ENVIRONMENTAL SCIENCE, ENGINEERING AND TECHNOLOGY

OIL

PRODUCTION, CONSUMPTION AND ENVIRONMENTAL IMPACT

ENVIRONMENTAL SCIENCE, ENGINEERING AND TECHNOLOGY

Additional books in this series can be found on Nova's website under the Series tab.

Additional e-books in this series can be found on Nova's website under the e-book tab.

ENVIRONMENTAL SCIENCE, ENGINEERING AND TECHNOLOGY

OIL

PRODUCTION, CONSUMPTION AND ENVIRONMENTAL IMPACT

SHUANGNING XIU
EDITOR

Nova Science Publishers, Inc.
New York

NOTICE TO THE READER

The Publisher has taken reasonable care in the preparation of this book, but makes no expressed or implied warranty of any kind and assumes no responsibility for any errors or omissions. No liability is assumed for incidental or consequential damages in connection with or arising out of information contained in this book. The Publisher shall not be liable for any special, consequential, or exemplary damages resulting, in whole or in part, from the readers' use of, or reliance upon, this material. Any parts of this book based on government reports are so indicated and copyright is claimed for those parts to the extent applicable to compilations of such works.

Independent verification should be sought for any data, advice or recommendations contained in this book. In addition, no responsibility is assumed by the publisher for any injury and/or damage to persons or property arising from any methods, products, instructions, ideas or otherwise contained in this publication.

This publication is designed to provide accurate and authoritative information with regard to the subject matter covered herein. It is sold with the clear understanding that the Publisher is not engaged in rendering legal or any other professional services. If legal or any other expert assistance is required, the services of a competent person should be sought. FROM A DECLARATION OF PARTICIPANTS JOINTLY ADOPTED BY A COMMITTEE OF THE AMERICAN BAR ASSOCIATION AND A COMMITTEE OF PUBLISHERS.

Additional color graphics may be available in the e-book version of this book.

Library of Congress Cataloging-in-Publication Data

Oil : production, consumption, and environmental impact / [edited by] Shuangning Xiu.
p. cm.
Includes bibliographical references and index.
ISBN 978-1-61942-877-5 (hardcover)
1. Oils and fats. I. Xiu, Shuangning.
TP670.O375 2011
664'.3--dc23

Published by Nova Science Publishers, Inc. † New York

CONTENTS

PREFACE

Petroleum accounts for a large percentage of the world´s energy consumption, ranging from a low of 32% for Europe and Asia to a high of 53% for the Middle East. The largest volume products in the industry are fuel oil and petrol, both important primary energy sources. However, rising oil prices and uncertainty over the security of existing fossil reserves, combined with concerns over global climate change, have created the need for new transportation fuels and for the manufacture of bioproducts to substitute for fossil-based materials.

The development of products derived from biomass is emerging as an important force component for economic development in the world. The United States currently consumes more than 140 billion gallons of transportation fuels annually. Conversion of cellulosic biomass to biofuels offers major economic, environmental, and strategic benefits. DOE and USDA predict that the U.S. biomass resources could provide approximately 1.3 billion dry tons of feedstock for biofuels, which would meet about 40% of the annual U.S. fuel demand for transportation. Against this backdrop, biofuels have emerged as one of the most strategically important sustainable fuels given their potential to increase the security of supply, reduce vehicle emissions and provide a steady income for farmers.

Several biorefinery processes have been developed to produce biofuels and chemicals from the initial biomass feedstock. Of all the various forms energy can take, liquid fuels are among the most convenient in terms of storage and transportation and are conducive to the existing fuel distribution infrastructure. This book comprehensively reviews the latest research progress on oil production, consumption, and environmental to readers at various levels. Special emphasis has been given to the state of the art, the use and drawbacks of biorefinery processes that are used to produce liquid fuels, specifically biodiesel and bio-oil.

The book is devoted to highlighting various aspects relevant to oil that can be used for fuel and energy purpose, including petroleum oil, biodiesel and bio-oil. Because accidents involving petroleum spill are very ordinary which produce severe impacts on the environment, new green materials for petroleum spill cleanup are discussed in Chapter 1. Flow assurance problems related to wax deposition during petroleum transportation are described in Chapter 2 and new experimental precipitation methods are developed. Chapter 3 focuses on key questions related to the environmental and socio-economic impacts of the biodiesel industry's consumption of vegetable oils as well as to emerging technologies and the transition to alternative feedstocks in pursuit of sustainable biodiesel production. Chapter 4 discusses the biodiesel production from inedible oils such as honge and mahua, which are having considerable potential for the biodiesel production in Asian countries in particular India. Chapter 5 and 6 are designed to introduce those readers requiring an in-depth knowledge on topics related to oil from biomass such as engineering process technologies, bio-oil characterization, upgrading and application. Factors influencing the fast pyrolysis are analyzed in Chapter 7. Chapter 8 introduces microwave-assisted pyrolysis oil, including process, characterization, and fractionation. Chapter 9 and 10 provided detailed studies of hydrothermal conversion (liquefaction) technology, covering the effect of biomass on bio-oil production and the production of Environment-Enhancing Energy (E^2-Energy).

The authors would like to acknowledge all their colleagues for their numerous and valuable suggestions to improve the quality of this book. The authors are also indebted to their friends, students, and technicians for all the support they provided.

In: Oil: Production, Consumption and Environmental Impact   ISBN: 978-1-61942-877-5
Editor: Shuangning Xiu   © 2012 Nova Science Publishers, Inc.

Chapter 1

MAGNETIC AND GREEN RESINS USEFUL FOR OIL SPILL CLEANUP

A. Varela,[1] M. C. Lopes,[1] T. Delazare,[1] G. E. Oliveira[2,•] and F. G. Souza, Jr[1,]*

[1]Instituto de Macromoléculas Professora Eloisa Mano,
Universidade Federal do Rio de Janeiro, Rio de Janeiro, Brasil
[2]Departamento de Química, Centro Ciências Exatas,
Universidade Federal do Espírito Santo, Vitória, Brasil

ABSTRACT

Petroleum has been consumed in large quantities by human kind for centuries and humanity is still very dependent on petroleum as a fuel and raw material for the petrochemical industry. Therefore, a large amount of oil needs to be transported across long distances by marine routes, increasing the chance of accidents, which are very common. These spills have a severe impact on the environment, being directly responsible for the destruction of marine life, since the interaction of lipophilic hydrocarbons with lipid layers of several flora and fauna organisms causes intoxication and even death. In addition, spills can also have an impact on the food and even the tourism industries. The extent of devastation caused by accidents shows that new strategies of remediation must be continuously studied. In this specific context, our group is focused on the use of renewable resources able to be transformed in polymer materials useful for the absorption of petroleum from the water, such as cashew nut shell liquid (CNSL); glycerol, a byproduct of the production of biodiesel by transesterification process; and the lignin removed by the Kraft process. Among these renewable resources, resins prepared using the cardanol from the cashew nut shell liquid provided good absorption results. From the environmental point of view, this strategy is interesting because it avoids the use of non-renewable materials at impacted areas.

---

[*] E-mail: fgsj@ufrj.br.
[•] E-mail: geiza.oliveira@ufes.br.

1. INTRODUCTION

Petroleum has been consumed in large quantities by human kind for centuries. Egyptians, Phoenicians, Babylonians, Greeks, Romans, Incas and Mayans are among the peoples that have used crude oil for different applications, such as mummification, waterproofing and military purposes. Today, humanity is still very dependent on petroleum as a fuel and raw material for the petrochemical industry, among other applications. However, a large amount of this non-renewable resource needs to be transported across long distances by marine routes, increasing the chance of accidents. Unfortunately, accidents involving petroleum spills are very common and the estimated amount of spilled oil around the world is equal to 400,000 tons per year [1]. These spills have a severe impact on the environment, being directly responsible for the destruction of marine life, since the interaction of lipophilic hydrocarbons with lipid layers of several flora and fauna organisms causes intoxication and even death. In addition, spills can also have an impact on the food and even the tourism industries. Figure 1 shows a spilled oil barrel on the water.

Among the traditional oil spill cleanup processes, the most used are (i) natural dispersion; (ii) containment and skimming; (iii) in situ burning; (iv) the use of sorbents; and (v) the use of detergents and dispersants.

The last one, as seen in the Terrey Canyon (1967) [1] and Alaska (1989) [2] spills, was not effective and also contributed to increasing the amount of toxic elements in the environment, making the bio-recovery of the ecosystem more difficult. The extent of devastation caused by accidents, as in Dalian (China) and the Gulf of Mexico, both in 2010, shows that new strategies of remediation must be continuously studied.

In this specific context, our group is focused on the use of renewable resources able to be transformed in polymer materials useful for the absorption of petroleum from the water, such as cashew nut shell liquid (CNSL); glycerol, a byproduct of the production of biodiesel by transesterification process; and the lignin removed by the Kraft process [4-7]. Natural sources of these chemicals are shown in Figure 2.

Among these renewable resources, resins prepared using the cardanol from the cashew nut shell liquid provided good absorption results. From the environmental point of view, this strategy is interesting because it avoids the use of non-renewable materials at impacted areas.

Figure 1. Spilled oil barrel on the water.

Figure 2. Some available resources: cashew nut and cashew– a source of cardanol (a); eucalyptus stem – a source of cellulose and lignin (b); and castor beans – a source of castor oil and glycerine (c).

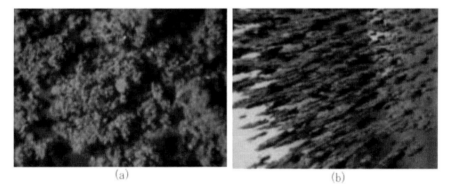

Figure 3. Maghemite nanoparticles (a) in the absence of a magnetic field and (b) in the presence of a magnetic field.

2. MAGNETIC PARTICLES

Among the available magnetic nanoparticles, maghemite is a very interesting example due to its high magnetic force and relatively low density, equal to (3.1 ± 0.8)g/cm^3. Among iron oxides particles, this density is one of the lowest observed. This low density is a crucial property in oil cleanup processes, since it allows improvement of the float ability of the composites, making easier the cleaning process. This material has a spinel structure and its composition is presented as $FeO.Fe_2O_3$, similar to magnetite. However, magnetite has a body-centred cubic crystallisation system, also referred to as α–iron, while maghemite crystallises according to the face-centred cubic system, also known as γ–iron [4,5]. These nanoparticles are prepared using the homogeneous precipitation technique. Initially, aqueous solutions of hydrochloric acid (2 mol/L), ferric chloride (2 mol/L) and sodium sulphite (1 mol/L) were prepared. In a typical procedure, 30 mL of the ferric chloride solution and 30 mL of deionised water were added into a beaker under continuous agitation. Soon afterwards, 20 mL of the sodium sulphite solution was added to the beaker, also under continuous agitation. The reaction product was precipitated using 50 mL of concentrated ammonium hydroxide, which was slowly poured into the beaker under continuous agitation. After 30 min, the medium was filtrated and the obtained particles were washed several times with water and finally dried at 60°C in an oven. Magnetite was converted into maghemite through annealing at 200°C for one hour. These maghemite nanoparticles were chosen because they present a good magnetic behaviour and after removing the applied magnetic field, they lose their alignment, as can be seen in Figure 3.

The maghemite WAXS pattern, Figure 4, presented peaks at 20.5°; 30.7°; 36.1°; 43.6°; 54.2°; 57.7° and 63.2°. According to Millan et al. [9], these peaks correspond to (111), (220), (311), (400), (422), (511) and (440) reflections of a spinel crystal structure such as that presented by maghemite or magnetite. Crystallinity degree was calculated according Ruland's method [10] while crystal sizes (CS) were calculated with Scherer's equation (Eq. 1) [8].

$$CS = K \times \lambda / \Delta\theta \times \cos(\theta) \qquad (1)$$

In this Equation, K is a constant (equal to 1.0), λ corresponds to the wavelength, θ is the Bragg angle ($2\theta/2$) and $\Delta\theta$ corresponds to the full width at half maximum (FWHM) of the (311) peaks. Pure maghemite presented crystallinity degree and crystal size equal to $(96\pm1)\%$ and (22 ± 2) nm, respectively. The crystal size was calculated with a R^2 equal to 0.96505. This result suggests that the maghemite nanoparticles are, predominantly, crystalline, but they have a small amorphous phase. It must be associated with the diminutive size of the nanoparticles that inserts some defects in the crystalline net of the maghemite.

Nanoparticles were also studied by Atomic Force Microscopy (AFM). AFM micrography of pure maghemite particles and particle size distribution of the maghemite are shown in Figure 5.

According to this figure, maghemite particles present spherical morphology and a low degree of aggregation. Particle diameters were calculated with the *ImageJ* software [4], while particle size distributions were computed as described in the literature [5]. Figure 5 also shows that particle size distribution presents an asymmetric mode, with 95% of the particles in the nm range.

The nanoparticles size was also studied by SAXS (see Figure 6). Appropriated corrections were performed and the particle size was determined using the Gnom® software. The average particle size was equal to (31.3 ± 0.7) nm. In spite of the differences, this result is in agreement with AFM, showed in Figure 5, indicating that nanoparticles were obtained.

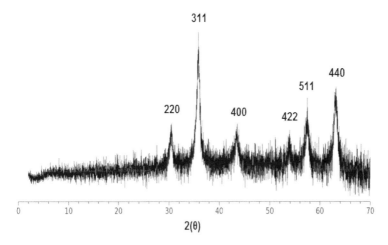

Figure 4. X ray diffractogram of the maghemite nanoparticles.

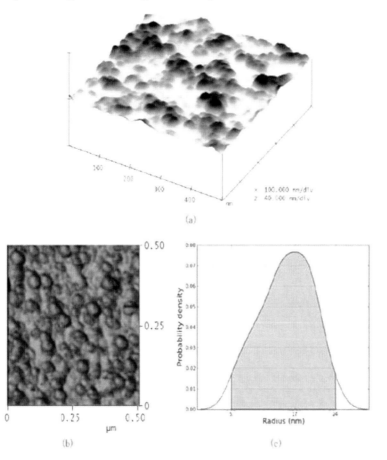

Figure 5. AFM of the maghemite nanoparticles in 3D (a) flatten (b) and respective probability density function of diameter.

Chemical structure of the maghemite was studied by FTIR and the spectrum is shown in Figure 7. Figure 7 shows a wide band at 3420cm^{-1} which corresponds to the O-H stretching, related to FeOH. In addition, there are others characteristic bands associated with structural water at $1632cm^{-1}$ and $1433cm^{-1}$. Thus, the spectrum shown in Figure 7 indicates that maghemite was obtained [4-7].

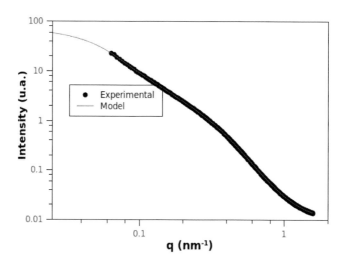

Figure 6. Maghemite nanoparticles SAXS profile.

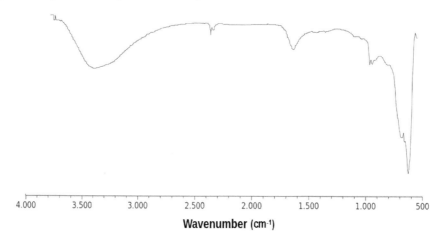

Figure 7. FTIR spectrum of the maghemite nanoparticles.

3. CARDANOL/FURFURALDEHYDE RESIN

The cardanol/furfuraldehyde resin is a thermoset material, which is a typical phenol/formaldehyde resin. These resins were prepared through acid catalysis. The syntheses were performed following a factorial design of experiments (DoE), shown in Table 1. In these expereiments, the lowest (-1); highest (+1) and central point (0) levels of furfural were equal to 0.344, 0.645 and 0.499 mol, respectively while the same levels for sulphuric acid were equal to 0.056, 0.066 and 0.061 mol, respectively.

Table 1. Furfuraldehyde and H_2SO_4 amounts used in the resin preparation

Experiment	Furfuraldehyde [a]	H_2SO_4 [a]
R1	-1	-1
R2	-1	1
R3	1	-1
R4	1	1
R5	0	0
R6	0	0
R7	0	0

(a) Lowest (-1); highest (+1) and central point (0) levels.

Table 2. Cure degree, time of preparation, density and oil removal capability (ORC) preliminary tests using the milled resins

Furfural	H_2SO_4	Cure degree (%)	Time (s)	Density *(g/cm^3)	ORC (g/g)
-1	-1	86±4	624±17	0.822±0.002	6.8±0.6
-1	1	93±5	346±36	0.823±0.001	6.4±1.4
1	-1	87±2	655±35	0.850±0.001	5.8±0.4
1	1	85±1	365±1	0.850±0.002	6.6±1.0
0	0	89±3	479±16	0.851±0.001	6.4±0.6
0	0	84±4	488±1	0.848±0.001	6.7±0.6
0	0	90±2	496±18	0.849±0.001	6.1±0.7

* Tests performed in 2-propanol d=0.7800 g/mL @ 20 °C.

The studied parameters were the furfuraldehyde and sulphuric acid (condensation catalyst) concentrations. The amount of cardanol was always equal to 100 mL. On the other hand, the lowest, the central and the highest levels of the furfuraldehyde were equal to 33, 48 and 62 phr, respectively, while the same levels to the H_2SO_4 were equal to 11, 12 and 13 phr, respectively. This (2^2 + 3) DoE produced seven resins. Among them, the first four are the combination of the lowest and highest levels, while the last three are replicates in the central point, as can be seen in the Table 1. Cardanol and furfuraldehyde were poured into a three-necked flask under continuous stirring. Soon afterwards, the medium was acidified with sulphuric acid and stirring was kept until the formation of a solid material. All the obtained materials were submitted to cure degree and density and oil removal capability tests.

Figure 8 shows the FTIR spectra of the resins. These spectra indicate that resins have the same chemical structure, which can be described as a typical phenol/formaldehyde resin [6-8]. Among the characteristic bands, a wide one, related to O-H stretching of the phenolic groups, takes place around 3400 cm^{-1}. The profile of this band is associated with the hydrogen bond that these compounds are able to form. In addition, the small characteristic band at 3000 cm^{-1} corresponds to C-H stretching and the doublet at 2925 cm^{-1} and 2855 cm^{-1} are associated with the stretching of the CH_2 and CH_3 groups. Another characteristic band can be seen at around 1615 cm^{-1}. This one corresponds to the C=C stretching of the aliphatic groups. Another doublet appears at 1460 cm^{-1} and 1544 cm^{-1}, characteristic of C=C stretching in aromatic rings. Bands around 1180 cm^{-1} and 1040 cm^{-1} are characteristic of the C=C stretching of the phenolic groups. Characteristic bands that appear around 970 cm^{-1} are related to asymmetric stretching of the C=C bond in the aromatic rings. These results indicate that the polymerisation occurred in the aromatic rings, preserving aliphatic unsaturated chains.

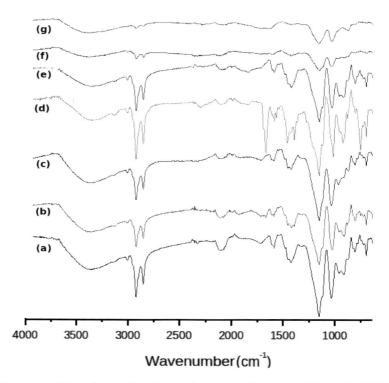

Figure 8. FTIR spectra of the resins produced according to conditions 1 to 7 shown in Table 1 (sequence (a) to (g), respectively).

Cure degree, time of preparation and density are shown in Table 2. Cure degree results presented very low correlation with the used chemical amounts of the furfuraldehyde and sulphuric acid. The calculated correlation was equal to 0.36. This value makes any further DoE calculations pointless. On the other hand, the average cure degree was equal to (87±4) %. This is an interesting result since the resin is insoluble in ordinary organic solvents, which means that petroleum may be extracted from the absorber using a washing process.

Table 3. Effects of the furfuraldehyde and H$_2$SO$_4$ concentrations on the preparation time, density, oil removal capability (ORC) and error associated with average oil removal capability (EORC) of the produced resins

	Effects			
	Time	**Density**	**ORC**	**EORC**
Mean/Interc.	**491.4**	**0.8250**	**638.6**	**0.7571**
Curvatr.	-19.5	**0.0281**	-	-
(1)Furfural	24.5	**0.0277**	-35.0	-0.3000
(2)H$_2$SO$_4$	**-280.5**	0.0010	20.0	**0.7000**
1 by 2	-3.5	0.0009	60.0	-0.1000

DoE results related to effects of the furfuraldehyde and H_2SO_4 concentrations on the preparation time, density, oil removal capability (ORC) and error associated with average oil removal capability (EORC) of the produced resins are shown in Table 3. Values presented in bold are statistically significant ($p \leq 0.05$). The effects of furfuraldehyde and H_2SO_4 concentrations on the preparation time, show that the preparation time is only statistically influenced ($p<0.05$) by catalyst concentration. The results showed, with a correlation larger than 0.97, that the increase of the catalyst concentration leads to a strong decrease of the preparation time. In addition, the raw data presented in Table 2 show that resins prepared using the lowest amount of catalyst consumes (10.5±0.5)min during preparation while the ones prepared using the highest level of the catalyst could be ready in (5.9±0.4)min. Beyond the cost decrease, the shorter preparation time may be very important when facing an environmental disaster, allowing faster responses.

Density results obtained using DoE calculations are also shown in Table 3. The results showed, with a correlation equal to 0.99568, that curvature and furfuraldehyde amount are statistically significant. Specifically, the increase in the furfuraldehyde concentration leads to an increase in the density. This phenomenon is possibly related to the closer packing provided by the additional cure points inside the resin [11]. Therefore, samples prepared using the lowest amount of furfuraldehyde presented the smaller density values, equal, in average, to $(0.811 \pm 0.002)g/cm^3$. This is a very good result, since the obtained value is lower than the one from the water, allowing the easier flotation of the material. Therefore, the resin obtained using the lowest amount of furfural, due to the lowest density values and the considerable cure degree, was chosen as the matrix for the preparation of the magnetic composites.

Oil removal capability tests (ORC) were performed using only the milled resins, and their results are also shown in Table 3. All analysed replicates presented a very small correlation, lower than 0.26517. Therefore tests were performed using the average values and their respective errors separately, as described previously [12]. This kind of variance analysis is very important to study complex and quite similar data [12], allowing infer, satisfactorily, the dispersion of the results caused by the studied variables, easing further decision making processes. Table 3 shows the effects of the furfuraldehyde and sulphuric acid concentration on the average oil removal capability of the produced resins. On the other hand, analysis of the errors associated with average oil removal capability is also shown in Table 3 and it presents a significant statistic influence of the catalyst amount over oil removal capability.

These results show that the increase of the catalyst amount is related, in a statistically significant way, to the increase of the error associated with the increasing of the average oil removal capability of the resins. Moreover, there is a good correlation ($R^2=0.87131$) between modelling and experimental data. This correlation allows production of the surface response shown in Figure 9, which makes clear that smaller errors are associated with smaller catalyst amounts.

This final information, associated with density results, allows inference that the most adequate resin for composite preparation is the one obtained through condition 1 (see Table 1), which corresponds to the use of the smallest catalyst and furfuraldehyde amounts. Therefore, materials presented in the next section were prepared using this resin as a matrix of composites containing different maghemite amounts.

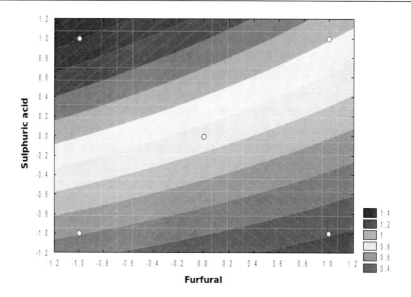

Figure 9. Response surface of the variance associated with the oil removal capability of the resins as a function of the catalyst and furfuraldehyde amount.

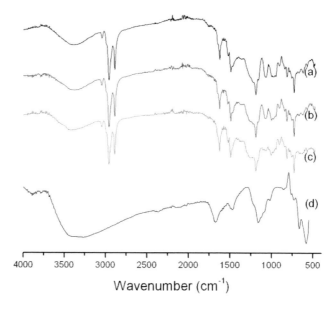

Figure 10. FTIR of the pure (a) magnetisable composites with 10% and (b) 20% (c) of the maghemite and pure maghemite (d).

4. MAGNETISABLE COMPOSITE

Distinct magnetisable composites are being prepared in several studies, pointing out numerous applications [4-8]. Among them, magnetisable composites useful to oil spill cleanup processes are attracting great interest due to their useful properties and easiness of preparation. In this study, the magnetisable composites were prepared using the resin which presented the lowest density associated with the highest oil absorption capability. The experimental procedure used to prepare the composites was similar to the one described for the resin preparation. Composites were prepared using the *in situ* technique. These composites posses four different amounts of the maghemite, equal to 5, 10, 15 and 20%. Maghemite nanoparticles were inserted in the reaction medium before acidification.

The chemical structure of each one of the magnetisable composites was characterised by FTIR and obtained spectra are shown in Figure 10. Aiming to make easier the study of these materials, the spectra of the resin and maghemite are also shown in Figure 10. Comparison among spectra of the pure resin and composites showed no significant differences, indicating the absence of chemical interactions between the matrix and the filler [8]. This same chemical behaviour is observed in other magnetisable composites, using maghemite nanoparticles as filler and other polymers obtained from glycerine, generated from biodiesel production, as the matrix [6-7].

The WAXS patterns of the resin, composites and maghemite are shown in Figure 11. The resin showed, as expected, a typical amorphous pattern while the maghemite particles are, predominantly, crystalline, as seen in Figures 4 and 11. Crystallinity degree was calculated according Ruland's method [10] while crystal sizes were calculated using Scherer's equation (Eq. 1) [8], as previously performed on the maghemite particles. As reported elsewhere [13], materials containing 0, 5, 10, 15, 20 and 100%wt of maghemite presented cristallinity degree equal to 27±2, 30±1, 36±1, 43±1, 55±2 and 96±1%, respectively. The crystal size of the composite containing 5wt% of the filler could not be calculated due to the low intensity of (311) peak. Other composites presented crystal sizes equal to 21±2 nm. This result is statiscally equal to the one of the pure maghemite (22±2 nm), indicating that the crystalline structure of the filler inside the composites remained essentially the same. These values are similar to the ones reported in other works of the group, where maghemite inside the polymer matrix presented a crystalline size equal to 19±1 nm [4], 21±2 nm dd5], 17±2 nm [6] and 21±3 nm [7]. The obtained results indicate that the maghemite properties are probably preserved in the hybrids. In addition, as expected, the increase of the maghemite content leads to the increase of the degree of crystallinity and rising of the characteristic diffraction peaks of the pure maghemite, as observed in Figure 11.

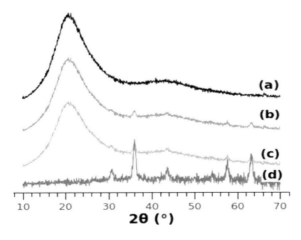

Figure 11. WAXS patterns of the resin (a) magnetisable composites with 10%, (b) and 20% (c) of the maghemite and pure maghemite (d).

Density of the composites was also determined elsewhere [13]. Composites containing 5, 10, 15 and 20wt% of maghemite presented density values equal to 0.861±0.009, 0.895±0.017, 0.931±0.001 and 0.970±0.002 g/cm^3, respectively. Figure 12 shows the linear relationship between the maghemite content and the density of the composite. Observed phenomenon can be described, with a correlation of 0.9995, according Equation 2.

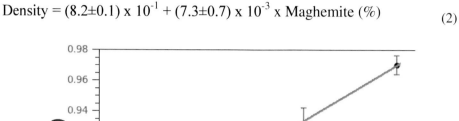

$$Density = (8.2\pm0.1) \times 10^{-1} + (7.3\pm0.7) \times 10^{-3} \times Maghemite \ (\%) \qquad (2)$$

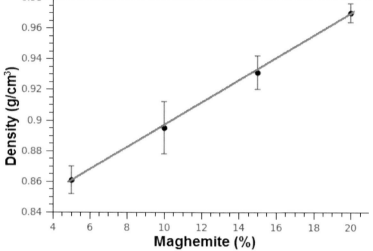

Figure 12. Relationship between the maghemite content and the density of the magnetisable composites.

All density values of the magnetisable composites are lower than 1g/cm^3. Therefore, densities of the composites, even using the largest amount of maghemite, were always lower than the ones of water. This information is important since the low density guarantees that the magnetisable composites are able to float. In addition, density of the composites can be easily adjusted, constituting a technological advantage in front of the enormous variety of crude oils.

The cure degree of the composites was also studied elsewhere [13]. Composites containing 5, 10, 15 and 20wt% of maghemite presented cure degree values equal to 92±4, 90±4, 85±4 and 88±6 %, respectively. The obtained values were statistically equal and the average cure degree was equal to (89±8) %. This high average result indicates that composites could be dispersed in ordinary organic solvents, allowing the recovery of the absorbed petroleum.

The magnetic force of the magnetisable composites was measured by weighing in two distinct moments: in the absence of the magnetic field and in the presence of the magnetic field. In both cases a known distance between the magnet and the sample was used. As described elsewhere [13], composites containing 5, 10, 15 and 20wt% of maghemite presented magnetic force values equal to 9.3±0.8, 13.1±0.4, 16.6±0.6 and 21.3±0.2 mN, respectively. These results show that larger amounts of maghemite produce higher magnetic forces. However the magnetic force values of the magnetisable composite are significantly lower than the one for the pure maghemite, which was equal to (349±2) mN. In spite of this difference, the magnetisable composites have a strong enough magnetic force to allow their use in the oil removal tests. Figure 13 presents the magnetic force as a function of the maghemite amount. The increase of the maghemite amount leads to a linear increase of the magnetic force. This upward trend can be described, with a correlation equal to 0.9991, by Equation 3.

$$\text{Magnetic Force} = (4,9\pm0,7)\times10^{0} + (8,2\pm0,4)\times10^{-1} \times \text{Maghemite (\%)} \qquad (3)$$

All the composites were used in the oil removal tests. These results are presented as grams of the oil removed by each gram of the composite. Thus, these results are dimensionless. As also described elsewhere [13], composites containing 5, 10, 15 and 20wt% of maghemite presented oil removal capability values equal to 8.73±0.17, 8.77±0.19, 9.57±0.18 and 10.20±0.20 g/g, respectively. Figure 14 shows these results as a function of the maghemite used in composites.

There is a linear relationship between the oil removal capability and the maghemite amount in the composite. This relationship can be described, with a correlation equal to 0.9039, by Equation 4.

$$\text{ORC} = (8.1\pm0.1) \times 10^{0} + (1.0\pm0.2) \times 10^{-1} \times \text{Maghemite (\%)} \qquad (4)$$

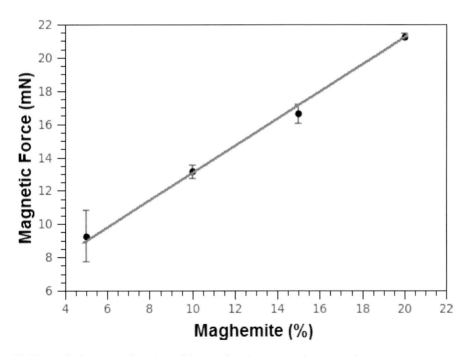

Figure 13. Magnetic force as a function of the maghemite amount in composites.

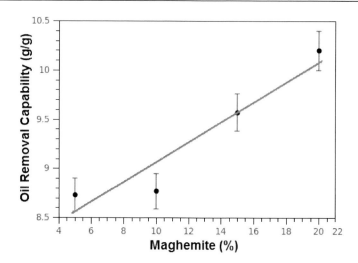

Figure 14. Oil removal capability of the magnetisable composites as a function of the maghemite amount.

Therefore, in the best case, each gram of the resin is able to remove around 10 g of the petroleum from the water. These results indicate that the increase of the maghemite concentration inside the magnetisable composite increases the removal efficiency of the oil from the water simply due to the larger magnetic attraction between the magnetic particles and the magnet [5]. Therefore, in this case, the oil removal capability seems to be the sum of two distinct effects, one of them related to the magnetic force and another related to the existing chemical affinity between the resin and the oil. In addition, this is a very encouraging result, since the magnetic composites based on polyurethanes and alkyd resins were able to remove (4.1 ± 0.1) g/g [5] and (8.33±0.19) g/g [4] of petroleum, respectively. Thus, the prepared material contributes to the environment, encouraging nobler uses for some of the available renewable resources besides reducing the environmental anthropogenic impact on areas degraded by oil spill accidents.

The amount of residual oil on the water was also studied. A calibration curve was built using the absorbances collected at 291.5 nm. This wavelength corresponds to the maximum absorbance of the petroleum solutions used in these tests. The obtained calibration curve can be described, with a correlation equal to 0.9756, by Equation 5.

$$\text{Absorbance} = (3.4\pm1.3) \times 10^{-2} + (1.18\pm0.02) \times 10^{-4} \times \text{Petroleum (ppm)} \qquad (5)$$

Residual oil amounts were calculated using Eq. 5 and obtained results are shown in Table 4 and Figure 15.

Table 4. Absorbance and residual oil amount on the water

Maghemite (%)	Absorbance at 291.5nm	Residual oil amount (ppm)
5	1.71	142±26
10	1.62	135±23
15	0.90	74±13
20	0.40	31±5

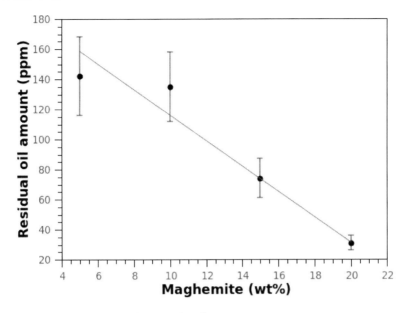

Figure 15. Residual oil as a function of the maghemite amount.

Figure 15 makes clear that the increasing of the amount of nanoparticles contributes to the decrease of the residual oil on the water. This behaviour can be described, with a correlation equal to 0.9938, by Equation 6.

$$\text{Residual oil (ppm)} = (2.0 \pm 0.3) \times 10^2 + -(8 \pm 1) \times 10^0 \times \text{Maghemite} \qquad (6)$$

This result is in complete agreement with that of the oil removal capability. Therefore, among the studied composites, the best is the one which possesses the largest amount of maghemite, being able to absorb the largest amount of petroleum, beyond producing the lowest amount of residual oil on the water.

4. FINAL REMARKS

Nature is fully capable of producing several useful resources and mankind, as the dominant species on Earth, should use these resources with the aim of building a better world for our children. Trying to contribute to this cause, the present work deals with a magnetisable nanocomposite produced using green resources such as cardanol, furfuraldehyde and maghemite nanoparticles. This material presents a low density associated with a considerable magnetic force and a good oil removal capability. Therefore, the produced nanomaterials are useful for the environment since they provide nobler uses of some of the renewable resources, which are often treated as waste, beyond being helpful in reducing the environmental anthropogenic impact on areas degraded by oil spill accidents.

ACKNOWLEDGMENTS

The authors thank Conselho Nacional de Desenvolvimento Científico e Tecnológico (CNPq), Coordenação de Aperfeiçoamento de Pessoal de Nível Superior (CAPES and CAPES-NANOBIOTEC). Financiadora de Estudos e Projetos (FINEP – PRESAL Ref. 1889/10) and Fundação Carlos Chagas Filho de Amparo à Pesquisa do Estado do Rio de Janeiro (FAPERJ) for the financial support and scholarships. The authors also thank LNLS for support on AFM (LNLS, Brazil – AFM / 9637/10) and SAXS experiments (D11A – SAXS1-9077, SAXS1-9078, SAXS1-11596 and SAXS1-11597).

REFERENCES

[1]   Coleman, J.; Baker, J.; Cooper, C.; Fingas, M.; Hunt, G.; Kvenvolden, K.; Michel, K.; Michel, J.; Mcdowell, J.; Phinney, J; Pond, R.; Rabalais, R.; Roesner, L.; Spies, R.B.; "Oil in the sea III." National Academy of Science; pg 16 (2003).

[2]   Bellamy, D. J.; Clarke, P. H.; John, D. M.; Jones, D.; Whittick, A. and Darke, T. "Effects of Pollution from the Torrey Canyon on Littoral and Sublittoral Ecosystems"; *Nature* 216, 1170 - 1173 (1967).

[3]   Bragg, J. R.; Prince, R. C.; Harner, E. J. and Atlas, R. M.; "Effectiveness of bioremediation for the Exxon Valdez oil spill"; *Nature* 368, 413 - 418 (1994).

[4]   Souza Jr., F.G.; Marins, J.A.; Rodrigues, C. H. M. ; Pinto, J. C. "A Magnetic Composite for Cleaning of Oil Spills on Water"; *Macromolecular Materials and Engineering*, 295, 10, 942-948 (2010).

[5]   Lopes, M. C.; Souza Jr, F. G.; Oliveira, G. E. "Magnetic foams useful in the environmental recovery processes". LOPES, Polímeros, São Carlos (2010). Available from http://www.scielo.br/scielo.php?pid=S0104-14282010005000054andscript=sci_arttext. Access on 05 Feb. 2011. Epub Nov 26, 2010. doi: 10.1590/S0104-14282010005000054. Polímeros (São Carlos. Impresso), 2010.

[6]   Souza Jr., F.G.; Oliveira, G.E; and Lopes., M.; "Environmental recovery by magnetic bio-resins"; Invited talk in the Second International Conference on Natural Polymers; India, 2010. Available from http://www.biopolymers.macromol.in/abstracts/fernandogomes.pdf; Access on 05 Feb. 2011.

[7]   Oliveira, G.E.; Souza Jr., F.G.; and Lopes., M.; "Biomaterials based on magnetic polyurethane foams useful in oil spill cleanup processes"; Invited talk in the Second International Conference on Natural Polymers; India (2010). Available from http://www.biopolymers. macromol.in/abstracts/geizaesperandiodeoliveira.pdf; Access on 05 Feb. 2011.

[8]   Fernando G. Souza Jr., Priscila Richa, Abner de Siervo, Geiza E. Oliveira, Cezar H. M. Rodrigues, Marcio Nele, Jose Carlos Pinto, "New in situ Blends of Polyaniline and Cardanol Bio-Resins "; *Macromol. Mater. Eng.* 2008, 293, 675–683.

[9]   Millan A, Palacio F, Falqui A, Snoeck E, Serin V, Bhattacharjee A, Ksenofontov V, Gutlich P and Gilbert I (2007) *Acta Materialia* 55:2201–2209.

[10]   Ruland W (1961) *Acta Cryst.* 14:1180-1185.

[11] S. Gopalakrishnana and R. Sujathaa; "Synthesis and thermal properties of polyurethanes from Cardanol- furfural resin "; *J. Chem. Pharm. Res.* (2010) 2(3):193-205.

[12] Souza Jr F.G., Pinto J.C., Oliveira G.E., Soares B.G, "Evaluation of electrical properties of SBS/Pani blends plasticized with DOP and CNSL using an empirical statistical model". *Polymer Testing*, v. 26, p. 720-728, 2007.

[13] Varela, A.; Oliveira, G; Souza Jr, F.G.; Rodrigues, C.H.M.; and Costa, M.A.S., "New petroleum absorbers based on cardanol-furfuraldehyde magnetic nanocomposites". *Polymer Engineering and Science* - Submitted

In: Oil: Production, Consumption and Environmental Impact   ISBN: 978-1-61942-877-5
Editor: Shuangning Xiu   © 2012 Nova Science Publishers, Inc.

Chapter 2

WAX PRECIPITATION IN FLOW ASSURANCE PROBLEMS

*Baudilio Coto,[*] Carmen Martos, Juan J. Espada
and María D. Robustillo*
Department of Chemical and Energy Technology, ESCET,
Universidad Rey Juan Carlos, Madrid, Spain

ABSTRACT

Flow assurance problems due to solid deposition are one of the main issues to address in crude oil production activities. Wax deposition is one of that flow assurance risks because paraffinic waxes present in petroleum mixtures can precipitate when temperature decreases during oil production. This issue is gaining increasing attention due to the impact in new offshore and cold environment developments.

Different methods have been reported to determine the main variables considered in wax precipitation studies (wax appearance temperature or WAT, and the amount of precipitated wax as a function of the temperature or wax precipitation curve). However, these methods are limited due to the use of solvents with great influence on the paraffin precipitation temperature, and alternative procedures have been developed using different experimental techniques (differential scanning calorimetry or DSC, nuclear magnetic resonance spectroscopy or NMR, and Fourier transformed infrared spectroscopy or FTIR).

Revision of different methodologies was carried out, with special focus on a new experimental wax precipitation method from non-diluted crude oils and DSC methods. Several crude oils were studied and the reliability of the different methods was confirmed from the good agreement obtained between the several experimental results as well as those predicted by thermodynamic models.

---

[*] To whom correspondence should be addressed: Phone: 34 91 4887089, Fax: 34 91 4887068. E-mail: baudilio.coto@urjc.es.

1. INTRODUCTION

The term "flow assurance" refers to ensure successfully and cost-effectively the flow of hydrocarbon streams from reservoir to processing facilities and to the selling point. It is extremely diverse and it comprises different aspects like hydraulic and thermal analyses (pressure and heat loss), operability (cooling down, slugging), blockages (mainly due to the presence of hydrates, asphaltenes, scales, sand and waxes), phase behavior and viscosity or mechanical aspects (corrosion, erosion) [1].

The scarcity of fossil resources has led to search for oil and gas into deeper and more hostile environments (high pressures, low temperatures...). This implies more difficulties to ensure a desirable flow for crude oil and gas and therefore deeper studies on this field.

Flow assurance problems due to solid deposition are one of the main issues to address in crude oil production activities. The evaluation of solid deposition risk affecting production and transport remains being a challenge, and it is affected not only by the fluid composition, but also by the type of reservoir and the development desired for the oil field. In this sense, wax deposition is one of the main flow assurance risks related to solid deposition.

Paraffin waxes contained in petroleum mixtures can precipitate when temperature decreases during oil production, transport through pipelines or storage. This problem is very well known within the petroleum industry since the presence of solid waxes increases fluid viscosity. Furthermore, its accumulation on the wall pipe reduces the flow line section, even causing the blockage of filters, valves and pipelines and reducing or even stopping oil production or transportation [1].

In general, the formation of any deposit (organic or inorganic), can be studied from three approaches: thermodynamics, kinetics and fluid dynamics. Thermodynamics defines the direction and balance of processes, whereas kinetics studies the rate at which the processes occur. Fluid dynamic, once satisfied the thermodynamic and kinetic conditions, helps to describe the flow preferential sites where deposition will take place.

The deposition sites are difficult to locate, and even once found it is difficult to access them, being necessary in most cases stop production. To minimize economic losses of oil companies due to the interruption of the production process, it is very important to design laboratory facilities in which obstructions could be properly studied, so the actual behavior of the fluid could be reproduced. Thus, it is possible to determine the effects of the deposits on the crude oil flow allowing the development of predictive models. The results of predictions facilitate the adoption of the appropriate prevention methods.

The design of production facilities or the development of remediation activities for paraffinic crude oils requires characterizing the fluid as accurately as possible. In-depth understanding about the conditions in which waxes can precipitate, as well as how and where deposition takes place, may reduce possible high operating costs, in case of undersized equipments and pipes, or high investment cots due to oversized facilities.

The deposition of waxes is more problematic in offshore wells where the distance between the platform and subsea facilities can be 20 to 60 km. Along that way, there is a potential risk of crude oil being cooled down below the temperature at which wax precipitates (Wax Appearance Temperature, WAT), thus appearing solid waxes. Despite the great variety of existing remediation methods their cost make them unaffordable. Therefore, significant research effort is being focused on developing new experimental techniques and predictive models which could anticipate the potential risk of wax formation [1-4].

Once described wax deposition problem, this chapter is focused on the evaluation of different existing methods to predict or experimentally determine the main variables involved in wax precipitation studies in order to develop a general methodology to check the potential risks of crude oil in flow assurance related to wax precipitation. These variables are the WAT, the total amount of waxes and the amount of wax precipitated as a function of the temperature, wax precipitation curve or WPC. Extended descriptions of new experimental precipitation methods and new methodologies based on DSC are also included. The reliability of all the studied methods is confirmed by applying them to some samples of different crude oils.

Finally, most used methods to remove waxes once deposited on the pipes are briefly reviewed and described.

2. PARAFFIN WAXES

Paraffins present in crude oils may be in gaseous, liquid or solid phase depending on temperature and pressure conditions. The precipitation or crystal formation is a thermodynamic process, while deposition is a kinetic phenomenon influenced by flow dynamics, heat and mass transfer and solid-surface interactions. The precipitation does not necessarily imply deposition. The main variables usually considered in wax precipitation studies are the wax appearance temperature (WAT), the total amount of waxes and the amount of wax precipitated as a function of the temperature (wax precipitation curve, WPC) [8]. These magnitudes can anticipate potential problems related to wax precipitation and they may be used as an indicator for the suitability of additives or alternative technologies to reduce the problem. *Figure 1* shows the aspect of a crude oil pipeline after having been subjected to a wax formation process [9].

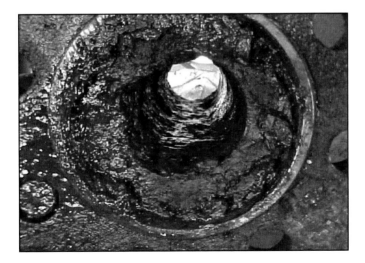

Figure 1. Crude oil pipeline blocked by a wax deposit.

The loss of the lighter constituents in a crude oil also affects wax precipitation, as it reduces the amount of paraffin that can be kept in solution at a given temperature. Generally, paraffinic compounds are more soluble in light crude oils than in heavy ones. For this reason, when a production area is getting older, lighter constituents are separated from the crude oil leading to saturation conditions for paraffinic components and increasing the risk of deposition problems.

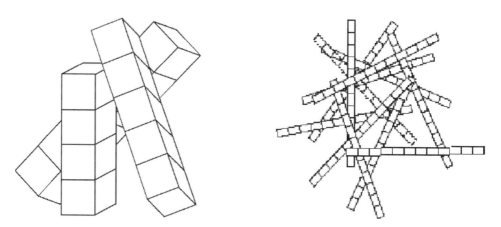

Figure 2. Crystalline structure of macrocrystalline and microcrystalline waxes.

In a crude oil two different types of waxes can be found: *microcrystalline* and *macrocrystalline* waxes (see *Figure 2* [10]). Macrocrystalline waxes, commonly known as paraffins, are present in petroleum distillates and they are usually composed of 40 to 90 % of n-paraffins with variable chain length and a very low proportion of iso-paraffins and naphthenes. For common operation temperatures (above 0 °C), macrocrystalline waxes are mainly composed of n-paraffins of more than 20 carbon atoms, with melting points in the range of 45 to 70 °C, an average molecular weight between 350 and 420 g·mol^{-1} and colorless [11]. The high melting points make these hydrocarbons to be the first precipitated and this makes *macrocrystalline* waxes to be of special relevance in the field of flow assurance.

Microcrystalline waxes are mixtures of n-alkanes, naphthenes and iso-alkanes in variable proportions. They are also called amorphous waxes because their constituents form small and irregular crystals. They are usually found in heavy petroleum fractions and have melting points in the range of 60 - 95 °C. Their average molecular weight is higher than macrocrystalline waxes since they contain 30 to 60 carbon atoms, ranging between 600 and 800 g·mol^{-1} [11-12]. These waxes differ from the microcrystallines in color and structure because they contain a considerable proportion of resins.

The wax crystallization process can be described by three different stages: nucleation, crystal growth and agglomeration [13]. The nucleation step is the process of gathering atoms, molecules or ions, which will form the new phase in the solution. As the oil temperature decreases, the mobility of molecules is progressively reduced and linear paraffin molecules tend to move close to each other forming clusters or cores of aligned chains disposed in an adjacent way. Molecules continue binding to these organized sites until the clusters reach a certain size and become stable. Once nuclei are formed and temperature decreases, additional molecules are deposited on the nucleation sites, making them grow and producing macroscopic size crystals in form of discrete platelets or needles. Finally, the crystals are agglomerated to form larger particles or gels that modify the oil rheological properties. The formation rate and the amount of precipitated wax crystals depend mainly on the following factors:

- Temperature (including metal surfaces).
- Pressure.
- Nucleation sites (presence of sand, porosity, wall roughness, etc.).
- Effect of other chemicals.

3. DETERMINATION OF COLD PROPERTIES

As mentioned before, the knowledge of the WAT, the total amount of waxes and the WPC is essential to prevent or mitigate flow assurance problems caused by the precipitation of these compounds.

The thermodynamic *wax appearance temperature* is defined as the maximum temperature at which a solid phase appears at a given pressure. However, the WAT measured experimentally corresponds to that temperature at which, under standard conditions of cooling, the crystallization of paraffinic compounds within the fluid is observed [14]. It depends on the composition of crude oil, the experimental technique used, the thermal history of the fluid, the cooling rate and the fluid properties related to the nucleation and crystal growth. Once the WAT value is reached, the fluid no longer has a Newtonian behavior.

A further cooling of the crude oil leads to the *pour point,* 3 °C above the temperature at which the crude oil stops flowing under the action of gravity due to the growth of the wax crystal network (it is determined by ASTM D97-02). It is assumed that the pour point corresponds to about 2% (wt) of precipitated paraffin [16-17]. At lower temperatures, the fluid has a pseudo-plastic behavior until it forms a semisolid gel which can not be broken unless considerable force is applied, reaching the so called gelation temperature [15].

The *WPC* is the representation of the percentage of precipitated solid as a function of temperature. WPC can be determined experimentally by direct or indirect methods. The existing methods are described in the following sections.

3.1. Experimental Determination of WAT

Although there are numerous techniques to determine the WAT [18], all of them have some limitations [19], making it difficult to decide which is the most reliable. The most frequently used methods to experimentally determine the WAT are described below:

ASTM D2500

Sometimes, WAT is measured in the same way than de cloud point. (the temperature at which turbidity appears due to the formation of paraffin crystals). The ASTM D2500 [20] method is based on visual observation of the wax crystals and for that reason it is only applicable to determine the cloud point for transparent petroleum fractions, not for dark and opaque samples like crude oils.

Light Transmission

WAT is determined by measuring the incident light fraction at a specified wavelength that passes through a sample according to the amount of paraffin precipitated [21-22]. This technique provides better results than visual observation made by the ASTM D2500, but it still requires a significant amount of crystals to reduce significantly transmitted light intensity [19]. It is applicable to both crude oil and petroleum fractions [23].

Cross Polarized Light Microscopy (CPM)

WAT determination by this technique is based on the fact that the wax crystals rotate polarized light but liquid hydrocarbons do not. The crystals are observed as small isolated spots of light on a black background and are identified visually or using a video camera. WAT is the temperature at which the first crystal is identified, although this technique also allows for an estimation of the amount of wax formed as a function of temperature [22, 24-28]. The method can be used either for crude oil and petroleum fractions, but since it is a visual method it tends to provide higher values of WAT than instrumental methods.

Fourier Transform Infrared Spectroscopy (FTIR)

Infrared spectroscopy allows determining the WAT and the WPC. The intensity of the bands obtained at a wavelength of 720 cm^{-1}, associated with the presence of CH_2 groups in hydrocarbon systems, increases with decreasing temperature. This phenomenon is attributed mainly to the increase of crystallinity of the solid phase. As methylene groups are the main constituents of the potential precipitated solids of crude oils, the integration of these signals between 735 and 715 cm^{-1} and its representation versus temperature yields the WAT and the WPC [29-30]. This method is applicable to both crude oil and petroleum fractions.

Nuclear Magnetic Resonance (NMR)

In this case, WAT determination is based on the fact that NMR signals are proportional to the mobility of protons in solution. The protons present in the liquid and solid phases can be then differentiated and used to determine the solid content at different temperatures [31]. However, this technique is not sensitive to a paraffin content lower than 5% (wt), and therefore can not be applied to crude oils with low paraffin content [32]. With this method WAT is underestimated.

Differential Scanning Calorimetry (DSC)

This technique estimates the WAT from the heat involved in paraffin by using an appropriate cooling rate precipitation [2, 8, 15, 32-36]. This method is applicable to crude oils and petroleum fractions, but it requires a minimum amount of paraffin for the WAT to be detected, so it is always underestimated. Since this technique allows obtaining more information besides the WAT, it is developed further in the next section.

Filter Plugging

This method follows the ASTM D6371 standard [37]. Crude oil sample is vacuum filtered and cooled down. The difference between initial pressure and pressure after temperature decrease is recorded. This variation is related to the formation of wax crystals [21]. One of the main drawbacks of this method is that the obtained results can be affected by the presence of sand and emulsions. Moreover, the technique is not quantitative unless the precipitate will remain trapped in a cold reservoir.

Viscosity

This technique yields the WAT value as a function of changes in the viscosity of the sample when paraffins precipitate. The crude oil has a Newtonian behavior and the formation of wax crystals makes it non-Newtonian. The dependence between viscosity and temperature follows the Arrhenius equation until the wax begins to precipitate [2, 8, 34-35, 38-41]. The detection of non-Newtonian behavior is only possible if there is a deviation of 2.5% compared to Newtonian fluid viscosity, which corresponds to a fraction of 1% by weight of precipitated paraffin. This amount of solid in some cases is enough to reach the pour point and therefore the WAT is underestimated [42-45].

Quarz Crystal Microbalance (QCM)

The quartz crystal microbalance is a very thin quartz crystal on which two separate metal coatings (gold, platinum, copper or silver) are deposited on both sides acting as electrodes. By applying an electrical potential across the quartz crystal, it undergoes a deformation that is proportional to the applied potential. The vibration of quartz crystal generates a transverse acoustic wave that is propagated through the interface located between the glass and the layer of the material deposited on its surface. Assuming that the acoustic speed and density of the deposited material are identical to those of quartz, the material deposited can be considered as an extension of the glass, so a change in the thickness of the deposited material is equivalent to a change in thickness of glass, which generates a change in the resonance frequency. Cassiède et al. have adapted this technique to study the solid-liquid equilibrium of n-paraffin compounds [46], but although the results are promising, the technique has not yet been applied to crude oils and petroleum fractions.

In general, the main problem of using the techniques explained before is the need to have a minimum amount of solid to detect a new phase, so that the WAT is often underestimated [19,47]. Moreover, most of them are indirect techniques and produce signals whose interpretation and relationship with the amount of wax is highly subjective [48]. Despite these drawbacks, differential scanning calorimetry and polarized light microscopy provide results with acceptable accuracy [19].

3.2. Experimental Determination of the Total Amount of Waxes

The total amount of wax is a key parameter used by thermodynamic models together with n-paraffin distribution to determine the WPC.

Many authors assume the total amount of waxes contained in a crude oil as the paraffin precipitated at -20 ° C [49]. This is really the amount of paraffin C_{20}^{+} [50], those paraffinic compounds of more than twenty carbon atoms, which potentially can generate flow assurance problems at the temperatures of interest (usually the minimum operation temperature is around 0 °C). The most used methods to determine the total amount of waxes are described below.

Gravimetric Method

Several procedures exist for the direct determination of the amount of waxes at different temperatures. In most cases, the precipitated wax is separated from the rest of the crude oil by filtering and then quantified by gravimetry. Different attempts have been made in order to separate precipitated waxes from crude oil by filtration. The problem is that viscosity of crude oil is too high even to flow, since pour point is usually reached. For this reason, crude oil has to be dissolved. The use of solvents shifts temperature towards lower values due to dilution effect. In order to reduce this problem, some authors have used a mixture of solvent/anti-solvent system. Next, we comment some of the methods reported in literature.

The most commonly used method for gravimetric determination of the precipitated wax was proposed by Burger et al. In this method, the crude oil is dissolved in a solvent mixture (petroleum ether/acetone), cooled at -20 °C and filtered at this temperature. This method is simultaneously a modification of UOP 46-85 standard [51].

Elsharkawy et al. [8] reported a modification of Burger's method, including previous crude oil dissolution in pentane. Nermen et al. [52] carried out a separation of waxes by fractional crystallization at low temperature using different solvents. Coto et al. reported a method using a mixture of acetone/n-pentane as solvent, the recovered solid is washed to remove other compounds[5]. Handoo et al. [53] reported a fractionation method using a mixture of solvents, recovering and re-crystallizing the soluble fraction at lower temperature.

Wax Cleaning Method

This method was proposed by Ronningsen and Bjorndal [2] and consists of dissolving the paraffin precipitated at -20 °C (obtained by Burger´s method [49]) in hexane. The mixture is passed through a chromatographic column containing silica as adsorbent and the resulting product is dried and weighted. The drawback of this technique is the low selectivity as not only the precipitated paraffin is removed but also other saturated compounds of present in the sample.

Gas Chromatography

Jokuty et al. [54] developed a method based on simulated distillation to determine the total wax content of a crude oil from the analysis of the saturated fraction obtained by SARA (saturates, aromatics, resins and asphalthenes) fractionation method. The relationship between the area corresponding to C_{18}^{+} and the total area of the chromatogram reports the total amount of paraffin waxes in the crude oil.

Cold Finger

This analysis consists of contacting the crude oil sample within a surface, which is cooled by a fluid from a cryostat. The oil is continuously stirred at a temperature above its WAT, while the paraffin deposit is formed on the cooled surface. The main drawback of this technique is the difficulty in quantifying the amount of the solid deposits and the reproducibility of the analysis under the same conditions [21, 56].

3.3. Experimental Determination of WPC

As mentioned above, the WPC represents the percentage of precipitated solid as a function of temperature and it can be determined by direct or indirect methods. Direct methods allow obtaining the amount of wax separated as a solid phase when the crude oil has been cooled down at a temperature below the WAT. Indirect methods measure the change that occurs in some properties of the fluid as a result of precipitation of waxes. The most used methods are described below.

Differential Scanning Calorimetry (DSC)

In recent years many thermodynamic models have been used to obtain both WAT and WPC [8, 15, 25, 57-59]. DSC is a fast indirect technique that provides good results. It measures the difference in heat flow between a sample of crude oil and a reference, or the power that must be provided or removed from the system. However, there are some difficulties regarding the experimental technique and the interpretation of the thermogram [1, 8, 15, 59], such as the low signal intensity obtained, the kinetic effects that influence the values of WAT, the wide temperature range of operation, the uncertainty in the calculation of precipitated mass of paraffin from heat flow or the non standard definition of the thermogram integration process.

A method reported in literature to determine the WAT and the WPC, developed by our team [15], is based on those reported by Elsharkawy´s [8] and Coutinho´s [58] but with some modifications. In the final optimized procedure, the temperature profile of the analysis follows several steps:

(1) Previous step: Sample is heated at 3 °C/min from 25 to 80 °C to completely dissolve possible solid phase and to remove any thermal history.
(2) Cooling step: Sample is cooled down from 80 to -120 °C at 3 °C/min.
(3) Heating step: Sample is heated up from -120 to 80 °C at the same rate, 3 °C/min.

The difference between the DSC curve and the baseline is a direct measurement of the total heat involved in the phase change, which is converted into the corresponding mass through an integration process which uses a calibration from pure n-paraffinic compounds. In the integration procedure the difference between the DSC curve and the baseline is a direct measurement of the total heat involved in the phase change and can be converted into the corresponding mass by means of the specific melting heat.

The integration procedure is carried out in terms of pure n-alkane components, which are considered to be the main precipitating compounds. Pure n-alkane properties from C_4 to C_{24} are taken from literature [60] and several correlations were checked for specific melting heat versus melting temperature [8, 61-64].

In the mass distribution representation, temperature is converted into an integer carbon atom number by using a correlation between pure n-alkane melting temperature and the number of carbon atoms [61].

The use of pure component correlations in the above procedure is not accurate and it has to be corrected. The precipitation temperature, $T_{p,i}$, at which an n-alkane precipitates in a mixture is highly dependent on the composition and it is different from the melting temperature. The melting heat also has to be modified because of the displacement of the solidification temperature using the melting heat capacities to correct such values.

In order to include this important effect of composition on precipitation properties, an iterative procedure which combines experimental data and calculation results is proposed. An initial n-alkane composition is determined for the crude oil sample from pure n-alkane parameters. Computationally, such mixture is set well above its WAT in order to have all the components in the liquid phase. A step by step decrease of temperature was simulated and the solid phase formation was computed for every component at each temperature considering the equilibrium and mass balance equations. Values for precipitation temperature and melting heat were determined for each n-alkane. The precipitation temperature is much lower than the melting temperature because of the low values of the mole fractions of individual components, and this large difference results also in a large difference between precipitation and melting heat values. New correlations can be obtained from the computed values for components in the mixture thus including the composition effect.

The iteration procedure described in *Figure 3* is proposed to integrate the DSC thermogram for crude oil mixtures. At the start point, the DSC thermogram is integrated according to the integration procedure and pure n-alkane correlations yielding a first n-alkane distribution curve. In the first iteration step, SLE equations are solved covering the whole temperature range and the process is carried out using as composition the obtained first n-alkane distribution. Values for the precipitation heat and temperature are determined for each n-alkane in the mixture. Correlations between precipitation temperature, precipitation heat and number of carbon atoms are determined. Experimental DSC thermogram is integrated again using that correlation and a second n-alkane distribution curve is obtained. The process is repeated till no changes are obtained in the determined distribution function. Usually, 3 or 4 iterations are enough to obtain convergence.

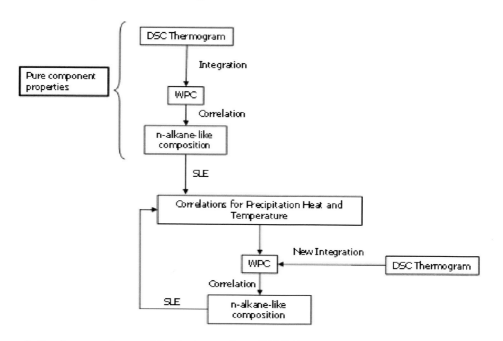

Figure 3. Iterative procedure used for the integration of DSC thermogram.

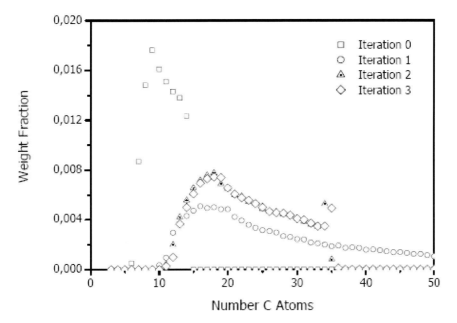

Figure 4. Change of the n-alkane distribution curves along the iteration procedure.

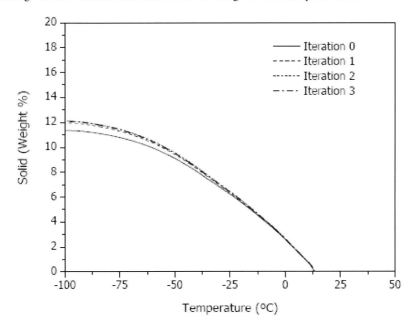

Figure 5. Change of the wax precipitation curve along the iteration procedure.

Figures 4 and *5* show the n-alkane distribution curves and the wax precipitation curves obtained in several iterations for the crude oil studied.

Fourier Transform Infrared Spectroscopy (FTIR)

FTIR is an indirect method to determine the WAT and the WPC by quantifying the increase of infrared absorbance motivated by the precipitation of waxes from the crude oil sample. It is considered that the increase of absorbance from 735 to 715 cm[-1] corresponds to the CH$_2$ bands of the n-paraffinic compounds, and it is linearly related with the increase of the precipitated wax [29]. However, it must be pointed out that the length of the n-paraffin considered limits the number of CH$_2$ groups and therefore the linear relationship is not accurate enough.

Gravimetric Methods

The results of indirect methods used to experimentally determine the WPC depends on the accuracy of the measurement of the property involved. Alternative methods are those based on centrifugation [65] or gravimetry as Burger´s method, previously described. However, one of the disadvantages of this gravimetric method is that the starting oil sample is dissolved, causing a displacement of the solid-liquid equilibrium. An alternative method, known as the *fractional precipitation method*, overcomes such limitations [66]. In this method, crude oil is not dissolved, and it consists of recovering the precipitated solid making consecutive filtration experiments while reducing the operation temperature.

Centrifugation and fractional precipitation methods allow determining directly the amount of precipitated wax. However, the precipitate contains a significant amount of trapped crude oil in its structure and therefore the use of additional techniques (^{1}H-NMR, DSC or HTGC) to determine the true amount of paraffin precipitated in the solid is required.

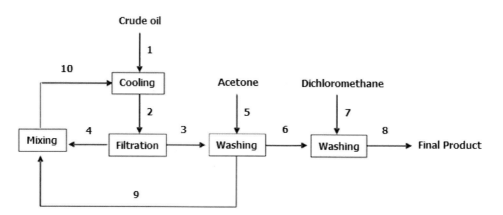

Figure 6. Experimental procedure of fractional precipitation.

The fractional precipitation method developed by our team was based on Burger´s method, but including some modifications to overcome its limitations. The data obtained were used as a benchmark to compare the data obtained by DSC technique. The main variables of the precipitation process are:

- Degree of crude oil dilution
- Influence of the solvent used to recover the waxes
- Influence of solvent
- Influence of pressure filtration
- Single or fractionated precipitation

The filtration procedure is shown in *Figure 6*. 50 g of crude oil (stream 1) are cooled in a cryostat at a slightly higher temperature than its wax appearance temperature (WAT) for 24 h.

The crude oil is then filtered using a glass microfibre Whatman filter N° 934 during at least 2 h. The solid phase (stream 3) is collected for further recovery of the precipitated waxes while liquid phase (stream 4) is used for next precipitation. The filtration area is washed with dichloromethane to recover the remaining crude oil and after that, solvent is removed by vacuum evaporation at 65–70 °C, and the obtained crude oil is mixed with the liquid phase (stream 4) obtained in the filtration process. The solid phase (stream 3) is washed with acetone to reduce the trapped crude oil. This washing process is carried out at room temperature in a Buchner funnel using vacuum. Acetone is removed by vacuum evaporation and the remaining crude oil is added (stream 9) to the next precipitation experiment fluid. The remaining solids (stream 6) are recovered by washing the filter with dichloromethane, and alter solvent removal by heating at 50–60 °C the final free-solvent product (stream 8) is weighted and stored for further characterization. The mixture (stream 10) formed by the rest of liquid crude oil is used for the next precipitation step at a lower temperature. This procedure can be repeated 4 or 5 times by decreasing system temperature about 3–5 °C in each step. This process allows obtaining the amount of solid precipitated at each temperature and therefore to obtain part of the precipitation curve and the WAT of a crude oil. The main part of the experimental system for fractional precipitation is the filter, which has to be temperature-controlled. Temperature is controlled by recirculation of a mixture of ethylenglicol –water from a thermostatic bath in the range of -30–50 °C. The top of the filter is covered and connected to a dry nitrogen stream in order to carry out filtration under a slight over pressure. A limitation of this new experimental procedure is that at very low temperatures the filtration process can not be applied due to the increase of the viscosity of the crude oils. For that reason, it is not possible to reach the temperature of -20 °C to determine the total wax content of crude oils. Such limitation does not affect the procedure of wax precipitation at -20 °C described by Burger due to the dilution of the sample. However, the results obtained by the fractional precipitation procedure are more realistic as it allows reproducing wax precipitation along a temperature profile similar to that in pipelines where flow assurance problems can appear.

3.4. Trapped Crude Oil Determination

The WPC obtained by DSC can not be directly compared to that obtained by fractional precipitation since the trapped crude oil remaining in the precipitated waxes has to be discounted. For that reason, the data obtained by fractional precipitation requires a correction by discounting the trapped crude oil. ^{1}H NMR [5] and DSC [1, 67] can be used for that purpose. Most literature data indicate that the trapped crude oil of real deposits varies in the range of 50 - 90 % [68].

4. STUDY OF CRUDE OILS APPLIED TO FLOW ASSURANCE

In this section, the methodology described before to determine the most important variables in flow assurance (WAT, total wax content and WPC), has been applied to study some crude oils.

4.1. WAT Determination

The results obtained by CPM and DSC to determine the WAT values of three paraffinic and two naphthenic crude oils are presented in *Table 1*.

Table 1. WAT values for the crude oils used as examples obtained by microscopy and DSC

CRUDE OIL	TYPE	WAT MICROSCOPY (°C)	WAT DSC (°C)
B-1	LIGHT/ NAPHTHENIC	17.8	16.3
B-3	LIGHT/ PARAFFINIC	54.1	54.9
B-5	VERY LIGHT/ PARAFFINIC	11.4	11.0
A-1	LIGHT/ PARAFFINIC	39.4	40.7
C-3	MEDIUM/NAPHTHENIC	12.2	13.3

Crude oils show different behavior depending on their composition. According to the WAT values obtained, crude oil B-5 has better behavior at low temperatures than crude oil B-1 because its waxes precipitate at lower temperature. Anyway, both samples have a WAT considerable lower than crude oil B-3. This sample has a WAT value of 54.1 °C and 54.9 °C obtained by microscopy and DSC, respectively and it may suppose a huge problem with regard to flow assurance, since it is highly paraffinic and its waxes precipitate at temperatures above room temperature. However, high values of WAT does not imply that the crude oil in question causes flow assurance problems around that temperature, because only a small amount of waxes may precipitate. For this reason, it is always necessary to complete the results with the WPC.

On the other hand, DSC WAT values are quite similar to those obtained by means of microscopy and it was not found a clear disagreement between both techniques. Nevertheless, in some cases such as crude oil B-1 and B-5, the WAT obtained by microscopy is higher than that provided by DSC. Some authors [35, 69] attribute these differences to the sensitivity of both techniques and the difficulty in distinguishing paraffin precipitates from other inorganic substances that may also be present in the crude oil. Another possible cause is the loss of volatile compounds during the analysis, which increases the concentration of paraffin in the sample since, unlike the DSC, the microscope is an open system.

The WAT values provided by both DSC and microscopy are not equilibrium values, since the detection of WAT requires the presence of a certain amount of precipitated paraffin which is greatly affected by the kinetic parameters of nucleation, especially when dealing with low paraffin content crude oils. However, as mentioned before, the cooling rate was optimized to 3 °C/min to minimize kinetic effects and a statistic study was carried out to determine the error associated to the visual detection of WAT. Results showed that interferences may occur due to the presence of other substances in the crude oil and the error made by using CPM was higher than that associated to the DSC.

4.2. WPC Determination

As an example, in this section the results obtained by different techniques such as DSC and fractional precipitation are presented for different type crude oils.

Differential Scanning Calorimetry

Figure 7 shows the WPC obtained during cooling for two crude oils: the paraffinic crude oil A-1 and the naphthenic crude oil C-3.

One of the possibilities to check the WPC obtained by DSC is the comparison of the amount of precipitated wax at the pour point (according to this technique), with those values proposed by other authors [16, 17], which are in the range of 2 to 4%. The results are shown in *Table 2*. In both cases it is verified that the amount of paraffin in the pour point is between the mentioned values.

Fractional Precipitation

WPC for crude oils A-1 and C-3 obtained by fractional precipitation, following the procedure described in *Section* 3.3 is presented in *Figure 8*.

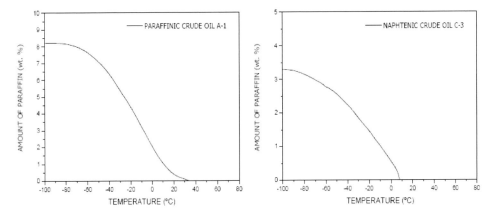

Figure 7. WPC of paraffinic A-1 and naphthenic C-3 crude oils.

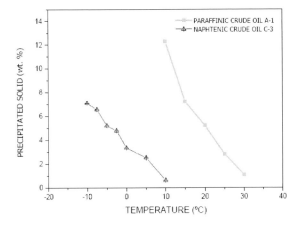

Figure 8. WPC of paraffinic crude oil A-1 and naphthenic crude oil C-3 obtained by fractional precipitation.

Table 2. Amount of precipitated wax at pour point for different crude oils

CRUDE OIL	TYPE	POUR POINT (°C)	% WAX IN POUR POINT ACCORDING TO WPC$_{DSC}$
A-1	LIGHT/ PARAFFINIC	-6	2.8
C-3	MEDIUM/ NAPHTENIC	<-38	2.2

The temperatures used for carrying out the experiments were different for each crude oil according to their characteristics. The onset temperature of fractional precipitation was established above the WAT and the temperature was decreased until the viscosity of the crude oil was high enough to stop oil flowing.

Figure 9 shows a picture of a paraffinic precipitated fraction and a saturated fraction of one of the crude oils studied. The dark color of the sample indicates the presence of trapped crude oil. Therefore, to compare the WPC obtained by fractional precipitation and DSC, the amount of trapped crude oil should be determined.

Figure 9. Appearance of a saturates sample (left) and a precipitated paraffin obtained by fractional precipitation (right).

4.3. Total Paraffin Content

Traditionally, it was considered that Burger´s method provides an estimation of the total amount of paraffin (C_{20}^{+}) because according to Jokuty et al [54], compounds with more than twenty carbon atoms precipitate at -20 °C. *Table 3* shows the amount of solid precipitated at -20 °C for a paraffinic and a naphthenic crude oil.

Table 3. Total wax amount at -20 °C for two crude oils

CRUDE OIL	SÓLID at -20 °C (%) (modified Burger´s method)	% PARAFFIN C_{20}^{+} (WPC DSC at -20°C)
A-1	15.3	4.4
C-3	7.6	1.5

The amount of solid paraffin obtained by Burger's method is larger than that provided by DSC. It means that it contains a large amount of trapped crude oil in its structure, which is necessary to determine previously to know the true amount of C_{20}^+ of each crude oil.

4.4. Determination of Trapped Crude Oil

As mentioned above, one of the drawbacks of the gravimetric determination of precipitated paraffin is the need to quantify the amount of crude oil trapped in the solid structure (porosity).

The average porosity obtained by the DSC method for the paraffinic crude oil A-1 was 87 %, and that obtained by ^{1}H-RMN was 86 %. With regard to the naphthenic crude oil C-3, the porosity obtained by DSC was 91 % and that obtained by ^{1}H-RMN corresponds to 87 %.

The average porosity values for the crude oil A-1 fractions obtained by Burger's method were 72 % and 75 % determined by DSC and ^{1}H-RMN, respectively. With regard to the naphthenic crude oil C-3, porosity values were 83 % and 81 %, determined by DSC and ^{1}H-RMN, respectively.

Moreover, when comparing the average porosity values of those fractions obtained by fractional precipitation with the porosity of fractions obtained at -20 °C it can be observed that the latter is always lower. The differences can be attributed to the presence of solvents (Burger's method), which reduce the inclusion of crude oil in the paraffinic structure.

Figures 10 and *11* show as an example the WPC of a paraffinic and a naphthenic crude oil obtained by DSC from the cooling thermogram and by fractional precipitation after discounting trapped crude oil obtained by DSC and ^{1}H-NMR.

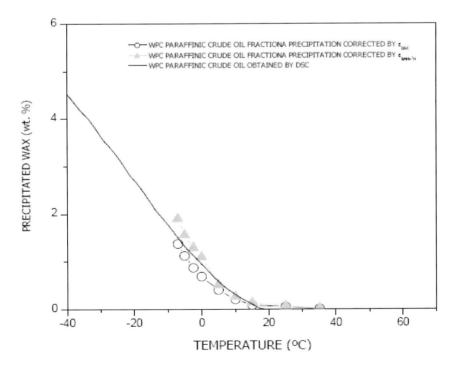

Figure 10. WPC of a paraffinic crude oil obtained by different techniques.

Generally, the method based on ^{1}H-NMR provides an amount of precipitated waxes slightly higher, being the differences more remarkable in the case of naphthenic crude oils. However, the results show that the corrected fractional precipitation curves, using both DSC and ^{1}H-NMR methods fit quite well to the curves obtained by the DSC analysis leading to consistent results despite of being so different techniques. This indicates that the method developed by our team to determine the WPC by DSC can be used since it is relatively rapid and provides reliable results.

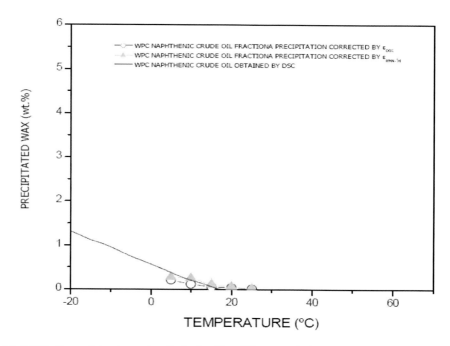

Figure 11. WPC of a naphthenic crude oil obtained by different techniques.

5. METHODS TO REMOVE WAX DEPOSITS

Although nowadays there are a wide variety of chemicals [70, 71] to inhibit wax deposition, none of them can be considered ideal. The most commonly used additives to reduce wax precipitates are polymeric materials such as polyethylene, which modify the growth of wax crystals during the cooling process. These compounds decrease the cohesive forces that hold joined the wax crystals and reduce the adhesive forces between the wax crystals and the deposition surface. The selectivity of these substances is high, so that their effectiveness is ensured.

Cho et al., in 1999, carried out a study of the effectiveness of different crude oil-soluble inhibitors by comparing their structure and concluded that the presence of an aliphatic long chain improves the inhibitor effect [72].

Pour point depressants (PPD) are other type of inhibitors. This group improves the flow properties of crude oils (viscosity and other rheological properties) and reduces gel formation at temperatures below the WAT. These compounds are incorporated into the paraffin network and make it weaker, which facilitates the breaking of the structure by shear stress. An example of this type of compound is polyethylene-co-vinyl acetate (EVA) [73, 74].

If the deposit has been already formed, the only solution is to use cleaning methods. The most commonly used are described below [75, 76].

Thermal Methods

Heat treatment only relocates the deposit, which can be or not satisfactory. A common method for removing paraffin deposits is the "hot oil" method. It is effective to dissolve wax and other hydrocarbons that are soluble in organic solvents [77]. The main drawback of this method is that the subsequent cooling of the crude oil causes again the deposition of paraffin in another part of the pipeline.

There is an alternative method where a solvent mixture is used to produce an acid-base exothermic reaction whose heat dissolves the paraffin deposited on the well or pipeline [77]. This method is not very effective because it is difficult to control the heat of reaction needed to provide the temperature to dissolve the paraffin without deposition occurring again elsewhere. Moreover, the temperatures generated can be high enough to burn the asphaltenic compounds present in the crude oil and cause permanent damage to the well.

Mechanical Methods

Mechanical removal techniques include tools and cutters with sharp points, or washing with jets of water at high pressure. None of these techniques provides a long-term solution to the problem of deposition. Wax scrapers placed on rods or wire cutters seem to be the most economical methods of control.

Solvent Use

The use of solvents containing surfactants can remove paraffin deposits [77, 78] and prevent further deposition. It is an expensive alternative and present important difficulties in the handle of the solvents. Carbon disulfide and other solvents containing halides, mainly chlorine and bromine, are the most used.

Bacterial Treatment

Bacterial treatment is a recent technique that involves the growing of special microorganisms that produce chemicals able to inhibit the formation of waxes and remove those already existing. However, microorganisms need water and adequate temperatures to survive, thus the application of this method is limited to water producing wells and temperatures below 93 °C [75, 79].

Electromagnetic Methods

The electromagnetic methods are based on the polarization of the paraffin molecules by passing the crude oil through a powerful electromagnetic field. Thus paraffin is oriented in the direction of flow and its migration to the pipe wall is prevented [75]. However, Cañas-Marín et al., in 2006, carried out a study of the influence of a static magnetic field on the WAT and the amount of precipitate, concluding that the presence of magnetic field increases the probability of formation of wax crystals [80]. For this reason it is still unknown whether the method is really effective or not.

Cold Flow

Another alternative to solve the flow assurance problems caused by waxes is called "Cold Flow". Merino et al. [81] carried out a review of this technology, which is based on the work made by Coberly in 1942 [82]. The presence of nucleation sites decreases the tendency of wax crystals to deposit on the wall. The nucleation sites make the paraffin to precipitate in the bulk solution, but reduce the amount of solids that adhere to the wall of the pipe.

The "Cold Flow" equipment is designed so that the temperature gradient between the crude oil and the wall is zero, thus avoiding deposition [83-85]. In a short distance, the crude oil is quickly cooled to the temperature of sea water and all precipitated paraffin is transported as a solid stable suspension that is not deposited. However, it can not be established that this system is to be economically viable at the field scale, since it is necessary to take into account other factors. Some of them are the considerable increase in viscosity, the tendency to gel of the oil and the influence on the deposition of other compounds such as hydrates and asphaltenes. Other limitations such as extreme operation conditions could make the maintenance difficult and expensive.

ACKNOWLEDGMENT

The authors thank Repsol for crude oil supply and financial support through the research project "Aseguramiento de flujo de crudos de petróleo: Estudio de la precipitación de parafinas".

REFERENCES

[1]   Robustillo, M. D. Ph.D. Thesis. *Flow Assurance in crude oil pipelines: wax precipitation study.* Universidad Rey Juan Carlos, ESCET, Móstoles, Madrid, Spain, July 2010.

[2]   Ronningsen, H. P.; Bjorndal, B. *Wax precipitation from Nord Sea crude oils. 1. Crystallization and dissolution temperatures and Newtonian and non-newtonian flow properties. Energy and Fuels*, 1991, 5, 895-908.

[3]   Pauly, J.; Dauphin, C.; Daridon, J. L. Liquid-solid equilibria in a decane + multi-paraffins system. *Fluid Phase Equilib.* 1998, *149*, 191-207.

[4]   Thanh NX, Hsieh M, Philip RP. *Waxes and asphaltenes in crude oils. Org. Geochem.* 1999; 30: 119-32.

[5]   Martos, C.; Coto, B.; Espada, J. J.; Robustillo, M. D.; Gómez, S.; Peña, J. L. *Experimental Determination and Characterization of Wax Fractions Precipitated as a Function of Temperature. Energy Fuels*, 2008, 22 (2), pp 708–714.

[6]   Martos, C.; Coto, B.; Espada, J. J.; Robustillo, M. D.; Peña, J. L.; Gómez, S. *Assessment of a Thermodynamic Model to describe Wax Precipitation in Flow Assurance Problems. Energy Fuels*, 2009, 23 (3), pp 1294–1298.

[7]   Martos, C.; Coto, B.; Espada, J. J.; Robustillo, M. D.; Peña, J. L.; Merino, D. *Characterization of Brazilian crude oil samples to improve the prediction of wax precipitation in flow assurance problems. Energy Fuels*, 2010, 24 (4), pp 2221–2226.

[8]   Elsharkawy, A. M.; Al-Sahhaf, T. A.; Fahim, M. A. *Wax Deposition from Middle East Crudes. Fuel* 1999, *79,* 1047–1055.

[9]   Courtesy of Repsol YPF.

[10]   http://tigger.uic.edu/~mansoori/Wax.and.Waxy.Crude_html

[11]   Martín Municio, A.; Colino Martínez, A.; *Diccionario Español de la Energía.* Repsol YPF, Madrid, 2004.

[12]   Riazi, M. R. *Characterization and Properties of Petroleum Fractions.* ASTM International Standards Worldwide. Philadelphia 2005.

[13]   Singhal, H. K.; Sahai, G.C.; Pundeer, G.S.; Chandra, K. *Designing and Selecting Wax Crystal Modifier for Optimum Field Performance Based on Crude Oil Composition.* SPE Annual Technical Conference and Exhibition, 6-9 October 1991, Dallas, Texas. SPE 22784.

[14]   Karan, K.; Ratulowski, J.; German, P. *Measurement of Waxy Crude Properties Using Novel Laboratory Techniques.* SPE 62945, 2000. Presented at the 75th Annual Technical Conference and Exhibition of the Society of Petroleum Engineers in Houston TX, October 1–4.

[15]   Coto, B.; Martos, C.; Espada, J. J.; Robustillo, M. D.; Peña, J. L. *Analysis of wax precipitation from crude oils by means of DSC: iterative procedure considering solid-liquid equilibrium equations. Fuel* 2010, *89,* 1087-1094.

[16]   Li, H.; Zhang, J.; Yan, D. *Correlations between the Pour Point / Gel Point and the Amount of Precipitated Wax for Waxy Crudes. Petroleum Science and Technology,* 2005, 23 (11-12), 1313-1322.

[17]   Kök, M. V.; Letoffe M. V., and Claudy, P. *Comparative methods in the determination of wax content and pour points of crude oils. Journal of Thermal Analysis and Calorimetry,* 2007. Volume 90, Number 3.

[18]   Uba, E. *Kingsley Ikeji. Measurement of Wax Appearance Temperature of an Offshore Live Crude Oil using Laboratory Light Transmission Method.* Nigeria Annual International Conference and Exhibition, 2-4 August 2004, Abuja, Nigeria. SPE 88963

[19]   Coutinho, J. A. P.; Daridon, J. L. *The Limitations of the Cloud Point Measurement Techniques and the Influence of the Oil Composition on its Detection. Petrol. Sci. Technol.* 23, 2005, 1113–28.

[20]   ASTM D2500 - 05 Standard Test Method for Cloud Point of Petroleum Products.

[21]   Becker, J. R. *Crude Oil Waxes, Emulsions and Asphaltenes.* PennWell, 1997.

[22]   Hammami, A.; Raines, M. *Paraffin Deposition from Crude Oils.* Comparison of Laboratory Results to Field Data. SPE 38776, 1997, 273-287.

[23]   Rizzo, H.; Carrier, J.; Castillo, S.; Acevedo, and J. Pauly. *A new experimental setup for the liquid–solid phase transition determination in crude oils under high pressure conditions. Fuel.* Volume 86, Issues 12-13, 2007, 1758-1764.

[24]   Erickson, D. D.; Niesen, V. G.; Brown, T. S. *Thermodynamic Measurement and Prediction of Paraffin Precipitation in Crude Oil.* 1993. SPE 26604.

[25]   Létoffé, J. M.; Claudy, P.; Garcin, M.; Volle, J. L. *Evaluation of crystallized fractions of crude oils by differential scanning calorimetry: correlation with gas chromatography. Fuel* 1995, 74, 1, 92-95.

[26]   Ferworn, K.; Hammami, A. *Control of Wax Deposition: An Experimental Investigation of Crystal Morphology and an Evaluation of Various Chemical Solvents.* SPE 37240, 1997, 291-310.

[27] García, M.; Orea, M.; Carbognani, L. *The Effect of Paraffinic Fractions On Crude Oil Wax Crystallization*. 3rd International Symposium on Colloid Chemistry in Oil Production (ISCOP), Huatulco, Oaxaca, Mexico, November 14-17, 1999.

[28] Magri, N.F., Kalpakci, B., Nuebling, L. *Evaluation of Paraffin Crystal Modifiers by Dynamic Videomicroscopy*. International Symposium on Oilfield Chemistry, 18-21 February 1997, Houston, Texas. SPE 37241.

[29] Roehner, R. M.; Hanson, F. V. *Determination of Wax Precipitation Temperature and Amount of Precipitated Solid Wax versus Temperature for Crude Oils Using FT-IR Spectroscopy*. Energy and Fuels 2001, 15, 756-763.

[30] Hanson, F. V.; Fletcher, J. V.; Karthik, R. *Determination Of Solid-Liquid Equilibria Data For Mixtures of Heavy Hydrocarbons in a Light Solvent*. Department of Chemical and Fuels Engineering. University of Utah. June 2003.

[31] Pedersen, K. S.; Skovborg, P. *Wax Precipitation from North Sea Crude Oils. 4. Thermodynamic Modeling*. Energy and Fuels 1991, 5, 924-932.

[32] Calange, S.; Ruffier-Meray, V.; Behar, E. *Onset Crystallization Temperature and Deposit Amount for Waxy Crudes: Experimental Determination and Thermodynamic Modeling*. SPE 37239, 1997, 283-290.

[33] Hansen, A. B.; Pedersen, W. B.; Larsen, E.; Nielsen, A. B.; Ronningsen, H. *Wax Precipitation from Nord Sea Crude Oils. 3. Precipitation and Dissolution of Wax Studied by Differential Scanning Calorimetry*. Energy and Fuels, 1991, 5 (6), 914-923.

[34] Kruka, V. R.; Cadena, E. R.; Long, T. E. *Cloud-Point Determination for Crude Oils*. J. Pet. Technol.; 1995, 681-687.

[35] Kok, M.; Létoffé, J. M.; Claudy, P.; Martin, D.; Garcin, M.; Volle, J. *Comparison of wax appearance temperatures of crude oils by differential scanning calorimetry, thermomicroscopy and viscometry*. Fuel, Vol. 75, No. 7, pp. 787-790, 1996.

[36] Coutinho, J. A. P.; Calange, S.; Ruffier-Meray, V. *Measuring the Amount of Crystallised Solution Using DSC*, Canadian, J. Chem. Engng. 1997; 75: 1075.

[37] ASTM D6371 - 05 Standard Test Method for Cold Filter Plugging Point of Diesel and Heating Fuels.

[38] Deo, M.; Wavrek, D. A. *Wax Precipitation: Compositional Study and Cloud Point Measurements*. 2nd International Symposium on Colloid Chemistry in Oil Production, SPE, Río de Janeiro 1997, paper 29.

[39] Adewusi, V. A. *Waxing Tendencies and Rheological Evaluation of Crude-Condensate Blends for an Offshore Pipeline Transportation*. Pet. Sci. Technol. 1998, 16 (6 and 8), 697-717.

[40] Singh, P.; Fogler, S. *Prediction of the Wax Content of the Incipient Wax-oil Gel in a Pipeline: An application of the Controlled-Stress Rheometer*. Department of Chemical Engineering, University of Michigan, 1999.

[41] Kulkarni, V. B. *Determination and Prediction of Wax Deposition From Alaska North Slope Crude Oil*. SPE 11972. 2008.

[42] Claudy, P.; Letoffe, J. M.; Bonardi, B.; Vassilakis, D., and Damin, B. *Interactions Between n-Alkanes and Cloud Point-Cold Filter Plugging Point Depressants in a Diesel Fuel. A Thermodynamic Study*. Fuel, 1993, 72:821.

[43] Coutinho, J. A. P.; Mirante, F.; Ribeiro, J. C.; Sansot, J. M., and Daridon, J. L. *Cloud and Pour Points in Fuel Blends*. Fuel, 2002, 81:963.

[44] Coutinho, J. A. P.; Da Silva, J. A. L.; Ferreira, A.; Soares, M. R., and Daridon, J. L. *Evidence for the Aging of Wax Deposits in Crude Oils by Ostwald Ripening. Pet. Sci. Tech.*, 2003, 21: 381.

[45] Da Silva, J. A. L., and Coutinho, J. A. P. *Dynamic Rheological Analysis of the Gelation Behaviour of Waxy Crude Oils. Rheologica Acta*, 2004, 43 (5): 433–441.

[46] Cassiède, M.; Pauly, J.; Milhet, M.; Rivaletto, M.; Marrucho, I. M.; Coutinho, J. A. P.; Daridon J. L. *A Quartz Crystal Microbalance Technique to Study Wax Crystallization in the Presence of Gas. Meas. Sci. Technol.* 19, 2008, 065704 (7 pp).

[47] Venkatesan, R.; Singh, P.; Fogler, H. S. *Delineating the Pour Point and Gelation Temperature of Waxy Crude Oils.* SPE 72237, 2002.

[48] Hammami, A.; Ratulowski, J.; Coutinho, J. A. P. *Cloud Points: Can We Measure or Model Them?. Petroleum Science and Technology*, 2003, 21 (3 and 4), 345–358.

[49] Burger, E. D.; Perkins T. K.; Striegler, J.H. *Studies of Wax Deposition in the Trans Alaska Pipeline. J. Petrol Technol.* 1981, *3*, 1075–86.

[50] Coutinho, J. A. P.; Daridon, J. L. *Low-Pressure Modeling of Wax Formation in Crude Oils. Energy and Fuels* 2001, *15*, 1454-1460.

[51] UOP Method 46-85. *Paraffin Wax Content of Petroleum Oils and Asphalts*, UOP Methods, UOP Inc., Des Plaines, 1985.

[52] Nermen, H. M.; Magdy, T. Z. *Separation of microcrystalline waxes from local crude petrolatums. Petrol Sci. Technol.* 2004, *11*, 15553–15569.

[53] Handoo, J.; Gupta, A. K.; Agrawal, K. M. *Characterization of total waxes derived from some Indian crude oils by fractionation. Petrol Sci. Technol.* 1997, 15–56.

[54] Jokuty, P.; Whiticar, S.; Wang, Z.; Landriault, M.; Sigouin, L.; Mullint, J. *A New Method for the Determination of Wax Content of Crude Oils.* SpillScience and Technology Bulletin, Vol. 3, No. 4, pp. 195-198, 1996.

[55] Espada, J. J.; Coutinho, J. A. P. and Peña, J. L. *Evaluation of Methods for the Extraction and Characterization of Waxes from Crude Oils. Energy Fuels* 2010, 24, 1837–1843

[56] Jennings, D.W., and Weispfennig, K. *Effects of Shear and Temperature on Wax Deposition: Coldfinger Investigation with a Gulf of Mexico Crude Oil. Energy Fuels* 2005, 19: 1376–1386.

[57] Chen, J.; Zhang, J.; Li, H. *Determining the Wax Content of Crude Oils by Using Differential Scanning Calorimetry. Thermochimica Acta* 410, 2004, 23-26.

[58] Coutinho, J. A. P.; Ruffier-Meray, V. *A new technique for measuring SLE phase diagrams using calorimetry. Fluid Phase Equilib.* 1998, *148*, 147–60.

[59] Queimada, A. J. N.; Dauphin, C.; Marrucho I. M.; Coutinho, J. A. P. *Low temperature behaviour of refined products from DSC measurements and their thermodynamical modelling. Thermochim. Acta* 2001, *372*, 93–101.

[60] Poling, B.E.; Prausnitz, J.M.; OConnell JP. *The properties of gases and liquids.* 5th ed. McGrawHill: New York; 2001.

[61] Won, K.W. *Thermodynamic calculation of cloud point temperatures and wax phase compositions of refined hydrocarbon mixtures. Fluid Phase Equilibria* 1989; 53:377–96.

[62] Marano, J.J.; Holder, G.D. *General equation for correlating the thermophysical properties of n-paraffins, n-olefins, and other homologous* series. *2. Asymptotic behavior correlations for PVT properties. Ind. Eng. Chem. Res.* 1997; 36:1895–907.

[63] Marrero J, Gani R. *Group-contribution based estimation of pure component properties. Fluid Phase Equilibria* 2001; 183–184:183–208.

[64] Ji, H.Y; Tohidi, B; Danesh, A; Todd, A. C. *Wax phase equilibria: developing a thermodynamic model using a systematic approach. Fluid Phase Equilibria* 2004; 216:201–17.

[65] Han, S.; Huang, Z; Senra, M.; Hoffmann, R. and Fogler, H. S. *Method to Determine the Wax Solubility Curve in Crude Oil from Centrifugation and High Temperature Gas Chromatography Measurements. Energy Fuels*, 2010, 24 (3), 1753–1761

[66] Coto, B.; Martos, C.; Peña, J. L.; Espada, J. J.; Robustillo, M. D. *A new method for the determination of wax precipitation from non-diluted crude oils by fractional precipitation. Fuel* 2008, *87*, 2090-2094.

[67] Coto, B.; Martos, C.; Espada, J. J.; Robustillo, M. D.; Merino-García, D.; Peña, J. L. *A new DSC-based method to determine the wax porosity of mixtures precipitated from crude oils. Energy Fuels*, 2011, 25 (4), pp 1707–1713

[68] Labes Carrier, C.; Ronningsen, H. P.; Kolnes, J.; Leporcher, E. *Wax deposition in north sea gas condensate and oil systems: comparison between operational experience an dmodel prediction.* SPE 77573. 2002.

[69] Paso, K.; Kallevik, H.; Sjöblom, J. *Measurement of Wax appearance temperature using near-infrared (NIR) Scattering. Energy Fuels* 2009, 23, 4988-4994.

[70] Fan, Y., and Llave, F. M.: *"Chemical Removal of Formation Damage From Paraffin Deposition Part I - Solubility and Dissolution Rate".* Latin American and Caribbean Petroleum Engineering Conference, 30 August-3 September 1997, Río de Janeiro, Brazil. SPE 31128.

[71] Nguyen Phuong Tung, Nguyen Thi Phuong Phong, Bui Quang Khanh Long, IMS-Vietnam NCST; Phung Dinh Thuc, Tong Canh Son, VietsovPetro. *Studying the Mechanisms of Crude Oil Pour Point and Viscosity Reductions When Developing Chemical Additives With the Use of Advanced Analytical Tools.* SPE International Symposium on Oilfield Chemistry, 13-16 February 2001, Houston, Texas. SPE 65024.

[72] Cho, S. Y.; Fogler, H. S. *Efforts on solving the problem of paraffin deposit. I: Using oil-soluble inhibitors. Journal of Industrial and Engineering Chemistry*, 5, 2, 1999, 123-127.

[73] Machado, A. L. C.; Lucas, E. F.; González, G. *Poly (Ethylene-co-Vinyl Acetate) (EVA) as Wax Inhibitor of a Brazilian Crude Oil: Oil Viscosity, Pour Point and Phase Behavior of Organic Solutions. Journal of Petroleum Science and Engineering*, 32, 2, 2001, 159-165 (7).

[74] Pedersen, K. S. *Influence of Wax Inhibitors on Wax Appearance Temperature, Pour Point, and Viscosity of Waxy Crude Oils. Energy and Fuels* 2003, 17, 321-328.

[75] Towler, B. F.; Rebbapragada, S. *Mitigation of paraffin wax deposition in cretaceous crude oils of Wyoming.* Journal of Petroleum Science and Engineering 2004, 45, 11-19.

[76] Biao, W.; Lijian, D. *Paraffin Characteristics of Waxy Crude Oils in China and the Methods of Paraffin Removal and Inhibition.* SPE 29954. 1995.

[77] Kruka, V. R. *Process for Removal of Wax Deposits.* United States Patent 4646837. Houston, Texas, 1987.

[78] Barker, K. M.; Newberry, K. M.; Yin, Y. R. *Paraffin Solvation in the Oilfield. SPE International Symposium on Oilfield Chemistry,* 13-16 February 2001, Houston, Texas. SPE 64995.

[79] Bishop, M. D., and Woodward, D. R. *Biological Paraffin Control Systems Show Production Increases in Addition to Controlling Paraffin.* Petroleum Society of CIM/Society of Petroleum Engineers, Calgary, June 10–13, 1990, Paper No. CIM/SPE 90-56, pp. 56-1 to 56-9.

[80] Cañas-Marin, W.A.; Ortiz-Arango, J. D.; Guerrero-Aconcha, U. E.; Lira-Galeana, C. *Thermodynamics of Wax Precipitation under the Influence of Magnetic Fields. Thermodynamics,* 2006. Vol. 52, No. 8, 2887- 2897.

[81] Merino-García, D.; Correra, S. *Cold Flow: A Review of a Technology to Avoid Wax Deposition. Petroleum Science and Technology,* 2008, 26: 446–459.

[82] Coberly, C. J. (1942). *Method for Preventing Wax Deposits in Tubing.* U.S. Patent 2303823, December 1, 1942.

[83] Brown, T. S.; Niesen, V. G. and Erickson, D. D. *Measurement and Prediction of the Kinetics of Paraffin Deposition.* SPE Paper 26548. Proceedings SPE 68th Annual Technical Conference and Exhibition, Houston, TX, October 3–6, 1993.

[84] Hsu, J. J. C. and Brubaker, J. P. *Wax Deposition and Scale-up Modelling for Waxy Live Crudes under Turbulent Flow Conditions.* SPE Paper 29976. SPE International Meeting Beijing, China, November 14–17, 1995.

[85] Bidmus, H. O.; and Mehrotra, A. K. *Heat-Transfer Analogy for Wax Deposition from Paraffinic Mixtures. Ind. Eng. Chem. Res.* 43: 791, 2004.

In: Oil: Production, Consumption and Environmental Impact
Editor: Shuangning Xiu

ISBN: 978-1-61942-877-5
© 2012 Nova Science Publishers, Inc.

Chapter 3

VEGETABLE OILS IN THE BIODIESEL INDUSTRY

*Verónica Leticia Colin**
PROIMI-CONICET, Tucumán, Argentina

ABSTRACT

Petroleum accounts for a large percentage of the world´s energy consumption, ranging from a low of 32% for Europe and Asia to a high of 53% for the Middle East. The largest volume products in the industry are fuel oil and petrol, both important primary energy sources. Over 50 species of plant produce oils that can be extracted from their seeds, nuts or kernels. All, technically, can be used as fuel or transformed into biodiesel. As part of the search for renewable energy sources, biodiesel compounds, which are commonly obtained from vegetable oils by transesterization with methanol or ethanol, represent an increase in energy input of about 30% and a reduction in CO_2 emissions of up to 60%, compared to conventional diesel. The main feedstocks include rapeseeds, sunflower seeds, soybeans and palm oil seeds, from which the oil is extracted chemically or mechanically. Although the global market for biodiesel has seen explosive growth in last year, there are lingering questions about feedstock availability, since the biodiesel industry now consumes a large percentage of vegetable oils produced. Besides, vegetable oils production is not sufficient to replace the demand for fossil fuels. Also, the environmental and socio-economic impacts of large-scale biodiesel production and commercialization include increased deforestation of native forests and threats to biodiversity, indiscriminate expansion of the agricultural frontier and displacement of other crops used for food or livestock feed. This chapter focuses on key questions related to the environmental and socio-economic impacts of the biodiesel industry's consumption of vegetable oils as well as to emerging technologies and the transition to alternative feedstocks in pursuit of sustainable biodiesel production.

---

* Corresponding author. Tel: +54 381 4344888; fax: +54 381 4344887. E-mail: veronicacollin@yahoo.com.ar.

1. INTRODUCTION

The world is now confronted with the twin crises of fossil fuel depletion and environmental degradation. The indiscriminate extraction and consumption of fossil fuels has led to a substantial reduction in petroleum reserves [1]. Petroleum-based fuels are obtained from limited reserves, and these finite reserves are also highly concentrated in certain regions of the world. Therefore, countries that naturally lack these resources are also facing a foreign trade crisis, mainly due to the import of petroleum crude oil. In this context, active research programs have arisen in order to reduce reliance on fossil fuels by the use of alternative and sustainable fuel sources, and thus to prolong the time over which fossil fuels will remain available [2].

In 1982, the first International Conference on Plant and Vegetable Oils as Fuels was held in Fargo, North Dakota [3]. The primary topics discussed at this meeting included fuel costs, oil seed processing and extraction, and the effects of vegetable oil fuels on engine performance and longevity. Over 50 species of plants produce oils that can be extracted from their seeds, nuts or kernels. Technically, vegetable oils as well as their derivatives can be used as fuel for diesel engines [4–8]. Among the various possible derivatives is biodiesel, a mixture of mono alkyl esters of long chain free fatty acids. Biodiesel has become increasingly attractive worldwide because it can be made from renewable resources and combines high performance with environmental benefits. Biodiesel represents an increase in energy inputs of 30% and CO_2 emission reductions of 40%-60% compared to those of petrodiesel. In commercial processes, highly refined vegetable oils, primarily consisting of triglycerides, are typically used as biodiesel feedstocks [9]. However, in order to make the use of biodiesel more economically viable, the use of virgin oils, which in terms of cost account for 80% of the total estimated production cost of biodiesel, could be replaced with more economical feedstock sources [10–13].

Although the global market for biodiesel has seen explosive growth in recent years, their production is currently the subject of a wide-ranging societal debate. Questions of costs, security of energy supply, greenhouse gas emissions, sustainability of production systems and impact on food production or biodiversity are some of the many issues that have been debated following renewed interest in biodiesel as a source of energy.

This chapter focuses on key questions related to the environmental and socio-economic impacts of the biodiesel industry's consumption of vegetable oils as well as to emerging technologies and the transition to alternative feedstocks in pursuit of sustainable biodiesel production.

2. VEGETABLE OILS

2.1. Chemical Composition and Properties as Fuel

Oils and fats are primarily water-insoluble, hydrophobic substances from the plant and animal kingdoms [14]. Triglycerides are esters of three fatty acids and one glycerol (Figure 1). From a chemical point of view, oils and fats consist of 90-98% triglycerides and a much smaller amount of mono- and diglycerides.

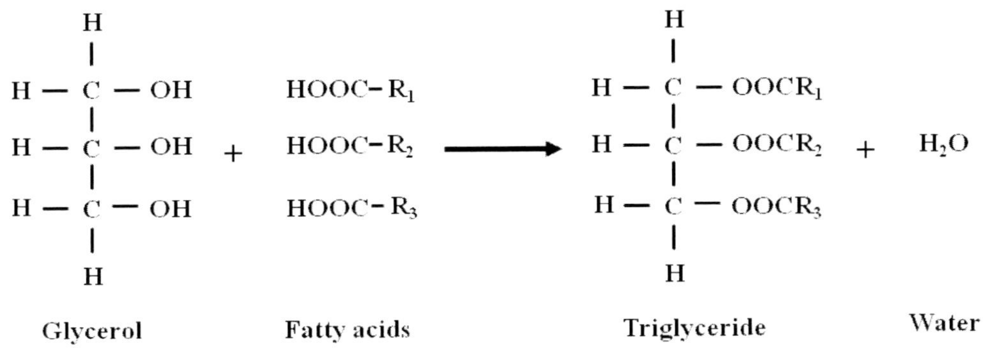

Figure 1. Synthesis of vegetable oils and fats.

Table 1. Chemical structure of common fatty acids

Name of fatty acid	Chemical name of fatty acids	Structure (xx:y)	Formula
Lauric	Dodecanoic	12:0	$C_{12}H_{24}O_2$
Myristic	Tetradecanoic	14:0	$C_{14}H_{28}O_2$
Palmitic	Hexadecanoic	16:0	$C_{16}H_{32}O_2$
Stearic	Octadecanoic	18:0	$C_{18}H_{36}O_2$
Oleic cis-9-	Octadecenoic	18:1	$C_{18}H_{34}O_2$
Linoleic cis-9,cis-12-	Octadecadienoic	18:2	$C_{18}H_{32}O_2$
Linolenic	cis-9,cis-12,cis-15 Octadecatrienoic	18:3	$C_{18}H_{30}O_2$
Arachidic	Eicosanoic	20:0	$C_{20}H_{40}O_2$
Behenic	Docosanoic	22:0	$C_{22}H_{44}O_2$
Erucle	cis-13-Docosenoic	22:1	$C_{32}H_{42}O_2$
Lignoceric	Tetracosanoic	24:0	$C_{24}H_{48}O_2$

(xx:y) carbon chain length: number of unsaturated bonds.

The fatty acids vary in their carbon chain length and in the number of unsaturated bonds they contain. Table 1 summarizes the fatty acid composition of some vegetable oils [15–18].

Oils from different sources have different fatty acid compositions (Table 2). When three fatty acids are identical, the product is simple triglycerides, when they are dissimilar the product possesses mixed triglyceride fatty acids, which are fully saturated with hydrogen have no double bonds. Those with one missing hydrogen molecule have one double bond between carbon atoms and are called monosaturated. Those with more than one missing hydrogen molecule and more than one double bond are called polyunsaturated.

Vegetative oils are generally characterized by certain fuel-related properties [19, 24–26] (Table 3). They have high molecular weights that vary in the range of 600-900 KD, which are three or more times higher than those of petrodiesel. The high viscosities possessed by vegetable oils are due to large molecular masses and chemical structures. The cloud, pour and flash points of vegetable oils are also generally higher. Cetane numbers are in the range of 34-42. The volumetric heating values of vegetatble oils are in the range of 39-40 MJ/kg, which are lower than those of petrodiesel (about 45 MJ/kg). The presence of chemically bound oxygen in vegetable oils also lowers their heating values by about 10%.

Table 2. Percentage of fatty acids for various vegetable oils

Oil	12:0	14:0	16:0	16:1	18:0	18:1	18:2	18:3	20:0	22:0	22:1	24:0	Other	Reference
Crambe	-	-	2.0	-	1.0	19.0	9.0	7.0	2.0	1.0	59.0	1.0	-	[19]
Peanut	-	-	11.4	-	2.4	48.3	32.0	0.2	-	-	-	-	9.1	[20]
Palm	-	-	42.6	0.3	4.4	40.5	10.1	0.2	-	-	-	-	-	[16]
Rapeseed	-	-	3.5	0.1	0.9	54.1	22.3	-	-	-	-	-	-	[21]
Sesame	-	-	13.1	-	3.9	52.8	30.2	-	-	-	-	-	0.2	[16]
Corn	-	-	6.0	-	2.0	44.0	48.0	-	-	-	-	-	-	[21]
Sunflower	-	-	6.4	0.1	2.9	17.7	72.9	-	-	-	-	-	-	[16]
Cottonseed	-	-	28.7	-	0.9	13.0	57.4	-	-	-	-	-	-	[16]
Soybean	-	-	11.9	0.3	4.1	23.2	54.2	6.3	-	-	-	-	-	[22]
Safflower	-	-	7.3	0.1	1.9	13.5	77.0	-	-	-	-	-	-	[21]
Babassu	48.0	16.0	10.0	-	2.0	14.0	5.0	-	-	-	-	-	5.0	[17]
Linseed	-	-	5.1	0.3	2.5	18.9	18.1	55.1	-	-	-	-	-	[16]
Jatropha	-	-	14.2	0.7	7.0	44.7	32.8	0.2	-	-	-	-	-	[23]
karanja	-	-	10.2	-	7.0	51.8	17.7	3.6	-	-	-	-	-	[20]
Rice bran	-	0.4-0.6	12-16.5	-	1.7-2.5	39-44	26-35	-	0.4-0.6	-	-	0.4-0.9	-	[24]
Castor	-	-	1.1	0	3.1	4.9	1.3	0	-	-	-	-	-	[16]
Mahua	-	-	16-28	-	20-25	41-51	9-14	-	0.0-3.3	-	-	-	89.6	[24]
Sesame	-	-	13.1	-	3.9	52.8	30.2	-	-	-	-	-	-	[16]
Peanut	-	0	11	-	2	48	32	1	1	2	0	1	-	[19]

Table 3. Physical properties of the most common vegetable oils

Vegetable oil	Kinematic viscosity (mm²/s)	Cloud point (°C)	Pour point (°C)	Flash point (°C)	Cetane number (°C)	Heating value (MJ/kg)	Carbon residue (wt·%)
Crambe	53.6	10.0	-12.2	274	44.6	40.5	0.23
Peanut	39.6	12.8	-6.7	271	41.8	39.8	0.24
Palm	39.6	31.0	-	267	42.0	-	0.23
Rapeseed	37.0	-3.9	-31.7	246	37.6	39.7	0.30
Sesame	35.5	-3.9	-9.4	260	40.2	39.3	0.24
Corn	34.9	-1.1	-40	277	37.6	39.5	0.24
Sunflower	33.9	7.2	-15.0	274	37.1	39.6	0.27
Cottonseed	33.5	1.7	-15	234	41.8	39.5	0.24
Soybean	32.6	-3.9	-12.2	254	37.9	39.6	0.25
Safflower	31.3	18.3	-6.7	260	41.3	39.5	0.25
Babassu	30.3	20.0	-	150	38.0	-	-
Linseed	27.2	1.5	-15.0	241	34.6	39.3	0.22
Jatropha	38.0	9	3	235	48	37.5	-
Karanja	7.3	9	3	228	-	-	-
Diesel	3.06	-15 to 5	-35 to -15	60–80	40-55	43.8	-

2.2. Performance of Vegetable Oils as Fuel

The use of vegetable oils as alternative fuels was first established in 1893, when the inventor of the diesel engine, Rudolph Diesel, first used peanut oil in his new compression-ignition engine [27]. In the 1930s and 1940s vegetable oils were used as diesel fuels, but usually only in emergency situations. During World War II, Seddon [28] experimented with using several different vegetable oils in a Perkins P6 diesel engine with great success. The results of this experiment showed that vegetable oils could be used to power a vehicle under normal operating conditions. However, not much more was done until the late 1970s and early 1980s, when concerns about high petroleum prices motivated extensive experimentation with oils and fats as alternative fuels. In these circumstances, Bruwer et al. [29] studied the use of sunflower seed oil as a renewable energy source. When operating tractors with 100% sunflower oil as fuel instead of petroleum diesel, an 8% power loss occurred after 1000 h of operation. Yarbrough et al. [30] experienced similar results when testing six different sunflower oils as petroleum fuel replacements. Raw sunflower oils were found to be unsuitable, while refined sunflower oil was found to be satisfactory. Bacon et al. [31] also evaluated the use of several vegetable oils as potential fuel sources. Although short-term engine test results were promising, Bacon recommended long-term engine testing to determine the overall effects of using vegetables oils as a fuel in diesel engines. Schoedder [32] used rapeseed oils to replace petroleum fuels in Germany with mixed results. Short-term engine tests indicated that rapeseed oil had similar energy outputs when compared to petroleum. However, initial long-term engine tests showed that difficulties arose in engine operation after 100 hours. The investigators indicated that further long-term testing was needed to determine whether these difficulties could be overcome.

Tahir et al. [33] tested sunflower oil as a fuel in agricultural tractors. Sunflower oil viscosity was 14% higher than petrodiesel at 37°C. Engine performance using the sunflower oil was similar to that of petrodiesel, but with a slight decrease in fuel economy. Oxidation of the sunflower oil left heavy gum and wax deposits on test equipment, which could lead to engine failure. Auld et al. [34] used rapeseed oil to study the effects of using an alternative fuel in diesel engines. An analysis of the rapeseed oil showed a relationship between viscosity and fatty acid chain length. Engine power and torque results using rapeseed oil were similar those of petrodiesel. Results of their short-term tests also indicated that further long-term testing was needed to evaluate rapeseed oil's effects on engine durability. Bettis et al. [35] evaluated sunflower, safflower, and rapeseed oils as possible sources for liquid fuels. The vegetable oils were found to contain 94-95% of the energy content of petrodiesel, and to be approximately 15 times more viscous. Although short-term engine tests indicated that power output for vegetable oils was nearly equivalent to that of petrodiesel, long-term durability tests revealed severe problems. Bettis et al. [35] and Engler et al. [36] reported that sunflower seed oil is acceptable only for short-term use as a fuel source, but long-term durability tests indicated severe problems due to carbonization within the combustion chamber. Pryor et al. [37] conducted short- and long-term engine performance tests using 100% soybean oil in a small diesel engine. Short-term results indicated that the soybean oil's performance was equivalent to that of petrodiesel. However, long-term engine testing was aborted due to power loss and carbon buildup on the injectors. Reid et al. [38] evaluated chemical and physical properties of 14 vegetable oils. They pointed out that the oils are very differently from petroleum-based fuel because of 'high viscosity'. As mentioned here, despite the general success seen when diesel engines are operated on vegetable oil during short-term performance tests, the real measure of success when using vegetable oil as a diesel fuel extender or replacement depends primarily on the performance of vegetable oils in engines over longer periods of time. However, various studies have indicated that potential problems such as stuck piston rings, carbon buildup on injectors, fuel system failure, and lubricating oil contamination existed when vegetable oils were used as alternative fuels. The main drawback of vegetable oils for direct utilization as fuel in conventional diesel engines is related to their high viscosity [39, 40], which causes incomplete fuel atomization, formation of carbon deposits on injectors, sticking piston rings and engine oil deterioration [41]. In this context, considerable efforts have been made to develop vegetable oil derivatives that approximate the properties and performance of hydrocarbon-based diesel fuels.

2.3. Derivatives of Vegetable Oils as Fuels

The problems with substituting vegetable oils for diesel fuels are mostly associated with their high viscosities (11-17 times higher than petrodiesel). Also, polymerization as a result of the reactivity of C-C double bonds that may be present can lower volatility, which causes the formation of carbon deposits in engines due to incomplete combustion, as well as oil ring sticking, while thickening and gelling of the lubricating oils as a result of contamination are also possible problems [7]. However, there are at least four different ways to reduce the viscosity of vegetable oils to improve their performance as diesel fuel:

2.3.1. Dilution with Petrodiesel

Vegetable oils can be blended with petrodiesel fuel, which can improve the physicochemical properties of the oils. Vegetable oil-petrodiesel fuel blending is a simple way to reduce the viscosity of straight vegetable oil, since this method does not require any chemical process [42]. Nevertheless, the long-term use of this blending method in a modern diesel engine becomes impractical because of the associated decrease in power output and thermal efficiency by carbon deposits.

Engelman et al. [43] presented data for 10-50% soybean oil-petrodiesel fuel blends tested in diesel engines. For the fuel blends studied, it was generally observed that vegetable oils could be used as a fuel source in low concentrations. However, fuel blends containing 60% or higher concentrations of vegetable oil caused the engine to sputter. Sims et al. [44] indicated that vegetable oils, particularly rapeseed oil, could be used as a replacement for petrodiesel. Their initial short-term engine tests showed that a 50% vegetable oil fuel blend had no adverse effects. However, in long-term tests they encountered injector pump failure and cold-starting problems. Bartholomew [45] reported that vegetable oils mixed with petrodiesel in small amounts did not cause engine failure. Short-term testing showed that 50/50 blends were successful, but that 20% vegetable oil fuel blends were better. Studies by Hofman et al. [46] and Peterson et al. [47] indicated that while vegetable oil fuel blends had encouraging results in short-term testing, problems occurred in long-term durability tests. Carbon buildup, ring sticking, and lubricating oil contamination combined to cause engine failure when vegetable oils were used in high percentages (50% or more) as diesel fuel substitutes. International Harvester Company [48] reported that cottonseed oil-petrodiesel fuel blends behaved like petroleum-based fuels in short-term performance and emissions tests. However, engine durability was an issue during extended use of these fuel blends because of carbon deposits and fueling system problems. Wagner and Peterson [49] reported mixed results when using rapeseed oil as a substitute fuel. Attempts to heat the oil fuel mixture prior to combustion exhibited no measurable improvements in the fuel injection process. Severe engine damage was also noted during short-term engine testing with rapeseed oil. However, a long-term test using a 70% rapeseed-petrodiesel fuel blend was successful for 850 hours with no apparent signs of wear, contamination of lubricating oil, or loss of power. Pestes and Stanislao [50] used a one-to-one blend of vegetable oil and diesel fuel to study piston ring deposits. Premature piston ring sticking and carbon buildup due to the use of the one-to-one fuel blend caused engine failure. Nag et al. [5] performed studies involving the use of seed oils from native plants from India. Performance tests using fuel blends with up to 50% seed oil from the Indian Amulate plant exhibited no loss of power. Sapaun et al. [51] reported that studies in Malaysia using palm oils as petrodiesel fuel substitutes, exhibited encouraging results. Performance tests indicated that power outputs were nearly the same for palm oil, blends of palm oil and petrodiesel, and 100% petrodiesel. Short-term tests using palm oil fuels showed no signs of adverse combustion-chamber wear, increases in carbon deposits, or lubricating oil contamination. McDonnell et al. [52] studied the use of a semi-refined rapeseed oil as a petrodiesel extender. Test results indicated that the rapeseed oil could serve as a fuel extender at mixture rates up to 25%. However, as a result of using rapeseed oil as a fuel source, injector life was shortened because of carbon buildup.

Based upon extensive experimentation, long-term engine testing research mostly shows that engine durability is affected when fuel blends contain more than 20% vegetable oil by volume. Therefore, more work is needed to determine whether fuel blends containing less than 20% vegetable oil can be used successfully as petrodiesel fuel extenders.

2.3.2. Microemulsion

Formation of microemulsions is another of the four potential solutions for solving problems related to vegetable oil viscosity. Microemulsions are isotropic, clear or translucent, thermodynamically stable dispersions of oil, water, a surfactant, and often a small amphiphilic molecule known as a co-surfactant [7, 53]. Microemulsion-based fuels are sometimes also termed "hybrid fuels", although blends of petrodiesel fuel with vegetable oils have also been called hybrid fuels [54].

To solve the problem of the high viscosity of vegetable oils, microemulsions using immiscible liquids, such as methanol, ethanol and ionic or non-ionic amphiphiles have been studied. It has been demonstrated that the short-term performance of both ionic and non-ionic microemulsions of aqueous ethanol in soybean oil are nearly equivalent to that of No. 2 petrodiesel fuel [19]. On the other hand, Ziejewski et al. [55] prepared a microemulsion containing 53% (v/v) alkali-refined and winterized sunflower oil, 13.3% (v/v) 190-proof ethanol and 33.4% (v/v) 1-butanol. This non-ionic microemulsion had a cetane number of 25 and an ash content of less than 0.01%. Lower viscosities and improved injector spray patterns were observed with an increase of 1-butanol. Ma and Hanna [6] prepared and evaluated a non-ionic fuel containing 50% No. 2 petrodiesel, 25% degummed and alkali-refined soybean oil, 5% 190-proof ethanol and 20% 1-butanol. Although the fuel passed the screening test, carbon and lacquer deposits on the injector tips, intake valves and tops of the cylinder liners represented major problems. The non-ionic fuel performed better than a 25% blend of sunflower oil in diesel oil. Engine performance was the same for a microemulsion of 53% sunflower oil and a 25% blend of sunflower oil in petrodiesel. A microemulsion fuel containing soybean oil, methanol, 2-octanol, and a cetane enhancer was the least costly vegetable oil-based alternative diesel fuel [54].

2.3.3. Pyrolysis

The pyrolysis of fats has been investigated for more than 100 years, especially in those areas of the world that lack petroleum deposits [6]. The goal of pyrolysis is the optimization of high-value fuel products from biomass by thermal and catalytic means [56]. The pyrolyzed material can be any type of biomass, such as vegetable oils, animal fats, wood, bio-waste, etc. Different types of vegetable oils show significant differences in the composition of the thermally decomposed oil that pyrolysis produces [7]. The main components are alkanes and alkanes, which account for approximately 60% of the total feeder weight, while carboxylic acids account for another 9.6-16.1%. The fuel properties of the liquid fractions of thermally decomposed vegetable oils are likely to be similar to those of diesel fuel. Many types of vegetable oil have been subjected to pyrolysis conditions, including soybean [7, 8, 57, 58], rapeseed [22, 59], palm [60], cottonseed [54], castor [8], safflower [59], olive [61], and tung [62].

2.3.4. Transesterification

In recent years, research interest in the use of raw vegetable oils as a fuel additive has greatly decreased. Because of engine durability problems encountered by researchers using raw vegetable oils as a diesel fuel in the early 1980's, most have opted to turn their attention to chemically modified vegetable fuels, more commonly known as biodiesel, instead of unrefined vegetable oils.

Harrington [63] reported that the fatty acid methyl esters obtained by transesterification of seed oils and other fats have been found suitable for usage as fuel in diesel engines, because transesterification provides a fuel viscosity that is close to that of petrodiesel. Therefore, the transesterification process, described below, is performed in order to lower the viscosity of vegetable oils, and is now the most commonly used method for manufacturing biodiesel.

3. BIODIESEL INDUSTRY

3.1. Chemical Composition and Properties of Biodiesel

Chemically, biodiesel comprises of a mixture of mono alkyl esters of long-chain fatty acids commonly derived from vegetable oils, which conform to the requirements set by ASTM D6751 (American Society of Testing and Materials). As depicted in table 4, biodiesel exhibits properties and characteristics that are comparable to conventional petrodiesel [64, 65], but it produces lower exhaust emissions [66, 67]. Consequently, it can be used as a substitute for petrodiesel, although it is more commonly used in fuel blends.

Table 4. American Society for Testing and Materials (ASTM) standards for maximum allowed quantities in petrodiesel and biodiesel

Fuel property	Diesel	Biodiesel
Standard	ASTM D975	ASTM D6751
Composition	HC [a] (C_{10}–C_{21})	FAME [b] (C_{12}–C_{22})
Kinematic viscosity at 40° C (mm^2/s)	1.9–4.1	1.9–6.0
Boiling point (°C)	188-343	182-338
Flash point (°C)	60-80	100-170
Cloud point (°C)	-15 to 5	-3 to 12
Pour point (°C)	-35 to -15	-15 to 16
Water (vol %)	0.05	0.05
Carbon (wt %)	87	77
Hydrogen (wt %)	13	12
Oxygen (wt %)	0	11
Sulfur (wt %)	0.05	0.05
Cetane number	40-55	48-60
Stoichiometric air/fuel ratio (AFR)	15	13.8
HFRR [c] (Dm)	685	314
BOCLE [d] scuff (g)	3600	>7000
Life-cycle energy balance (energy units produced per unit energy consumed)	0.83/1	3.2/1

[a] Hydrocarbons.
[b] Fatty Acid Methyl Esters.
[c] High Frequency Reciprocating Rig.
[d] Ball-on-Cylinder Lubricity Evaluator.

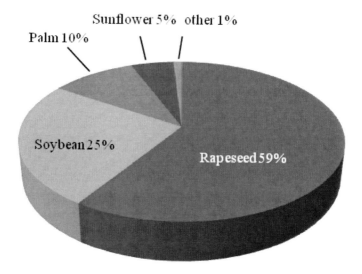

Figure 2. Total global biodiesel feedstock sources.

Biodiesel is a cleaner burning alternative to petroleum-based diesel fuel that also offers further advantages such as: 1) a higher cetane number and a higher flash point, meaning better and safer performance; 2) higher lubricity, which prolongs engine life and reduces the frequency of engine part replacement; 3) lower sulfur and aromatic content; 4) higher combustion efficiency and lower levels of CO and hydrocarbon emissions due to the presence of oxygen in biodiesel ($\approx$10%); and 5) renewability of the feedstock sources and higher overall biodegradability. In terms of effective use of fossil energy resources, biodiesel yields around 3.2 units of fuel product energy for every unit of fossil energy consumed in the life cycle. By contrast, petroleum diesel's life cycle yields only 0.83 units of fuel product energy per unit of fossil energy consumed. Such measures confirm the "renewable" nature of biodiesel.

Viscosity is the most problematic property of biodiesel since it affects the operation of the fuel injection equipment, particularly at low temperatures when the decrease in viscosity affects the fluidity of the fuel. In other words, the main disadvantage of biodiesel as diesel fuel is the fact that its viscosity varies greatly with temperature. Also, lower energy content, higher cloud point and pour point, higher nitrogen oxide emissions, lower engine speed and power, injector coking, engine compatibility, high price, and higher engine wear are other potential disadvantages of biodiesel use [22].

3.2. Feedstock for Biodiesel Production

3.2.1. Edible Oils

To overcome the problems associated with high viscosities, low volatility and the polyunsaturated character of unrefined vegetable oils; they can be used as feedstock for the production of refined biodiesel. More than 95% of global biodiesel production now begins with edible vegetable oils [9]. In 2008, 59% of total global biodiesel production used rapeseed oil as the feedstock, followed by soybean, palm, and sunflower oils [68] (Figure 2). It is important to remark that rapeseed oil is known in North America as canola oil.

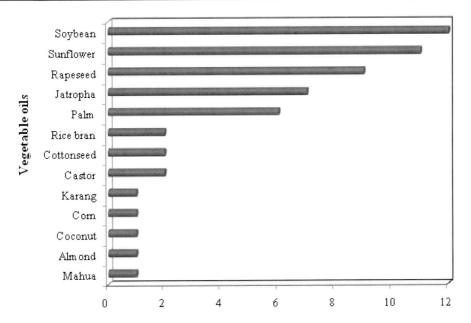

Figure 3. Vegetable oils cited in scientific articles for biodiesel production.

The source of biodiesel usually depends upon which crops are amenable to the producing locality's regional climate. In 2009 soybean oil accounted for approximately 90% of the biodiesel produced in the US [56]. High levels of oleic acid (Table 2) make soybean oil more resistant to oxidation and hence more suitable for processes requiring high oxidative stability at high temperatures, such as in biodiesel and biolubricant applications. On the other hand, high linoleic acid content (less stable to oxidation) also gives soybean oil excellent drying properties, which is also a desirable property for applications involving paints, inks and varnishes [69].

Biodiesel production in the European Union (EU) is based primarily on rapeseed oil (80%) [70]. In fact, about 65% of rapeseed oil is used for this purpose [71]. On the other hand, while China, a major producer of rapeseed, is also starting to produce biodiesel from this source; palm oil predominates in biodiesel production in the region and in most tropical countries [72].

Although the global market for biodiesel has seen explosive growth in recent years, prices continue to be much higher than those of petrodiesel due to the high prices of edible vegetable oil feedstocks. For this reason, many researchers are increasingly interested in investigating new ways to synthesize biodiesel from alternative feedstock sources, as discussed next.

3.2.2. Non-Edible Oils

The production of biodiesel from a variety of non-edible oilseed crops has been extensively investigated over the last few years. Non-edible oils can be obtained from plant and tree sources including the jatropha tree (*Jatropha curcas*) [73, 74], karanja (*Pongamia pinnata*) [75, 76], tobacco seed (*Nicotiana tabacum* L.) [77], rice bran [67, 78], mahua (*Madhuca indica*) [79], neem (*Azadirachta indica*) [80] and rubber tree seed tree (*Hevea brasiliensis*) [81]. Two of these trees, *Jatropha curcas* and *Pongamia pinnata*, are notable for their ability to thrive in any type of soil, their need for minimum inputs and management, and their low moisture demands [82]. Their seeds contain about 30-40% oil, which has been identified as a feedstock source for biodiesel. *Madhuca indica* and *Madhuca longifolia* are the two major species of the genus *Madhuca* found in India [22]. Mahua oil generally contains about 20% free fatty acids (FFAs) and therefore some sort of conversion procedure is definitely needed for its use as biodiesel [79]. Rice bran oil is also an underutilized non-edible vegetable oil. Although this oil is available in large quantities in rice-cultivating countries, very little research has been done regarding utilization of this oil as a replacement for petrodiesel [67]. Figure 3 summarizes the vegetable oils cited in scientific articles related to biodiesel production over the last decade [73, 74, 83–135].

In addition to vegetable oils, serious attention has been directed recently to the exploration of microbial oils, also called single-cell oils, which are produced by some oleaginous microorganisms such as microalgae, bacteria, yeast and fungi [136]. Although there are many microorganisms that have the ability to accumulate oils under specific cultivation conditions, these taxa have different prospects for the biodiesel industry in terms of oil yield, volumetric lipid productivity, biomass production, etc. Autotrophic microalgae are photosynthetic microorganisms that convert sunlight, water and carbon dioxide into algal biomass [137]. They have long been recognized as good potential sources for biodiesel production because of their high oil content and rapid biomass production. It has been established that autotrophic microalgaes vary in their ability to produce oil. Apart from this basic species-based variability, other cultivation-based parameters such as temperature, light intensity, pH, salinity, and mineral and nitrogen sources also influence on oil production [137–141]. The oil contents of some microalgae are given in table 5.

Table 5. Oil accumulation produced by different microalgaes [141–144]

Microalga	Oil content (wt·% dry cell weight)
Botryococcus braunii	25–75
Chlorella sp.	28–32
Crypthecodinium cohnii	20
Cylindrotheca sp.	16–37
Dunaliella primolecta	23.0
Isochrysis sp.	25–33
Monallanthus salina	>20
Nannochloris sp.	20–35
Nannochloropsis sp.	31–68
Neochloris oleoabundans	35–54
Nitzschia sp.	45–47
Phaeodactylum tricornutum	20–30
Schizochytrium sp.	50–77
Tetraselmis sueica	15–23
Parietochloris incisa	62
Monodus subterraneus	≈40
Nitzschia laevis	≈70

Compared to plant oils, microbial oils have many advantages such as higher growth rates and productivity when compared to conventional forestry, agricultural crop farming, and other aquatic plant cultivation. Their cultivation also requires much less land area than other biodiesel feedstocks of agricultural origin [145]. According to Benemann [146] total world commercial microalgal biomass production is about 10,000 tons per year. However, one of the major differences between autotrophic microalgaes and heterotrophic microorganisms is that the scaling-up process for autotrophic microalgaes is more complicated, since light is needed during the cultivation process. To minimize costs, microbial oil production must rely upon available free sunlight, despite daily and seasonal variations in light levels [142]. Raceway ponds [147] and tubular photobioreactors [148] are therefore usually adopted for large-scale cultivation of autotrophic microalgaes.

By altering cultivation conditions or using genetic engineering, some autotrophic microalgaes can be converted to heterotrophic microalgaes. This is important because such heterotrophic microalgaes can accumulate oils using organic carbon as the carbon source instead of sunlight [148]. Generally speaking, heterotrophic microalgaes are easily cultivated and controlled in normal fermenters. However, they require organic carbon sources for oil accumulation, which might limit their application to oil production as a biodiesel feedstock source.

To summarize, with the rapid expansion of interest in biodiesel production, microbial oils might become an important source of feedstocks in the future. However, a significant amount of work remains to be done in order to understand and improve this potential.

3.2.3. Waste Cooking Oil

In order to reduce production costs, waste cooking oils (WCO) is a promising alternative to vegetable oil for biodiesel production [150]. Its price is 2-3 times less than that of virgin vegetable oils [151]. Management of waste cooking oils poses a significant challenge because of disposal problems and possible contamination of water and land. In the past, large amounts of WCO have been illegally dumped into rivers and landfills, causing environmental pollution. The use of WCO in production of biodiesel thus offers another significant advantage in terms of reduction in environmental pollution [152]. The conversion of waste oil into methyl esters through the transesterification process reduces its molecular weight by two-thirds, reduces its viscosity by about one-seventh, reduces its flash point slightly, increases its volatility marginally, and reduces pour point considerably [1]. However, the production of biodiesel from waste oil is also challenging due to the presence of undesirable components such as FFAs and water [12].

3.2.4. Animal Fats

Another potential source of feedstock for biodiesel production is fats derived from animals. Animal fats used to produce biodiesel include tallow, choice white grease or lard, poultry fat, fish oil and yellow grease. Compared to plant crop oils, these fats frequently offer an economic advantage because they are more favorably priced for conversion into biodiesel. Animal fat methyl ester has some other advantages, such as high cetane number, non-corrosivity, and renewability [13]. Animal fats tend to be low in FFAs and water, but there is a limited amount of these oils available, meaning these would never be able to meet the fuel needs of the world [153]. Finally, table 6 summarizes the sources of biodiesel feedstock discussed above in the form of edible oils, non-edible oils, and WCO and animal fats.

Table 6. Biodiesel feedstock

Edible oils	Non-edible oils	Animal fats/WCO
Rapeseed [116, 125, 128]	Jatropha curcas [74, 106, 114]	Tallow [166, 167]
Soybean [86, 96, 103]	Karanja [90, 160]	Lard [168]
Sunflower [83, 84, 88, 95]	Tobacco seed [24, 161]	Poultry [18]
Safflower [154, 155]	Rice bran [101, 162]	Fishoil [53, 169]
Cottonseed [118, 156]	Mahua [79, 124, 160]	Chicken fat [170]
Coconut [105, 157, 158]	Almond [16, 102]	Yellow grease [171]
Barley [159]	Babassu [7, 17, 53]	WCO [172–174]
Palm [93, 99]	Jojoba oil [163]	
Sesame [158]	Microalgaes [164, 165]	

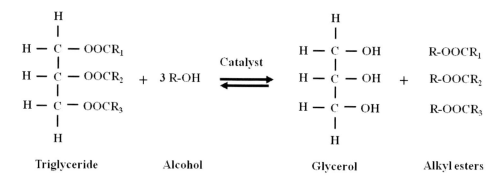

Figure 4. The triglyceride transesterification reaction.

3.3. Transesterification Process

As mentioned above, the most commonly used method to produce biodiesel is the transesterification process, where triglycerides (vegetable oils, animal fats or waste oils) are combined with a short chain alcohol to form fatty esters such as methyl ester. Specifically, a triglyceride molecule reacts with a low molecular weight alcohol, yielding a mono alkyl ester and a glycerol byproduct (Figure 4), which can be used for pharmaceutical and cosmetic industry applications.

Different types of alcohols can be used for transesterification, such as methanol, ethanol, butanol, etc. [105, 133, 175]. Among these alcohols, methanol is used most frequently [73, 74, 83, 84, 85]. Because the transesterification reaction is reversible, it is necessary to add a little excess alcohol in order to shift the equilibrium towards the formation of alkyl esters. Generally, a catalyst is needed to improve the reaction rate and yield [176]. However, the transesterification process can be carried out even without a catalyst. The transesterification process using a catalyst is called catalytic transesterification, whereas transesterification without a catalyst is called non-catalytic transesterification. Non-catalytic transesterification usually uses a supercritical alcohol such as supercritical methanol [177, 178] or supercritical ethanol [179], in order to produce the fatty acid alkyl esters. On the other hand, catalytic transesterification is divided into two types based on the processes applied: homogenous and heterogeneous. The homogenous transesterification process usually uses catalysts such as sodium hydroxide (NaOH), potassium hydroxide (KOH) [85], sulfuric acid (H_2SO_4) [180] or hydrochloric acid (HCl) [181]. The biggest issue of homogeneous catalyst is, however, the purification step of biodiesel for removing soaps, glycerine and unreacted catalyst, as well as the processes high demand for water and energy. Moreover, homogeneous catalysts cannot be regenerated or reused. In this context, research into improving biodiesel production processes has focused on the use of heterogeneous catalysts because they can be easily separated by filtration, and also because of their less corrosive nature, leading to safer, cheaper and more environmentally friendly operations [182]. Heterogeneous transesterification processes uses solid catalysts such as metal oxides [98, 183], active metals supported on various media [184], zeolites [185], resins [186], membranes [187] and enzymes [109–135]. The methods used in the transesterification process are summarized in figure 5.

In general, homogeneous catalysis is more active than heterogeneous catalysis since the active sites are within a liquid phase and are capable of moving freely in the reagents. Meanwhile, the active sites of solid catalysts are confined to the surface, making the reactions limited by the effects of internal mass-transfer resistance. Industrial processes favor, however, the use of solid catalysts to carry out chemical transformations due to the relative ease of separating them from any reaction mixture. Table 7 shows a comparison between homogeneous and heterogeneous catalysis methods for biodiesel fuel production [188].

Another way of categorizing the transesterification process is by division into alkaline, acid or enzymatic catalysis. Currently, most commercial biodiesel production is performed using alkali-catalyzed transesterification. Figure 6 shows a simplified flow chart of the alkali-catalyst process.

The alkali catalysts most widely used are sodium hydroxide (NaOH), potassium hydroxide (KOH), sodium metoxide (NaOCH$_3$) and potassium metoxide (KOCH$_3$) (Table 8), which have higher activity levels, lower required processing temperatures, and good rates of conversion. Alkaline catalysis has disadvantages, however, since these catalysts produce soaps, requiring a purification step that uses a significant amount of water. Also, alkali catalysts are hygroscopic and form water when they are dissolved in alcohol, which affects yields. They are very sensitive to FFAs, requiring pretreatment steps for the raw materials, especially used oils. As depicted in the figure 6, if the percentage of FFAs is over 2.5% by weight, pretreatment is necessary to reduce the content of FFAs [189, 190]. The results of this step also determine the amount of catalyst required in the neutralization step.

An alternative process is the use of an acid catalyst, as some researchers have claimed that these are more tolerant of FFAs [191–193] and can thereby reduce the formation of soaps. Currently, the catalysts most commonly used in biodiesel production are the organic acids, such as the derivates of toluenesulfonic acid and, more often, mineral acids such as sulfuric acid [194]. However, acid catalysts require higher temperatures as well as higher amounts of alcohol. Because of the fact that the reaction rate of acid-catalyzed transesterification has been found to be up to 4000 times slower than using alkali-catalysts [53], and because of their more corrosive nature compared to alkali liquids, these catalysts are rarely used on an industrial scale.

Although the most common route to biodiesel production is through alkali-catalyzed transesterification, as mentioned above there are several problems associated with this kind of production. These problems can be partially overcome by using lipase as biocatalyst. Varieties of immobilized lipases are commercially available and can be employed as heterogeneous catalysts for biodiesel production (table 9).

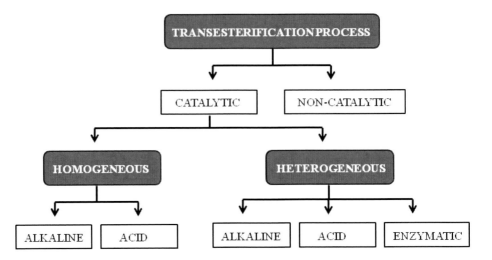

Figure 5. Classification of methods in the transesterification process.

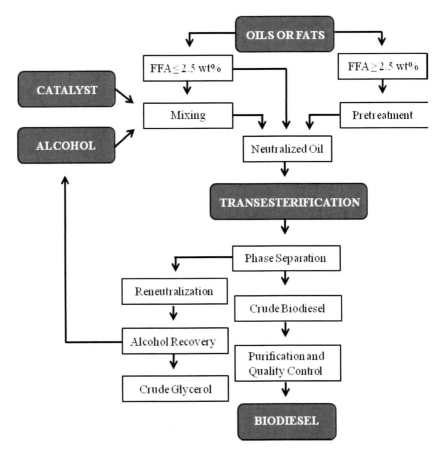

Figure 6. Simplified process flow chart for alkali-catalyzed biodiesel production.

Table 7. Comparison between homogeneous catalysis and heterogeneous catalysis methods for biodiesel production

Process characterists	Homogeneous catalysis	Heterogeneous catalysis
Temperature and pressure	Moderately low	Higher
Free fatty acids in raw materials	Saponified products	Alkyl esters
Water in raw materials	Interference with the reaction	More tolerant
Production cost of catalyst	Cheap	Relatively expensive
Catalyst effective	High	Less than catalyst in solution
Catalyst reusable	Non-possible	Easy
Undesired side reactions	Fewer	Higher
Recovery of glycerol	Difficult	Easy
Yield of alkyl esters	Low	Higher

Table 8. Transesteritication reactions using various alkali catalysts

Oil	Alcohol	Catalysis	Yield (%)	Reference
Jatropha	Methanol	NaOH	99.3	[73]
Jatropha	Methanol	NaOH	≈98.0	[74]
Sunflower	Methanol	$NaOH/Al_2O_3$	88.0	[83]
Sunflower	Methanol	$K_2CO_3/Al–O–Si$	92.0	[84]
Sunflower	Methanol	NaOH	97.1	[85]
Soybean	Ethanol	KOH	95.0	[86]
Sunflower	Methanol	KOH	90.0	[87]
Sunflower	Methanol	$NaOCH_3$	>98.0	[88]
Canola	Methanol	KOH	87.0	[89]
Karang	Methanol	KOH	92.0	[90]
Sunflower	Methanol	NaOH	≈93.0	[91]
Canola	Methanol	$KOCH_3$	95.8	[92]
Palm	Ethanol	KOH	96.0	[93]
Sunflower	Methanol	NaOH	≈98.0	[94]
Sunflower	Methanol	NaOH	>97.0	[95]
Soybean	Methanol	$CaOCH_3$	98.0	[96]
Palm	Methanol	$NaOCH_3$	96.8	[97]
Canola	Methanol	KOH/MgO	99.4	[98]
Palm	Methanol	NaOH	95.0	[99]
Cottonseed	Methanol	$NaOCH_3$	96.9	[100]
Rice bran	Methanol	$NaOCH_3$	83.3	[101]
Almond	Methanol	KOH	88.0	[102]
Soybean	Methanol	KOH	>99.0	[103]
Castor	Methanol	$NaOCH_3$	>96.0	[104]
Coconut	Methanol	KOH	99.0	[105]
Jatropha	Methanol	$NaOCH_3$	94.0	[106]
Rapeseed	Methanol	KOH	95.0	[107]
Palm	Methanol	KOH/bentonite	90.7	[108]

**Table 9. Transesteritication reactions using various lipases,
based on research results published over the last decade**

Oil	Alcohol	Microorganism/Lipase	Yield (%)	Reference
Rice bran	Methanol	*Candida antarctica* (Novozym 435)	>98.0	[78]
Sunflower	Methanol	Novozym 435	97.0	[109]
Soybean	Methanol	*Thermomyces lanuginosus* (Lipozyme TL IM)	92.0	[110]
Palm	Methanol	*Rhizopus oryzae*	55.0	[111]
Soybean	Methyl acetate	Novozym 435	92.0	[112]
Soybean	Methanol	Lipozyme TL IM	98.0	[113]
Jatropha	Ethanol	*Chromobacterium viscosum*	92.0	[114]
Sunflower	Methanol	Novozym 435	93.2	[115]
Rapeseed	Methanol	Novozyme 435 and Lipozyme TL IM	95.0	[116]
Palm	Ethanol	*Pseudomonas fluorescens*	98.0	[117]
Cottonseed	Methanol	Novozym 435	97.0	[118]
Jatropha	Methyl acetate	Novozym 435	91.3	[119]
Soybean	Methanol	Novozym 435	90.0	[120]
Corn	Methanol	*Penicillium expansum*	85.0	[121]
Jatropha	Ethanol	*Pseudomonas cepacia*	98.0	[122]
Soybean	Ethanol	*Rhizomucor miehei* (Lipozyme RM IM)	≈60.0	[123]
Mahua	Ethanol	*Pseudomonas cepacia*	96.0	[124]
Rapeseed	Methanol	*Candida rugosa*	95.0	[125]
Sunflower	Methanol	Novozym 435	99.6	[126]
Castor	Methanol	*Pseudomonas* sp.	85.0	[127]
Rapeseed	Methanol	Novozym 435	90.0	[128]
Soybean	Methanol	*Pseudomonas fluorescens*	98.0	[129]
Soybean	Methanol	Novozym 435	97.0	[130]
Jatropha	Methanol	*Enterobacter aerogenes*	94.0	[131]
Rapeseed	Methanol	Novozym 435	96.5	[132]
Soybean	Methanol	Novozyme 435 and Lipozyme TL IM	97.2	[133]
Canola	Methanol	Novozym 435	72.0	[134]
Soybean	Methanol	Novozym 435	83.3	[135]

**Table 10. Comparison between alkali-catalysis and lipase-catalysis methods
for biodiesel production [53]**

Process characterists	Alkali-catalysis	Lipase-catalysis
Reaction temperature (°C)	60–70	30–40
Free fatty acids in raw materials	Saponified products	Methyl esters
Water in raw materials	Interference with the reaction	No influence
Yield of methyl esters	Normal	Higher
Recovery of glycerol	Difficult	Easy
Purification of methyl esters	Repeated washing	None
Production of catalyst	Cheap	Relatively expensive

There is also substantial interest now in naturally immobilized catalysts such as cell-bound microbial lipases [195, 196]. Such systems are potentially cost effective because the biomass can be directly utilized as an enzyme source, eliminating the complex procedures of enzyme isolation, purification and immobilization [197]. The main disadvantages of lipases when used for industrial-scale production, however, include higher costs and longer reaction times [198–200]. In table 10, a comparison between alkali catalysis and lipase-based catalysis methods for biodiesel production is presented.

3.4. Main Factors Affecting the Yield of Biodiesel

3.4.1. Molar Ratio of Alcohol to Oil

One of the main factors affecting the yield of biodiesel is the alcohol-to-triglyceride molar ratio [10, 173]. Theoretically, the transesterification reaction requires a ratio of 3 mol of alcohol for 1 mol of triglyceride to produce 3 mol of fatty acid ester and 1 mol of glycerol. Since transesterification is an equilibrium process, an excess of alcohol is used to drive the reaction to completion. The yield of biodiesel is thus increased and reaches a maximum when the alcohol-triglyceride ratio is raised beyond 3. Further increase in the alcohol content beyond the optimal ratio will not increase the yield further, but will only increase costs for alcohol recovery [173]. The molar ratio is associated with the type of catalyst used. Thus, the alcohol-to-triglyceride molar ratio typically used for research purposes is 6:1, with the use of an alkali catalyst [88, 94, 106]. In addition, when the percentage of free fatty acids in the oils or fats is high, such as in the case of WCOs, a higher molar ratio is needed when using acid-catalyzed transesterification [173, 200]. Although the optimum alcohol-to-oil molar ratio has not yet been established, a wide range from 2:1 to 30:1 has been adopted in scientific studies [73, 83, 84, 201].

3.4.2. Reaction Time and Temperature

Freedman et al. [202] found that the conversion rate of fatty acid esters increases with reaction time. Normally, the yield reaches a maximum at a reaction time of <90 min, and then remains relatively constant or even decreases with a further increases because of the initiation of reverse reaction [1, 151, 199]. Temperature also clearly influences the reaction and resulting yield of the biodiesel product. A higher reaction temperature can decrease the viscosities of oils and result in an increased reaction rate, and thus a shortened reaction time. Optimal temperature range has been reported as between 50 °C and 60 °C [173], while higher temperatures tend to accelerate soap formation [1, 199, 203].

3.4.3. Catalyst Concentration

In addition to the type of catalyst used (alkali, acid or enzyme) catalyst concentration levels can also affect the yield of the biodiesel product. The most commonly used catalyst is sodium hydroxide. However, Freedman et al. [202] found that sodium methoxide was more effective than sodium hydroxide. This is because upon mixing sodium hydroxide with methanol, a small amount of water will be produced, which will affect the product yield because of the hydrolysis reaction created [204]. This problem can be addressed by first adding the catalyst into the methanol first and then adding this mixture to the oil.

As the catalyst concentration increases the conversion of triglyceride and the yield of biodiesel increase. This is because an insufficient amount of catalysts result in an incomplete conversion of the triglycerides into the fatty acid esters [173, 204]. Usually, the yield reaches an optimal value when the catalyst (NaOH) concentration reaches 1.5% by weight and then decreases a little with further increases in catalyst concentration. The reduction of the yield of the biodiesel is due to the addition of excessive alkali catalyst, which causes more triglycerides to react with the alkali catalyst and thus formation of more soap [173, 205].

4. BIODIESEL SUITABILITY FROM VEGETABLE OILS

In recent years, a rapid expansion in biodiesel production capacity is being observed not only in developed countries but also in developing countries such as China, Brazil, Argentina, Indonesia and Malaysia. On the whole, biodiesel feedstock sources should fulfill two basic requirements: low production costs and large-scale production potential. There are two fundamental inputs to the cost of biodiesel: the cost of feedstocks and the cost of processing. The major economic factor to consider for input costs of biodiesel production is the feedstock, which accounts for about 80% of the total cost. Other important costs those related to methanol and the catalyst, which must be added to the cost of the feedstock.

As mentioned above, biodiesel is mainly prepared from conventionally grown edible oils, which have high production costs and low production scales. The estimated increase in edible oil use for biodiesel production was 6.6 million tons from 2004 to 2007 [71]. However, global use of edible oils increased even faster during this same period, in excess of increases in production. A rough estimate suggests that about 7.8 million hectares (Mha) were used to provide biodiesel feedstocks in the four major producing countries in 2007 [206] (Figure 7), with biodiesel production using around 4.3 Mha of arable land in the EU. Between 2005 and 2017, biodiesel use of edible oils has been projected to account for more than a third of the expected growth in edible oil use [207].

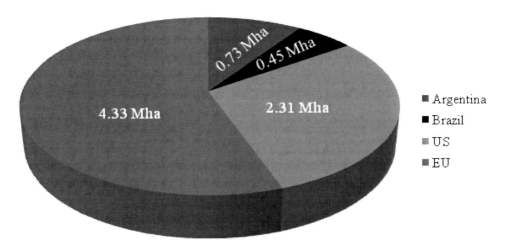

Figure 7. Numbers of million hectares (Mha) used to provide biodiesel feedstocks in the four major producing countries in 2007.

Oil yield per hectare is an important parameter to consider for biodiesel production. Soybeans, which represent the most common biodiesel feedstock in the U.S., only produce about 0.52 tons of oil per hectare [208]. Based on current U.S. diesel consumption of about 227 billion liters per year, this would require more than 500 Mha of land in soybeans or more than half the total U.S. land area planted just to produce this amount of soybeans [209].

Biodiesel production in the EU, on the other hand, is based primarily on rapeseed oil. Rapeseed, produces 1 ton of oil per hectare [208], giving it the highest yield of any conventional oilseed field crop. Total EU rapeseed production was 15.3 million tons in 2006/2007 [210]. Although Chinese production of rapeseed biodiesel is limited because of less advanced technology, scientists are working at improving technologies to increase their biodiesel production from rapeseed oil [211].

Palm oil is produced from the fruit of the oil palm, (*Elaeis guineensis*). This tree is native to West Guinea, but was introduced into other parts of Africa, Southeast Asia and Latin America during the 15th century [212]. Palm oil is now increasingly being produced on large-scale plantations in tropical lowland regions, especially in tropical East Asia. China is the largest consumer of palm oil in the world. Other large-scale consumers of palm oil include Indonesia, India, Malaysia and the EU. These five major consumers account for 55% of global palm oil consumption. The palm oil system generates more biodiesel per hectare than the rapeseed system [213]. Palm, which can produce an astounding 4000 l of oil per hectare, has the highest oil yield of plants grown for biodiesel feedstock.

Continuous and large-scale production of biodiesel from edible oils has been of great concern because over the long term they compete with the food supply [152, 214]. Extensive use of edible oils may cause significant problems in developing countries, even starvation. Nearly 60% of humans in the world are malnourished, so the need for grains and other basic foods is critical [209]. Expansion of biofuel production in general, has coincided with recent sharp increases in prices for food grains, feed grains, oil seeds, and vegetable oils. The credibility of this association is heightened by the fact that practically all biofuels in the world are produced from feedstocks that could be used to produce food or that are produced on land that could produce food. The truth about food prices and biofuels is more complicated than critics of biofuels may want to believe. However, for oil seeds, a link certainly exists. There is no doubt that vegetable oil prices are much higher than they would have been without expansion of the biodiesel sector in this area.

Use of non-edible vegetable oils when compared with edible oils is very significant in developing countries [215] because of the tremendous demand for edible oils as food, which are therefore far too expensive to be used as fuel at the present time [216, 217]. *Jatropha curcas* can thrive on any type of soil, and plantations are already being developed in several arid regions. Because it is both non-edible and can be grown on marginal lands, *Jatropha* is potentially a sustainable source of biofuel that will not compete with food crops. However, the serious problem with jatropha oil, in addition to the low yield (about 0.5 ton per hectare), is that it is highly toxic to people and livestock. The comparatively high price of jatropha oil is also still a drawback [218]. Karanja (*P. pinnata*) is native to a number of countries including India, Malaysia, Indonesia, Taiwan, Bangladesh, Sri Lanka and Myanmar. It is a fast-growing leguminous tree with the potential for high oil seed production and the added benefit of the ability to grow on marginal land. These properties support the suitability of this plant for large-scale vegetable oil production, as required by a sustainable biodiesel industry [219]. *Madhuca indica* is one of the forest tree-based non-edible oils with a high production potential (about 60 million tons per annum in India) [220]. The yield of *M. indica* seeds varies depending upon the size and age of the individual tree [221]. The kernel constitutes about 70% of the seed and contains about 50% oil [222].

Although biodiesel from oil crops is being produced in increasing amounts, there are also problems of environmental harm and sustainability with respect to biofuel production in general. Environmental problems such as increased deforestation of native forests, threats to biodiversity, soil erosion and water pollution from fertilizers and pesticides could become worse with increasing biofuel production. Biodiesel production depends on land use and availability even greater than other biofuels such as bioethanol. The fact is that even if all available crops, forests and grasses were used for biofuels, we could not become independent of fossil fuels if current rates of petroleum usage are maintained.

Impacts of large-scale biodiesel production from vegetable oils can be significantly lowered by substituting of alternative feedstocks such as WCO and animal fats. The use of these feedstocks to produce biodiesel can not only reduce the costs of production but can also offer significant advantages because of the potential reduction in environmental pollution. Biodiesel derived from WCO has taken a commercial patent as an alternative fuel to petroleum-based diesel fuel for diesel engines in the markets of Europe and the US [223]. The amount of waste oil generated in each country is huge and varies depending on the use of vegetable oil. An estimate of the potential amount of WCO from collection in the EU is approximately 0.7-1.0 million tons per year [11]. Chhetri et al. [152] reported that approximately 135,000 tons per year of WCO is produced in Canada. According to a report by the USDA Foreign Agricultural Service [224], WCO accounts for about 80,000 tons of China's biodiesel production. However, it must be remembered that the quality of these low-cost feedstocks can generate processing problems in existing industrial-scale biodiesel production methods because the alkali-catalyzed system is very sensitive to water, free fatty acids and other impurities [173].

According to the American Society of Testing and Materials (ASTM), biofuel composed of mono-alkyl esters of long-chain fatty acids derived from vegetable oils, animal fats or WCOs is technically described as first-generation biodiesel. However, the global markets for biodiesel are entering a period of rapid transitional growth, creating both uncertainty and opportunity. Production of synthetic biodiesel by biomass gasification and catalytic conversion to liquid using the Fischer-Tropsch process offers a variety of potential biofuel applications. This second-generation biofuel can be made from almost any form of biomass, especially wood and wood waste. Unlike vegetable oils, these sources do not compete with food crops and their available volume is much higher. However, if made from dedicated energy crops, they do in fact compete for land and water resources. Fischer-Tropsch fuel production was developed in Germany in 1935, and involves conversion of synthesis gas (CO and H_2) into hydrocarbon products by highly exothermic reactions in the presence of a catalyst [203]. The catalysts most commonly used on an industrial scale are iron and cobalt. In order to improve catalytic performance, bimetallic catalysts containing Fe, Co, Ni and Ru can be used [198]. The Fischer-Tropsch process is summarized in Figure 8.

$$nCO \; + \; 2n\,H_2 \; \xrightarrow{\text{Catalyst}} \; -(CH_2)n- \; + \; nH_2O$$

Figure 8. The Fischer-Tropsch mechanism.

Production of biodiesel by FT synthesis is a good alternative for producing biofuels, by using non-edible lignocellulosic raw materials, many of them considered to be waste products. However, although second-generation processes can make use cheaper feedstock sources, these processes also tend to be complex and very expensive, so that they would not be economically competitive by the year 2020.

CONCLUSION

Although biodiesel is better than petrodiesel in terms of sulfur content, flash point, aromatic content and biodegradability, sourcing of feedstock for their production carries diverse problems too. These include impacts on biodiversity, land use and competition with food crops. An increasing number of second-generation biodiesel projects are now emerging in response to growing sustainability concerns by governments, and in response to market demands for more efficient processes and greater feedstock production yields. However, these new processes also carry with them many unresolved issues. In these circumstances, a cost-benefit analysis requires forecasts of the future to be made, considering various scenarios in relation to feedstock sources and processing methods, as well as consideration of the environmental and socio-economic impacts of large-scale biodiesel production. Further research and discussion between those involved in these various lines of research will be needed to resolve these issues.

REFERENCES

[1]   Demirbas, A. Progress and recent trends in biodiesel fuels. *Energy Convers. Manage.* 2009, *50*, 14–34.

[2]   Namasivayam, A.M.; Korakianitis, T.; Crookes, R.J.; Bob-Manuel, K.D.H.; Olsen, J. Biodiesel, emulsified biodiesel and dimethyl ether as pilot fuels for natural gas fuelled engines. *Appl. Energy.* 2010, *87*, 769–778.

[3]   Vegetable Oil Fuels, Proceedings of the International Conference on Plant and Vegetable Oils As Fuels, August 2-4, 1982, Holiday In *Fargo, North Dakota* (Asae Publication, 82-4).

[4]   Goering, C.E.; Schwab, A.W.; Daugherty, M.J.; Pryde, E.H.; Heakin, A.J. Fuel properties of eleven oils. *Trans. ASAE* 1982, *25*, 1472–1483.

[5]   Nag, A.; Bhattacharya, S.; De, K.B. New utilization of vegetable oils. *J. Am. Oil. Chem. Soc.* 1995, *72*, 1591–1593.

[6]   Ma, F.; Hanna, M.A. Biodiesel production: a review. *Bioresour. Technol.* 1999, *70*, 1–15.

[7]   Srivastava, A.; Prasad, R. Triglycerides-based diesel fuels. *Renew. Sustain. Energy. Rev.* 2000, *4*, 111–133.

[8]   Lima, D.G.; et al. Diesel-like fuel obtained by pyrolysis of vegetable oils. *J. Anal. Appl. Pyrol.* 2004, *71*, 987–996.

[9]   Gui, M.M.; Lee, K.T.; Bhatia, S. Feasibility of edible oil vs. non-edible oil vs. waste edible oil as biodiesel feedstock. *Energy* 2008, *33*, 1646–1653.

[10] Zhang, Y.; Dube, M.A.; McLean, D.D.; Kates, M. Biodiesel production from waste cooking oil: 2. Economic assessment and sensitivity analysis *Bioresour. Technol.* 2003, *90*, 229–240.

[11] Jacobson, K.; Gopinath, R.; Meher, L.C.; Dalai, A.K. Solid acid catalyzed biodiesel production from waste cooking oil. *Appl. Catal. B Environ.* 2008, *85*, 86–91.

[12] Oner, C.; Altun, S. Biodiesel production from inedible animal tallow and an experimental investigation of its use as alternative fuel in a direct injection diesel engine. *Appl. Energy* 2009, *86*, 2114–2120.

[13] Guru, M.; Koca, A., Can, O.; Cinar, C.; Sahin, F. Biodiesel production from waste chicken fat based sources and evaluation with Mg based additive in a diesel engine. *Renew. Energy* 2010, *35*, 637–643.

[14] Sonntag, N.O.V. Structure and composition of fats and oils. In *Bailey's industrial oil and fat products*, 4th ed.; John Wiley and Sons: New York, 1979; Vol. 1; pp 407–409.

[15] Bagby, M.O. Vegetable oils for diesel fuel: opportunities for development. In *International Winter Meeting of the ASAE*. Hyatt Regency Chicago, December 15-18, 1987.

[16] Demirbas, A. Biodiesel fuels from vegetable oils via catalytic and non-catalytic supercritical alcohol transesterifications and other methods: a survey. *Energy Covers. Manage.* 2003, *44*, 2093–2109.

[17] Abreu, F.R.; Lima, D.G.; Hamu, E.H.; Wolf, C.; Suarez, P.A.Z. Utilization of metal complexes as catalysts in the transesterification of Brazilian vegetable oils with different alcohols. *J. Mol. Catal. A Chem.* 2004, *209*, 29–33.

[18] Goodrum, J.W.; et al. Rheological characterization of animal fats and their mixtures with 2 fuel oil. *Biomass Bioenergy* 2003, *24*, 249–256.

[19] Goering, C.E.; Camppion, R.N.; Schwab, A.W.; Pryde, E.H. In *Vegetable oil fuels*, Proceedings of the International Conference on Plant and Vegetable Oils as Fuels, Fargo, North Dakota. American Society of Agricultural Engineers, St. Joseph, MI: 4, 1982; pp 279–286.

[20] Akoh, C.C.; Chang, S.W.; Lee, G.C.; Shaw, J.F. Enzymatic approach to biodiesel production. *J. Agric. Food. Chem.* 2007, *55*, 8995–9005.

[21] Pinto, A.C.; et al. Biodiesel: an overview. *J. Bra. Chem. Soc.* 2005, *16*, 1313–1330.

[22] Demirbas, A. Biodiesel: a realistic fuel alternative for diesel engine. London: Springer Publishing Co, 2008.

[23] Edem, D.O. Palm Oil: biochemical, physiological, nutritional, hematological, and toxicological aspects: a review. *Plant Foods Hum Nutr.* 2002, *57*, 319–341.

[24] Giannelos, P.N.; Zannikos, F.; Stournas, S.; Lois, E.; Anastopoulos, G. Tobacco seed oil as an alternative diesel fuel: physical and chemical properties. *Indus. Crops Prod.* 2002, *16*, 1–9.

[25] Ali, Y.; Hanna, M.A.; Cuppett, S.L. Fuel properties of tallow and soybean oil esters. *J. Am. Oil Chem. Soc.* 1995, *72*, 1557–1564.

[26] Kumar, N. Performance and emission studies of an agriculture diesel engine on pre-heated jatropha oil. Ph.D. Dissertation, Department of Mechanical Engineering Faculty of Technology, University of Delhi Delhi-110 007, India, 2008.

[27] Shay, E.G. Diesel fuel from vegetable oils: status and opportunities. *Biomass Bioenergy* 1993, *4*, 227–242.

[28] Seddon, R.H. Vegetable oil in commercial vehicle. Gas Oil Power, 1942, *37*, 136–141.

[29] Bruwer, J.J. The utilization of sunflower seed oil as renewable fuel diesel engines, In *Biomass Energy/Crop Production*, St. Joseph, MI: ASAE, 1981, Vol. 2; pp 44–81.

[30] Yarbrough, C.M.; Lapori, W.A.; Engler, C.R. Compression ignition performance using sunflower seed oil. In *ASAE*, paper number 81–576. St. Joseph, MI: ASAE, 1981.

[31] Bacon, D.M.; Brear, F.; Moncrieff, I.D.; Walker, K.L. The use of vegetable oils in straight and modified forms diesel engine fuel: Beyond the energy crisis–opportunity and challenges. In *Fazzolre RA, Smith CR, editors*, proceedings of the Third International Conference on Energy Use Management, Berlin (West). Oxford: Pergamum Press, 1981; Vol. 3 pp 1525–1533.

[32] Schoedder, C. Rapeseed oil as an alternative fuel for agriculture. Beyond the energy crises-opportunity and challenges. In *Fazzolre RA, Smith CR, editors*, proceedings of the Third International Conference on Energy Use Management, Berlin (West). Oxford: Pergamon Press, 1981; Vol. 3; pp 1815–1822.

[33] Tahir, A.R.; Lapp, H.M.; Buchanan, LC. Sunflower oil as a fuel for compression ignition engines. In *Vegetable oils fuels*, proceeding of the International Conference on Plant and Vegetable Oils Fuels. St. Joseph, MI: ASAE, 1982.

[34] Auld, D.L.; Bettis, B.L.; Peterson, C.L. Production and fuel characteristics of vegetative oil seeds crop in the Pacific North West vegetable oil fuel. In *International Conference on Plant and Vegetable Oils Fuels*, St. Joseph, MI: ASAE, 1982.

[35] Bettis, B.L.; Peterson, C.L.; Auld, D.L.; Driscoll, D.J.; Peterson, E.D. Fuel characteristics of vegetable oil from oil seed crops in the Pacific Northwest. *Agron. J.* 1982, *74*, 335–339.

[36] Engler, C.R.; Johnson, L.A.; Lepori, W.A.; Yarbought, C.M. Effect of processing and chemical characteristics of plant oil on performance of an indirect injection diesel engines. *J. Am. Oil Chem. Soc.* 1983, *60*, 1592–1596.

[37] Pryor, R.W.; Hanna M.A.; Schinstock, J.L.; Bashford, L.L. (1983). Soybean oil fuel in a small diesel engine. *Trans. ASAE* 1983, *2*, 333–337.

[38] Reid, J.F.; Hensen, A.C.: Goering, C.E. Quantifying diesel injection coking with computer vision. *Trans. ASAE* 1989, *32*, 1503–1506.

[39] Dunn, R.O. Low-temperature flow properties of vegetable oil/co-solvent blends diesel fuels. *J. Am. Oil Chem. Soc.* 2002, *79*, 709–715.

[40] Meher, L.C.; Vidya Sagar, D.; Naik, S.N. Technical aspects of biodiesel production by transesterification –A review. *Renew. Sustain. Energy Rev.* 2006, *10*, 248–268.

[41] Murugesan, A.; Umarani, C.; Subramanian, R.; Nedunchezhian, N. Biodiesel as an alternative fuel for diesel engines –A review. *Renew. Sustain. Energy Rev.* 2009, *13*, 653–662.

[42] Hariharan, V.S.; Reddy, K.V.; Rajagopal, K. Study of the performance, emission and combustion characteristics of a diesel engine using sea lemon oil based fuels. *Indian J. Sci. Technol.* 2009, *2*, 43–47.

[43] Engelman, H.W.; Guenther, D.A.; Silvis, T.W. Vegetable oil as a diesel fuel. In *Diesel and Gas Engine Power Division of ASME*, paper Number 78-DGP-19. New York, NY: ASME, 1978.

[44] Sims, R.E.H.; Raine, R.R.; McLeod, R.J. Rapeseed oil as a fuel for diesel engines. In *SAE-Australia*, paper presented at the National Conference on Fuels from Crops of the Society of Automotive Engineers, Australia, 1981.

[45] Bartholomew, D. Vegetable oil fuel. *J. Am. Oil Chem. Soc.* 1981, *58*, 286–288.

[46] Hofman, V.; Kaufman, D.; Helgeson, D.; Dinusson, W.E. Sunflower for power. In NDSU Cooperative Extension Service, Circular AE-735, Fargo, ND, 1981.

[47] Peterson, C.L.; Thompson, J.C.; Wagner, G.L.; Auld, D.L.; Korus, R.A. Extraction and utilization of winter rape (*BRASSICA NAPUS*) as a diesel fuel extender, Proceedings of the American Oil Chemists' Society Annual Meeting in Toronto, Canada, May 2-6, 1982.

[48] Fort, E.F.; Blumberg, P. N.; Staph, H. E.; Staudt, J.J. Evaluation of cottonseed oils as diesel fuel. In *SAE Technical*, paper Series 820317, Warren dale, PA: SAE, 1982.

[49] Wagner, G.L.; Peterson, C.L. Performance of winter rape (*BRASSICA* NAPUS) based fuel mixtures in diesel engines. In *Vegetable oil fuels*, proceeding of the International Conference on Plant and Vegetable Oils Fuels. St. Joseph, MI: ASAE, 1982.

[50] [50] Pestes, M.N.; Stanislao, J. Piston ring deposits when using vegetable oil as a fuel. *J. Test. Eval.* 1984, *12*, 61–68.

[51] Sapaun, S.M.; Masjuki, H.H.; Azlan, A. The use of palm oil as diesel fuel substitute. *Part A: J. Power Energy* 1996, *210*, 47–53.

[52] McDonnel, K.P.; Ward, S.M.; Mc Nully, P.B.; Howard-Hildige, R. Results of engine and vehicle testing of semi refined rapeseed oil. *Trans. ASAE* 2000, *43*, 1309–1316.

[53] Fukuda, H.; Konda, A.; Noda, N. Biodiesel fuel production by transestirification of oils. *J. Biosci. Bioeng.* 2001, *92*, 405–416.

[54] Knothe, G.; Dunn, R.O.; Bagby, M.O. Biodiesel: the use of vegetable oils and their derivatives as alternative diesel fuels. In *Fuels and Chemicals from Biomass*, proceedings of the ACS symposium series no. 666, Washington, DC, USA, 1997; p. 172–208.

[55] Ziejewski, M.; Kaufman, K.R.; Schwab, A.W.; Pryde, E.H. Diesel engine evaluation of a nonionic sunflower oil-aqueous ethanol microemulsion. *J. Am. Oil Chem. Soc.* 1984, *61*, 1620–1626.

[56] Balat, M. Prospects for worldwide biodiesel market development. *Energy Sources,* Part B 2009, *4*, 48–58.

[57] Schwab, A.W.; Dykstra, G.J.; Selke, E.; Sorenson, S.C.; Pryde, E.H. Diesel fuel from thermal decomposition of soybean oil. *J. Am. Oil Chem. Soc*. 1988, *65*, 1781–1786.

[58] Da Rocha Filho, G.N.; Brodzki, D.; Djega-Mariadassou, G. Formation of alkanes, alkylcycloalkanes and alkylbenzenes during the catalytic hydrocracking of vegetable oils. *Fuel* 1993, *72*, 543–549.

[59] Billaud, F.; Dominguez, V.; Broutin, P.; Busson, C. Production of hydrocarbons by pyrolysis of methyl esters from rapeseed oil. *J. Am. Oil Chem. Soc.* 1995, *72*, 1149–1154.

[60] Alencar, J.W.; Alves, P.B.; Craveiro, A.A. Pyrolysis of tropical vegetable oils. *J. Agric. Food Chem.* 1983, *31*, 1268–1270.

[61] Akdeniz, F.; Küçük, M.M.; Demirbas, A. Liquids from olive husk by using supercritical fluid extraction and thermochemical methods. *Energy Educ. Sci. Technol.* 1998, *2*, 17–22.

[62] Chand, C.C.; Wan, S.W. China's motor fuels from tung oil. *Ind. Eng. Chem.* 1947, *39*, 1543–1548.

[63]   [63] Harrington, K.J. Chemical and physical properties of vegetable oil esters and their effect on diesel fuel performance. *Biomass* 1986, *9*, 1–1.

[64]   Lotero, E.; Liu, Y.J.; Lopez, D.E.; Suwannakarn, K.; Bruce, D.A.; Goodwin, J.G. Synthesis of biodiesel via acid catalysis. *Ind. Eng. Chem. Res.* 2005, *44*, 5353–5363.

[65]   Kiss, A.A.; Dimian, A.C.; Rothenberg, G. Biodiesel by catalytic reactive distillation powered by metal oxides. *Energy Fuels* 2008, *22*, 598–604.

[66]   Stevens, C.V.; Verhe, R. Renewable bioresources: Scope and modification for non food application. In *England*, Wiley: New York, 2004.

[67]   Sinha, S.; Agarwal, A.K.; Garg, S. Biodiesel development from rice bran oil: transesterification process optimization and fuel characterization. *Energy Convers. Manage.* 2008, *49*, 1248–1257.

[68]   Pahl, G. Biodiesel: growing a new energy economy. Vermont (USA): Chelsea Green Publishing Company, 2008.

[69]   Marvey, B.B. Sunflower-based feedstocks in nonfood applications: perspectives from olefin metathesis. *Int. J. Mol. Sci.* 2008, *9*, 1393–1406.

[70]   Van der Velde, M.; Aloe, A.; Bouraoui, F. Pan-European regional-scale modelling of water and N efficiencies of rapeseed cultivation for biodiesel production. *Global Change Biol.* 2009, *15*, 306–318.

[71]   Mitchell, D. A. Note on Rising Food Prices. In *World Bank policy research working*, paper no. 4682, World Bank-development economics group (DEC), Washington (DC), August 27, 2008.

[72]   Cao, P.; Dube, M.A.; Tremblay, A.Y. High-purity fatty acid methyl ester production from canola, soybean, palm, and yellow grease lipids by means of a membrane reactor. *Biomass Bioenergy* 2009, *32*, 1028–1036.

[73]   Budiman, A.; Kusumaningtyas, R.D.; Rochmadi, S.; Purwono, S. Second generation of biodiesel production from indonesian jatropha oil by continuous reactive distillation process. *A. J. Ch. E.* 2009, *9*, 35–48.

[74]   El-Diwani, G.; Attia, N.K.; Hawash, S.I. Development and evaluation of biodiesel fuel and by-products from jatropha oil. *Int. J. Environ. Sci. Tech.* 2009, *6*, 219–224.

[75]   Naik, M.; Meher, L.C.; Naik, S.N.; Das, L.M. Production of biodiesel from high free acid Karanja (*Pongamia pinnata*) oil. *Biomass Bioenergy* 2008, *32*, 354–357.

[76]   Agarwal, A.K.; Rajamanoharan, K. Experimental investigations of performance and emissions of karanja oil and its blends in a single cylinder agricultural diesel engine. *Appl. Energy* 2009, *86*, 106–112.

[77]   Veljkovic, V.B., Lakicevic, S.H.; Stamenkovic, O.S.; Todorovic, Z.B.; Lazic, M.L. Biodiesel production from tobacco (*Nicotiana tabacum L.*) seed oil with a high content of free fatty acids. *Fuel* 2006, *85*, 2671–2675.

[78]   Lai, C.C; Zullaikah, S.; Vali, S.R.; Ju, Y.H. Lipase catalyzed production of biodiesel from rice bran oil. *J. Chem. Technol. Biotechnol.* 2005, *80*, 331–337.

[79]   Ghadge, S.V.; Raheman, H. Biodiesel production from mahua (*Madhuca indica*) oil having high free fatty acids. *Biomass Bioenergy* 2005, *28*, 601–605.

[80]   Agarwal, D.; Kumar, L.; Agarwal, A.K. Performance evaluation of a vegetable oil fuelles compression ignition engine. *Renew. Energy* 2008, *33*, 1147–1156.

[81]   Ramadhas, A.S.; Jayaraj, S.; Muraleedharan, C. Biodiesel production from high FFA rubber seed oil. *Fuel* 2005, *84*, 335–340.

[82]   Mukherjee, P. Remote village electrification through the biofuels route: the WII experience, Proceedings of the 5th International Biofuels Conference, New Delhi, February 7–8, 2008.

[83]   Arzamendi, G.; Campo, I.; Arguiñarena, E.; Sanchez, M.; Montes, M.; Gandia, L.M. Synthesis of biodiesel with heterogeneous NaOH/alumina catalysts: Comparison with homogeneous NaOH. *Chem. Eng. J.* 2007, *134*, 123–130.

[84]   Lukić, I.; Krstić, J.; Glišić, S.; Jovanović, D.; Skala, D. Biodiesel synthesis using K_2CO_3/Al–O–Si aerogel catalysts. *J. Serb. Chem. Soc.* 2010, *75*, 789–801.

[85]   Dias, J.M.; Alvim-Ferraz, M.C.M.; Almeida, M.F. Comparison of the performance of different homogeneous alkali catalysts during transesterification of waste and virgin oils and evaluation of biodiesel quality. *Fuel* 2008, *87*, 3572–3578.

[86]   Zagonel, G.F.; Peralta-Zamora, P.G.; Ramos, L.P. Production of ethyl esters from crude soybean oil: optimization of reaction yields using a 23 experimental design and development of a new analytical strategy for reaction control. *Preprints Symp: Am. Chem. Soc. Div. Fuel Chem.* 2002, *47*, 363–364.

[87]   Tomasevic, A.V.; Siler-Marinkovic, S.S. Methanolysis of used frying oil. *Fuel Process Technol.* 2003, *81*, 1–6.

[88]   Vicente, G.; Martínez, M.; Aracil, J. Integrated biodiesel production: a comparison of different homogeneous catalysts systems. *Bioresour. Technol.* 2004, *92*, 297–305.

[89]   Dmytryshyn, S.L.; Dalai, A.K.; Chaudhari, S.T.; Mishra, H.K.; Reaney, M.J. Synthesis and characterization of vegetable oil derived esters: evaluation for their diesel additive properties. *Bioresour. Technol.* 2004, *92*, 55–64.

[90]   Sarma, A.K.; et al. A comprehensive analysis of fuel properties of biodiesel from koroch seed oil. *Energy Fuels* 2005, *19*, 656–657.

[91]   Georgogianni, K.G.; Kontominas, M.G.; Avlonitis, D.; Gergis, V. Transesterification of sunflower seed oil for the production of biodiesel: effect of catalyst concentration and ultrasonication, Proceedings of the International Conference on Energy and Environmental Systems, Chalkida, Greece, May 8-10, 2006; pp 425–429.

[92]   Singh, A.; He, B.; Thompson, J.; Van Gerpen, J. Process optimization of biodiesel production using alkaline catalysts. *Appl. Eng. Agric.* 2006, *22*, 597–600.

[93]   Alamu, O.J.; Waheed, M.A.; Jekayinfa, S.O.; Akintola, T.A. Optimal transesterification duration for biodiesel production from Nigerian palm kernel oil. *Agric. Eng. Int.: the CIGR E journal* 2007, *9*, 1–11.

[94]   Bambase, M.E., Jr.; Nakamura, N.; Tanaka, J.; Matsumura, M. Kinetics of hydroxide-catalyzed methanolysis of crude sunflower oil for the production of fuel-grade methyl esters. *J. Chem. Technol. Biotechnol.* 2007, *82*, 273–280.

[95]   Rashid, U.; Anwar, F.; Moser, B.R.; Ashraf, S. Production of sunflower oil methyl esters by optimized alkali-catalyzed methanolysis. *Biomass Bioenergy* 2008, *32*, 1202–1205.

[96]   Liu, X.; Piao, X.; Wang, J.; Zhu, S.; He, H. Calcium methoxide as a solid base catalyst for the transesterification of soybean oil to biodiesel with methanol. *Fuel* 2008, *87*, 1076–1082.

[97] Ríos, L.A.; Castrillon, A.F.; Zuleta Suárez, E. Productions of palm oil biodiesel whit heterogeneous basic catalysts compared to conventional homogeneous catalysts. *Energetic* 2009, *42*, 45–52.

[98] Ilgen, O.; Akin A.N. Transesterification of canola oil to biodiesel using MgO loaded with KOH as a heterogeneous catalyst. *Energy Fuels 2009, 23*, 1786–1789.

[99] Lubes, Z.I.Z.; Zakaria, M. Analysis of parameters for fatty acid methyl esters production from refined palm oil for use as biodiesel in the single- and two stage processes. *Malaysian J. Biochem. Mol. Biol.* 2009, *17*, 5–9.

[100] Rashid, U.; Anwar, F.; Knothe, G.H. Improving the performance of alternative fuels and co-products from vegetable oils. *Energy Fuels* 2009, *90*, 1157–1163.

[101] Rashid, U.; Anwar, F.; Ansari, T.M.; Arif, M.; Ahmad, M. Optimization of alkaline transesterification of rice bran oil for biodiesel production using response surface methodology. *J. Chem. Tech. Biotechnol.* 2009, *84*, 1364–1370.

[102] Laiz-Saldaña, J.C.; Tovar-Miranda R.; Durán-de-Bazúal, M.C.; Solís-Fuentes, J.A. Using of agroindustrial residues: Biodiesel production by alkaline transesterification of Zapote Mamey (*Pouteria sapota*) raw "almond" oil. *Tecnol. Ciencia Ed.* (IMIQ) 2009, *24*, 48–56.

[103] Hossain, A.B.M.S.; Boyce, A.N. Biodiesel production from waste sunflower cooking oil as an environmental recycling process and renewable energy. *Bulgarian J. Agric. Sci.* 2009, *15*, 312–317.

[104] Peña, R.; Romero, R.; Martinez, S.L.; Ramos, M.J.; Martinez, A.; Natividad, R. Transesterification of castor oil: Effect of catalyst and co-solvent. *Ind. Eng. Chem. Res. 2009, 48*, 1186–1189.

[105] Kumar, G.; Kumar, D.; Singh, S.; Kothari, S.; Bhatt, S.; Singh, C.P. Continuous low cost transesterification process for the production of coconut biodiesel. *Energies* 2010, *3*, 43–56.

[106] Rashid, U.; Anwar, F.; Jamil, A.; Bhatti, H.N. *Jatropha curcas* seed oil as a viable source for biodiesel. *Pak. J. Bot.* 2010, *42*, 575–582.

[107] Vlad, E.; Bildea, C.S.; Pleşu, V.; Marton, G.; Bozga, G. Process design of biodiesel production from rapeseed oil. *Chem. Eng. Trans.* 2010, *21*, 1267–1272.

[108] Soetaredjo, F.E.; Ayucitra, A.; Ismadji, S.; Maukar, A.L. KOH/bentonite catalysts for transesterification of palm oil to biodiesel. *Appl. Clay Sci.* 2010, doi: 10.1016/j.clay.2010.12.018.Bako, K.B.; Kova, F.C.S.; Gubicza, L.; Hansco, J.K. Enzymatic biodiesel production from sunflower oil by *Candida antarctica* lipase in a solvent free system. *Biocatal. Biotransform.* 2002, *20*, 437–439.

[110] Du, W.; Xu, Y.Y.; Liu; D.H. Novozym 435-catalyzed transesterification of soybean oil for biodiesel production in a solvent-free medium. *Prepr. Pap.-Am. Chem. Soc., Div. Fuel Chem.* 2003, *48*, 532.

[111] Lara Pizarro, A.V.; Park, E.Y. Lipase-catalyzed production of biodiesel fuel from vegetable oils contained in waste activated bleaching earth. *Process Biochem.* 2003, *38*, 1077–1082.

[112] Du, W.; Xu, Y.; Liu, D.; Zeng, J. Comparative study on lipase catalyzed transformation of soyabeen oil for biodiesel production with acyl acceptors. *J. Mol. Catal. B: Enzym.* 2004, *30*, 125–129.

[113] Xu, Y.; Du, W.; Zeng, J.; Liu, D. Conversion of soyabeen oil to biodiesel fuel using lipozyme TL IM in a solvent free medium. *Biocatal. Biotransform.* 2004, *22*, 45–48.

[114] Shah, S.; Sharma, S.; Gupta, M.N. Biodiesel preparation by lipase-catalyzed transesterification of jatropha oil. *Energy Fuels* 2004, *18*, 154–159.

[115] Deng, L.; Xu, X.B.; Haraldsson, G.G.; Tan, T.W.; Wang, F. Enzymatic production of alkyl esters through alcoholysis: A critical evaluation of lipases and alcohols. *J. Am. Oil Chem. Soc.* 2005, *82*, 341–347.

[116] Li, L.; Du, W.; Liu, D.; Wang, L.; Li, Z. Lipase-catalyzed transesterification of rapeseed oils for biodiesel production with a novel organic solvent as the reaction medium. *J. Mol. Catal. B: Enzym.* 2006, *43*, 58–62.

[117] Moreira, A.B.R.; Perz, V.H.; Zanin, GM.; de Castro H.F. Biodiesel synthesis by enzymatic transesterification of palm oil with ethanol using lipases from several sources immobilized on silica-PVA composite. *Energy Fuels 2007*, *21*, 3689–3694.

[118] Royon, D.; Daz, M.; Ellenrieder, G.; Locatelli, S. Enzymatic production of biodiesel from cotton seed oil using t-butanol as a solvent. *Bioresour. Technol.* 2007, *98*, 648–653.

[119] Modi, M.K.; Reddy, J.R.C.; Rao, B.V.S.K.; Prasad, R.B.N. Lipase mediated conversion of vegetable oils into biodiesel using ethyl acetate. *Bioresour. Technol.* 2007, *98*, 1260–1264.

[120] Hama, S.; Yamaji, H.; Fukumizu, T.; Numata, T.; Tamalampudi, S.; Kondo, A.; Nodac, H.; Fukuda, H. Biodiesel fuel production in a packed-bed reactor using lipase-producing *Rhizopus oryzae* cells immobilized within biomass support particles. *Biochem. Eng. J.* 2007, *34*, 273–278.

[121] Li, N.; Wu, H.; Zong, M.; Lou, W. Immobilization of lipase from *Penicillium expansum* and its application to transesterification of corn oil. *Chin. J. Catal.* 2007, *28*, 333–338.

[122] Shah, S.; Gupta, M.N. Lipase catalyzed preparation of biodiesel from Jatropha oil in a solvent-free system. *Process Biochem.* 2007, *42*, 409–414.

[123] Bernardes, O.L.; Bevilaqua, J.V.; Leal, M.C.M.R.; Freire, D.M.G.; Langone, M.A.P. Biodiesel fuel production by the transesterification reaction of soybean oil using immobilized lipase. *Biochem. Biotechnol.* 2007, 137-140, 105–114.

[124] Kumari, V.; Shah, S.; Gupta, M.N. Preparation of biodiesel by lipase catalyzed transesterification of high free fatty acid containing oil from *Madhuca indica*. *Energy Fuels* 2007, *21*, 368–372.

[125] Shao, P.; Meng, X.; He, J.; Sun, P. Analysis of immobilized *Candida rugosa* lipase catalyzed preparation of biodiesel from rapeseed soap stock. *Food Bioprod. Process* 2008, *86*, 283–289.

[126] Ognjanović, N.D.; Šaponjić, S.V.; Bezbradica, D.I.; Knežević, Z.D. Lipase-catalyzed biodiesel synthesis with different acyl acceptors. *BIBLID: 1450-7188* (2008), *39*, 161–169.

[127] Gao, L.F.; et al. Primary study on producing biodiesel with castor oil by enzymatic catalysis. *J. Anhui Agric. Sci.* 2008, *36*, 6950–6952.

[128] Gog, A.; Roman, M.; Paizs, C.; Chintoanu, M.; Luca, E.; Irimie, F.D. Enzymatic production of biodiesel from rapeseed oil. Bulletin UASVM, Horticulture, 2008.

[129] Salis, A.; Pinna, M.; Monduzzi, M.; Solinas, V. Comparison among immobilised lipases on macroporous polypropylene toward biodiesel síntesis. *J. Mol. Catal. B: Enzymatic.* 2008, *54*, 19–26.

[130] Zheng, Y.; Quan, J.; Ning, X.; Zhu, L.M.; Jiang, B.; He, Z.Y. Lipase-catalyzed transesterification of soybean oil for biodiesel production in *tert*-amyl alcohol. *World J. Microbiol. Biotechnol.* 2009, 25, 141–146.

[131] Kumari, A.; Mahapatra, P.; Garlapati, V.K.; Banerjee, R. Enzymatic transesterification of Jatropha oil. *Biotechnol. Biofuels* 2009, 2, 1.

[132] Simas, A.; Lapa, N.; Oliveira, A.C. Optimization of enzymatic transesterification of rapeseed oil using response surface methodology, Proceedings of the 17th European Biomass Conference and Exhibition, 2009; p. 1532–1537.

[133] Huang, Y.; Zheng, H.; Yan, Y. Optimization of lipase-catalyzed transesterification of lard for biodiesel production using response surface methodology. *Appl. Biochem. Biotechnol.* 2010, *160*, 504–515.

[134] Ruzich, N.I.; Bassi, A.S. Investigation of lipase-catalyzed biodiesel production using ionic liquid [BMIM][PF$_6$] as a co-solvent in 500 ml jacketed conical and shake flask reactors using triolein or waste canola oil as substrates. *Energy Fuels 2010*, *24*, 3214–3222.

[135] Chen, H.C. Continuous production of lipase-catalyzed biodiesel in a packed-bed reactor: Optimization and enzyme reuse study. *J. Biomed. Biotechnol.* 2011, doi:10.1155/2011/950725.

[136] Ma, Y.L. Microbial oils and its research advance. *Chin. J. Bioprocess Eng.* 2006, *4*, 7–11.

[137] Chisti, Y. Biodiesel from microalgae beats bioethanol. *Trends Biotechnol.* 2008, *26*, 126–131.

[138] Illman, A.M.; Scragg, A.H.; Shales S.W. Increase in *Chlorella* strains calorific values when grown in low nitrogen medium. *Enzyme Microb. Technol.* 2000, *27*, 631–635.

[139] Liu, B.; Zhao, Z.B. Biodiesel production by direct methanolysis of oleaginous microbial biomass. *J. Chem. Technol. Biotechnol.* 2007, *82*, 775–780.

[140] Li, J.; Liu, H.J.; Zhang, J.A.; Liu, J. Progress in and prospect of microbial lipid production by fermentation. *Mod. Chem. Indust.* 2007, *27*, 133–136.

[141] Solovchenko, A.E.; Khozin-Goldberg, I.; Didi-Cohen, S.; Cohen, Z.; Merzlyak, M.N. Effects of light intensity and nitrogen starvation on growth, total fatty acids and arachidonic acid in the green microalga *Parietochloris incisa*. *J. Appl. Phycol.* 2008, *20*, 245–251.

[142] Christi, Y. Biodiesel from microalgae. *Biotechnol. Adv.* 2007, *25*, 294–306.

[143] Khozin-Goldberg, I.; Cohen, Z. The effect of phosphate starvation on the lipid and fatty acid composition of the fresh water eustigmatophyte *Monudus subterraneus*. *Phytochem.* 2006, *67*, 696–701.

[144] Chen, G.Q.; Jiang, Y.; Chen, F. Variation of lipid class composition in *Nitzchia laevis* as a response to growth temperature change. *Food Chem.* 2008, *109*, 88–94.

[145] Mata, T.M.; Martins, A.A.; Caetano, N.S. Microalgae for biodiesel production and other applications: a review. *Renew. Sustain. Energy Rev.* 2010, *14*, 217–232.

[146] Benemann, J.R. Microalgae biofuels: a brief introduction. In *Benemann Associates and Microbio Engineering*, Walnut Creek (CA), January 1, 2009.

[147] Sheehan, J.; Dunahay, T.; Benemann, J.; Roessler, P. A look back at the US Department of Energy's Aquatic Species Program: Biodiesel from algae. US Department of Energy, Washington, D. C. NREL: NREL/TP-580-24190, 1998.

[148] Pulz, O. Photobioreactors: production systems for phototrophic microorganisms. *Appl. Microbiol. Biotechnol.* 2001, *57*, 287–293.

[149] Miao, X.L.; Wu, Q.Y. Bio-oil fuel production from microalgae after heterotrophic growth. *Renew. Energy Resour.* 2004, *4*, 41–44.

[150] Hameed, B.H.; Goh, C.S.; Chin, L.H. Process optimization for methyl ester production from waste cooking oil using activated carbon supported potassium fluoride. *Fuel Process Technol.* 2009, *90*, 1532–1537.

[151] Phan, A.; Phan, T.M. Biodiesel production from waste cooking oils. *Fuel* 2008, *87*, 3490–3496.

[152] Chhetri, A.B.; Watts, K.C.; Islam, M.R. Waste cooking oil as an alternate feedstock for biodiesel production. *Energies* 2008, *1*, 3–18.

[153] Sheedlo, M. A review of the processes of biodiesel production. *MMG 445 Basic Biotechnol. Journal* 2008, *4,* 61–65.

[154] Antolin, G.; Tinaut, F.V.; Briceño, Y.; Castaño, V.; Pérez, C.; Ramírez, A.I. Optimization of biodiesel production by sunflower oil transesterification. *Bioresour. Technol.* 2002, *83*, 111–114.

[155] Mohamed, M.; Soumanoua, B.; Uwe, T.; Bornscheuer, A. Improvement in lipase catalyzed synthesis of fatty acid methyl esters from sunflower oil. *Enzyme Microb. Technol.* 2003, *33*, 97–103.

[156] Köse, O.; Tüter, M.; Askoy, H.A. Immobilized *Candida Antarctica* lipase-catalized alcoholysis of cotton seed oil in a solvent-free medium. *Bioresour. Technol.* 2002, *83*, 125–129.

[157] Tan, R.R.; Culuba, A.B.; Purvis, M.R.I. Carbon balance implications of coconut biodiesel utilization in the Philippine automotive transport sector. *Biomass Bioenergy* 2004, *26*, 579–587.

[158] Haas, M.J. Improving the economics of biodiesel production through the use of low value lipids as feedstocks: vegetable oil soapstock. *Fuel Process Technol.* 2005, *86*, 1087–1096.

[159] Ugarte, D.G.T.; Ray, D.E. Biomass and bioenergy applications of the POLYSYS modeling framework. *Biomass Bioenergy* 2000, *18*, 291–308.

[160] Karmee, S.K.; Chadha, A. Preparation of biodiesel from crude oil of Pongamia pinnata. *Bioresour Technol.* 2005, *96*, 1425–1429.

[161] Usta, N. Use of tobacco seed oil methyl ester in a turbocharged indirect injection diesel engine. *Biomass Bioenergy* 2005, *28*, 77–86.

[162] Cravotto, G.; Binello, A.; Merizzi, G.; Avogadro, M. Improving solvent-free extraction of policosanol from rice bran by high intensity ultrasound treatment. *Eur. J. Lipid Sci. Technol.* 2004, *106*, 147–151.

[163] Canoira, L.; et al. Biodiesel from Jojoba oil-wax: transesterification with methanol and properties as a fuel. *Biomass Bioenergy* 2006, *30*, 76–81.

[164] Scragg, A.H.; Morrison, J.; Shales, S.W. The use of a fuel containing *Chlorella vulgaris* in a diesel engine. *Enzyme Microb. Technol.* 2003, *33*, 884–889.

[165] Meng, X.; Yang, J.; Xu, X.; Zhang, L.; Nie, Q.; Xian, M. Biodiesel production from oleaginous microorganisms. *Renew. Energy* 2009, *34*, 1–5.

[166] Nelson, R.G.; Schrock, M.D. Energetic and economic feasibility associated with the production, processing, and conversion of beef tallow to a substitute diesel fuel. *Biomass Bioenergy* 2006, *30*, 584–591.

[167] Han, J. Lipase-catalyzed production of biodiesel from tallow. *J. ASTM Inter.* 2010, *7*, 10.

[168] Lu, J.; Nie, K.; Xie, F.; Wang, F.; Tan, T. Enzymatic synthesis of fatty acid methyl esters from lard with immobilized *Candida* sp. 99–125. *Process Biochem.* 2007, *42*, 1367–1370.

[169] Kamini, N.R.; Fujii, T.; Kurosu, T.; Iefuji, H. Production, purification and characterization of an extracellular lipase from the yeast, *Cryptococcus* sp. S-2. *Process Biochem.* 2000, *36*, 317–324.

[170] Guru, M.; Artukoglu, B.D.; Keskin, A.; Koca, A. Biodiesel production from waste animal fat and improvement of its characteristics by synthesized nickel and magnesium additive. *Energy Convers. Manage.* 2009, *50*, 498–502.

[171] Diaz-Felix, W.; Riley, M.R.; Zimmt, W.; Kazz, M. Pretreatment of yellow grease for diesel engine. *Appl. Energy* 2009, *86*, 2114–2120.

[172] Shimada, Y., Watanabe, Y.; Sugihara, A.; Tominaga, Y. Enzymatic alcoholysis for biodiesel fuel production and application of the reaction to oil processing. *J. Mol. Catal. B: Enzym.* 2002, *17*, 133–142.

[173] Leung, D.Y.C.; Guo, Y. Transesterification of neat and used frying oil: optimization for biodiesel production. *Fuel Process Technol.* 2006, *87*, 883–890.

[174] Kondamudi, N.; Mohapatra, S.K.; Misra, M. Quintinite as a bifunctional heterogeneous catalyst for biodiesel synthesis. *Appl. Catal. A: Gen.* 2011, 393, 236–243.

[175] Cardoso, A.L.; Gonzaga Neves, S.C.; da Silva, M.J. Esterification of oleic acid for biodiesel production catalyzed by $SnCl_2$: A kinetic investigation. *Energies* 2008, *1*, 79–92.

[176] Xiangmei, M. Biodiesel production from waste cooking oil via alkali catalyst and its Engine test. *Fuel Process in Tech.* 2008, *9*, 851–857.

[177] Demirbas, A. Biodiesel production from vegetable oils via catalytic and non-catalytic supercritical methanol transesterification methods. *Prog. Energy Comb. Sci.* 2005, *31*, 466–487.

[178] Saka, S.; Kusdiana, D. Biodiesel fuel from rapeseed oil as prepared in supercritical methanol. *Fuel* 2001, *80*, 225–231.

[179] Madras, G.; et al. Synthesis of biodiesel in supercritical fluids. *Fuel* 2004, *83*, 2029–2033.

[180] Marchetti, J.M.; Errazu, A.F. Comparison of different heterogeneous catalysts and different alcohols for the esterification reaction of oleic acid. *Fuel* 2008, *87*, 15–16.

[181] Al-Widyan, M.I.; Al-Shyoukh, A.O. Experimental evaluation of the transesterification of waste palm oil into biodiesel. *Bioresour. Technol.* 2002, *85*, 253–256.

[182] Zabeti, M. Activity of Solid Catalysts for Biodiesel Production: A Review. *Fuel Process. Technol.* 2009, *90*, 770–777.

[183] Liu, X.; He, H.; Wang, Y.; Zhu, S. Transesterification of soybean oil to biodiesel using SrO as a solid base catalyst. *Catal. Commun.* 2007, *8*, 1107–1111.

[184] Park, E.Y.; Sato, M.; Kojima, S. Lipase-catalyzed biodiesel production from waste activated bleaching earth as raw material in a pilot plant. *Bioresour. Technol.* 2008, *99*, 3130–3135.

[185] Suppes, G.J.; et al. Transesterification of soybean oil with zeolite and metal catalysts. *Appl. Catal. A: Gen.* 2004, *257*, 213–223.

[186] Shibasaki-Kitakawa, N.; Honda, H.; Kuribayashi, H.; Toda, T.; Fukumura, T.; Yonemoto, T. Biodiesel production using anionic ion-exchange resin as heterogeneous catalyst. *Bioresour. Technol.* 2007, *98*, 416–421.

[187] Guerreiro, L.; et al. Transesterification of soybean oil over sulfonic acid functionalised polymeric membranes. *Catal. Today* 2006, *118*, 166–171.

[188] Marchetti, J.M.; Miguel, V.U.; Errazu, A.F. Heterogeneous esterification of oil with high amount of free fatty acids. *Fuel* 2007, *86*, 906–910.

[189] Turkay, S.; Civelekoglu, H. Deacidification of sulfur olive oil. I. Single-stage liquid–liquid extraction of miscella with ethyl alcohol. *J. Am. Oil Chem. Soc.* 1991, *68*, 83–86.

[190] Zhang, Y.; Lu, X.H.; Yu, Y.L.; Ji, J.B. Study on the coupling process of catalytic esterification and extraction of high acid value waste oil with methanol. In: *Zhuang X, editor*, proceeding of the International Conference on Biomass Energy Technologies, Guangzhou, China, 2008.

[191] Freedman, B.; Pryde, E.H. Fatty esters from vegetable oils for use as a diesel fuel, Proceedings of International Conference on Plant and Vegetable oils as Fuels. St. Joseph, MI: ASAE, 1982; pp 117–122.

[192] Aksoy, H.A.; Kahraman, I.; Karaosmanoglu, F.; Civelekoglu, H. Evaluation of Turkish sulphur olive oil as an alternative diesel fuel. *J.A.O.C.S.* 1988, *65*, 936–938.

[193] Liu, K. Preparation of fatty acid methyl esters for gas chromatographic analysis of lipids in biological material. *JAOCS* 1994, *71*, 1179–1187.

[194] Soriano, N.U.; Vendittia, R.; Argyropoulos, D.S. Biodiesel synthesis via homogeneous Lewis acid catalyzed transesterification. *Fuel* 2009, *88*, 560–565.

[195] Tamalampudi, S.; Talukder, M.; Hama, S.; Tanino, T.; Suzuki, Y.; Kondo, A.; Fukuda, H. Development of recombinant *Aspergillus oryzae* whole-cell biocatalyst expressing lipase-encoding gene from *Candida antarctica*. *Appl. Microbiol. Biotechnol.* 2007, *75*, 387–395.

[196] Hama, S.; Tamalampudi, S.; Suzuki, Y.; Yoshida, A.; Fukuda, H.; Kondo, A. Preparation and comparative characterization of immobilized *Aspergillus oryzae* expressing *Fusarium heterosporum* lipase for enzymatic biodiesel production. *Appl. Microbiol. Biotechnol.* 2008, *81*, 637–645.

[197] Colin, V.L.; Baigorí, M.D.; Pera, L.M. Mycelium-bound lipase production from *Aspergillus niger* MYA 135, and its potential applications for the transesterification of ethanol. *J. Basic Microbiol.* 2011, *51*, 1–7.

[198] Das, P.C.; Pradhan, N.C.; Dalai, A.K.; Bakhshi, N.N. Carbon monoxide hydrogenation over various titania-supported Ru-Ni bimetallic catalysts. *Fuel Process. Technol.* 2004, *85*, 1487–1501.

[199] Bondioli, P.; Gasparoli, A.; Bella, L.D.; Silvia, T. Evaluation of biodiesel storage stability using reference methods. *Eur. J. Lipid Sci. Technol.* 2002, *104*, 777–784.

[200] Ferella, F. Optimization of the transesterification reaction in biodiesel production. *Fuel* 2010, *89*, 36–42.

[201] Lien, Y.Y.; Hsieh, L.S.; Wu, J.C.S. Biodiesel synthesis by simultaneous esterification and transesterification using oleophilic acid catalyst. *Ind. Eng. Chem. Res.* 2010, *49*, 2118–2121.

[202] Freedman, B.; Pryde, E.H.; Mounts, T.L. Variables affecting the yields of fatty esters from transesterified vegetable oils. *J. Am. Oil Chem. Soc.* 1984, *61*, 1638–1643.

[203] Demirbas, A. Hydrogen production from carbonaceous solid wastes by steam reforming. *Energy Sources, Part A*, 2008, *30*, 924–931.

[204] Guo, Y. Alkaline-catalyzed production of biodiesel fuel from virgin canola oil and recycled waste oils. Ph.D. Dissertation, Department of Mechanical Engineering the University of Hong Kong, Hong Kong, 2005.

[205] Eevera, T.; Rajendran, K.; Saradha, S. Biodiesel production process optimization and characterization to assess the suitability of the product for varied environmental conditions. *Renew. Energy* 2009, *34*, 762–765.

[206] Trostle, R. Global agricultural supply and demand: factors contributing to the recent increase in food commodity prices. USDA Economic Research Service, report WRS-0801, Washington (DC), July, 2008.

[207] Food and Agriculture Organization of the United Nations (FAO). The market and food security implications of the development of biofuel production, Proceeding of the FAO Committee on Commodity Problems, Sixty-seventh Session, Rome, April 20–22, 2009.

[208] Rapier, R. Renewable diesel. In *Biofuels, solar and wind as renewable energy systems: benefits and risks*, Ed.; Springer Verlag; September 11, 2008.

[209] Pimentel, D.; Pimentel, M. Corn and cellulosic ethanol cause major problems. *Energies* 2008, *1*, 35–37.

[210] European Commission. Agriculture in the European Union: statistical and economic information. Directorate-General for Agriculture and Rural Development, Brussels, February 2007.

[211] US Environmental Protection Agency (EPA). A comprehensive analysis of biodiesel impacts on exhaust emissions. Draft Technical Report, EPA420-P02-001; October 2002. www.biodiesel.org/resourcesgen/20021001_gen (accessed October 2009).

[212] Abdullah, S.; Tiong, F.C. Prediction of palm oil properties using artificial neural network. *IJCSN* 2008, *8*, 101–106.

[213] Thamsiriroj, T.; Murphy, J.D. Is it better to import palm oil from Thailand to produce biodiesel in Ireland than to produce biodiesel from indigenous Irish rape seed? *Appl. Energy* 2009, *86*, 595–604.

[214] Refaat, A.A. Correlation between the chemical structure of biodiesel and its physical properties. *Int. J. Environ. Sci. Technol.* 2009, *6*, 677–694.

[215] Chincholkar, S.P.; Srivastava, S.; Rehman, A.; Dixit, S.; Lanjewar, A. Biodiesel as an alternative fuel for pollution control in diesel engine. *Asian J. Exp. Sci.* 2005, *19*, 13–22.

[216] Pramanik, K. Properties and use of Jatropha curcas oil and diesel fuel blends in compression ignition engine. *Renew. Energy* 2003, *28*, 239–248.

[217] Mahanta, P.; Mishra, S.C.; Kushwah, Y.S. An experimental study of Pongamia pinnata L. oil as a diesel substitute. *Proc. Inst. Mech. Eng. J. Power. Eng.* 2006, *220*, 803–808.

[218] Van Eijck, J.; Romijn, H. Prospects for jatropha biofuels in Tanzania: an analysis with strategic niche management. *Energy Policy* 2008, *36*, 311–325.

[219] Scott, P.T.; Pregelj, L.; Chen, N.; Hadler, J.S.; Djordjevic, M.A.; Gresshoff, P.M. *Pongamia pinnata*: an untapped resource for the biofuels industry of the future? *Bioenergy Res.* 2008, *1*, 2–11.

[220] Ghosal, M.K.; Das, D.K.; Pradhan, S.C.; Sahoo, N. Performance study of diesel engine by using mahua methyl ester (biodiesel) and its blends with diesel fuel. *Agri. Eng. Int. CIGR Ejournal*, 2008, *10*, 1–9.

[221] Puhan, S.; Vedaraman, N.; Ram, B.V.B.; Sankarnarayanan, G.; Jeychandran, K. Mahua oil (*Madhuca Indica* seed oil) methyl ester as biodiesel-preparation and emission characteristics. *Biomass Bioenergy* 2005, *28*, 87–93.

[222] Pandey, A. Handbook of plant-based biofuels. Boca Raton (FL): CRC Press, Taylor and Francis LLC, 2008.

[223] Canakcı, M.; Ozsezen, A.N. Evaluating waste cooking oils as alternative diesel fuel. *G.U. J. Sci.* 2005, *18*, 81–91.

[224] Latner, K.; O'Kray, C.; Jiang, J. China, peoples republic of bio-fuels an alternative future for agriculture 2006. In *USDA Foreign Agricultural Service*, GAIN report-CH6049, August 8, 2006.

In: Oil: Production, Consumption and Environmental Impact   ISBN: 978-1-61942-877-5
Editor: Shuangning Xiu   © 2012 Nova Science Publishers, Inc.

Chapter 4

HONGE AND MAHUA BIODIESEL

N. Kapilan[1], and R. P. Reddy[2]*

[1]Nagarjuna College of Engineering and Technology, Bangalore, India
[2]Reva Institute of Technology and Management, Bangalore, India

ABSTRACT

The rapidly increase in consumption and depletion of fossil fuels have promoted research for alternative fuels. Among the alternative fuels, biodiesel has considerable potential and can be used as a renewable fuel. In developing and under developed countries, inedible oils are used for the biodiesel production. In this work, biodiesel was derived from high acid value honge and mahua oils. From the property analysis, it is observed that the honge and mahua biodiesel satisfy the ASTM biodiesel specifications. The engine tests were carried out on a single cylinder diesel engine. The engine performance with biodiesel is comparable to fossil diesel with significant reduction in CO, UBHC and smoke emissions. From this work, it is concluded that the honge biodiesel and mahua biodiesel are promising alternative fuel to replace petroleum-based diesel that are obtained from renewable sources.

1. INTRODUCTION

The analysis of Shahriar and Erkan [2009] indicates that the fossil fuel reserves depletion time for oil is approximately 35 year. The rapid depletion of fossil fuels and the environmental pollution caused by burning these fuels and sharp escalation in the petroleum prices have led to an intensive search for alternative fuels, IEO [2008]. Among the different alternative fuels, biodiesel is considered as a potential sustainable renewable substitute for the fossil diesel. Biodiesel is defined as mono-alkyl esters of long chain fatty acids derived from vegetable oils or animal fats, which conform to ASTM D6751 specifications. Vegetable oil is water-insoluble hydrophobic substances primarily composed of trigylcerides. The commonly present fatty acids in vegetable oils are, palmitic, oleic, stearic, arachidic, behenic, linoceri,

* Email: kapil_krecmech@yahoo.com.

erucic, myristic, linoleic and linoleinic. The variation in viscosity of the vegetable oils is due to fatty acid chain length, the number of unsaturated bonds and interaction between the combinations. The triglyceride molecules have molecular weights between 800 and 900 and are thus nearly four times larger than the diesel ($C_{16}H_{34}$), Ulf Schuchart et al. [1998].

Generally, Biodiesel is produced from vegetable oil by a chemical process called transesterification. This process is a reaction of the oil with an alcohol, in the presence of a catalyst, such as potassium hydroxide, to chemically break the molecule of an oil or fat into an ester (biodiesel) and glycerol. Transesterification consists of three equivalent, consecutive and reversible reactions. The triglyceride is converted stepwise to diglyceride, monoglyceride and finally glycerol. At each reaction step, one molecule of methyl or ethyl ester is produced for each molecule of methanol or ethanol consumed. Marchetti et al. [2007] made a review of the alternative technological methods that could be used to produce biodiesel. They reported that a two-step transesterification can be used to produce biodiesel. The biodiesel is an oxygenated compound because it has 17% oxygen by weight. As a mixture with low-sulfur diesel, biodiesel can act as a lubricity improver. The absence of sulfur allows more efficient use of oxidation catalysts. The viscosity of biodiesel is less than that of virgin oils and closer to diesel. The biodiesel is safe to store and handle due to its higher flash point. The neat biodiesel contains almost no sulfur and no aromatics. Also biodiesel is biodegradable and non-toxic.

Use of indigenously made alternative fuels will increase the growth of country's economy and increases job opportunities and meet the local and regional energy requirements of each country. In India, biodiesel is derived from inedible oils as there is a demand for the edible oils, Subramanian et al. [2005]. This paper discusses the biodiesel production from inedible oils such as honge and mahua, which are having considerable potential for the biodiesel production in Asian countries in particular India.

2. POTENTIAL OILS

In India, different types of inedible oils are available. Among these, honge oil and mahua oil are having considerable potential for the production of biodiesel and discussed in the following sub-chapter.

2.1. Honge

Honge is a medium sized tree that generally attains a height of about 8 m and is one of the few nitrogen fixing trees and is shown in Figure 1(a). It is commonly called pongam, pongamia pinnata, or karanj. It grows in areas having an annual rainfall ranging from 0.5 to 2.5 m. The natural production is profuse by seed and common by root suckers. It is native to the Asian subcontinent. The trunk is generally short with thick branches spreading into a dense hemispherical crown of dark green leaves. The alternate, compound pinnate leaves consist of 5 or 7 leaflets which are arranged in 2 or 3 pairs, and a single terminal leaflet. Leaflets are 5-10 cm long, 4-6 cm wide and pointed at the tip. Flowers are light purple, or white in colour and is shown in Figure 1(b). Pods are elliptical and contain a single seed. The seeds are 10-20 cm long, oblong, and light brown in color and is shown in Figure 1(c). A thick yellow-orange to brown oil is extracted from the seeds. The oil yield from the seeds using mechanical expeller is around 25%. The number of plants that can be planted is 200 plants per acre, with the spacing between the plants is 5 m x 4 m. The seed yield is 25 to 40 kg per tree, depends upon the age and other parameters, svlele [2010]. The major fatty acids present in the honge oil are palmitic (9.77 %), stearic (7.33 %), oleic acid (351.72%), linoleic (19.17 %), linolenic (4.17 %) and Behenic acid (5.84 %).

(a) Honge.

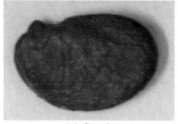

(b) Flower.

(c) Seed.

Figure 1.

(a) Mahua.

(b) Seed.

Figure 2.

2.2. Mahua

Mahua is a medium to larger tree and is available in large quantities in Asian countries. It belongs to madhuca longifolia of family sapotaceae with wider and round canopy. The variety latifolia is common throughout the Indian sub-continent and is shown in Figure 2(a). The tree may attain a height of upto 20 metres. Simple lanceolate leaves grow in cluster at the tip of the branches and is 7.5 to 23 cm long. The flowers are fleshy and the fruit is a kind of berry, egg shaped, contains 1 to 4 seeds. The kernel constitutes 70% the seed and contains 50% oil. The seed oil is obtained from the seed kernels and is a common ingredient of hydrogenated fat in India, novodboard [2010]. It has palmitic (19%), stearic (15%), oleic (42%) and linoleic (24%) as major fatty acids. The seed is shown in Figure 2(b).

Table 1. Properties of the biodiesel

Property	ASTM D6751	Mahua Biodiesel	Honge Biodiesel	Diesel
Flash point (°C)	>130	132	145	71
Pour point (°C)	--	6	8	-14
Calorific Value (MJ/kg)	--	36.73	36.9	42.5
Viscosity at 40° C (mm^2/sec)	1.9-6	4.71	4.8	2.36
Density at 15°C (kg/m^3)	--	885	889	845
water content (mg / kg)	<500	130	144	105
Acid number (mg KOH/ g)	<0.50	0.41	0.44	0.31
Copper strip corrosion, 3hr at50°C	>No.3	1	1	1
Ash Content (%)	<0.02	0.01	0.01	0.01

3. BIODIESEL PRODUCTION

There are different ways of producing biodiesel from vegetable oils, Marchetti et al. [2007] and Balat [2010]. Both honge and mahua oils are inedible in nature and hence in developing and under developed countries located in Asia; biodiesel is derived from these types of oils. These oils are generally unrefined and contain higher acid value. For base catalyst transesterification, the acid value should be less than 1 mg KOH/g of oil. A two-step transesterification is one of the better methods to produce biodiesel from high acid value vegetable oil. The acid value of honge and mahua oils was 12 and 15 mg KOH per g of oil respectively and hence, two-step transesterification was used in this work.

In the first step called acid catalyst transesterfication, acid value of the oil was reduced below 1 mg KOH/g of oil. The sulfuric acid was used as the catalyst and the quantity used was 1% of the weight of the oil. The quantity of the methanol used was 1/3 rd of the quantity of the oil used. These reactions were carried-out for 90-120 min, until the acid value of the oil was reduced below 1 mg KOH /g of the oil. The reaction was carried-out in a 25litre capacity biodiesel plant, which consists of reactor vessel, settling tank and washing tank. The required quantity of vegetable oil (honge or mahua oil) was poured into the reactor vessel and heated below the boiling point of the alcohol (60°C). Then required quantity of methanol and sulfuric acid was poured into the reactor vessel. The reactants were mixed vigorously using the mechanical stirrer. This reaction was carried-out upto 120 min, until the acid value was reduced below 1 mg KOH /g of the oil.

The pretreated oil of the first step was used in the second step called base catalyst transesterification. The sodium hydroxide (NaOH) was used as the catalyst and the quantity used was 1% of the weight of the oil and reaction was carried-out for 90 min. This reaction was carried-out in the reactor vessel. The pretreated vegetable oil was poured into the reactor vessel and heated to 60°C. The required quantity of methanol and NaOH pallets were mixed thoroughly so that the NaOH completely dissolves in the methanol. After the reaction, the products of transesterification were heated above 100°C, to remove the excess methanol and allowed to settle for 5 h. After settling, two layers were observed. The top layer (biodiesel) was removed and added with warm distilled water to remove the impurities and soap. Finally, the water washed biodiesel was heated above 100°C, for 15 min, to remove the moisture from the biodiesel. The biodiesel yield obtained in this method was 91 and 88% respectively for honge and mahua oils. The by-product of this reaction is glycerin.

3. BIODIESEL PROPERTIES

The important properties of biodiesel were determined as per ASTM methods and the values are shown in Table 1. From the table, it is observed that the properties of the biodiesel satisfy the ASTM Biodiesel standards. The higher flash point of the biodiesel indicates the reduced risk of fire hazard and safe transportation of biodiesel as compared to diesel. The calorific value of the biodiesel is lower than the diesel. Generally biodiesel contains 10 to 15% oxygen in its molecular structure. The presence of oxygen in the biodiesel reduces its calorific value. The viscosity of the biodiesel is higher than the diesel due to heavier molecules present in their molecular structure. The water content, acid number, copper corrosion and ash content are within the biodiesel standards.

4. ENGINE TESTS AND PERFORMANCE ANALYSIS

The engine tests were conducted on a 3.5 kW, single cylinder, four stroke, naturally aspirated, diesel engine which is most widely used in agricultural machinery in India. The engine was loaded using an eddy current dynamometer. The fuel flowrate was measured using a burette and a stop watch. The engine exhaust emissions were measured using a MRU make emission analyzer. The engine was started by hand cranking with diesel as fuel and allowed to warm-up. After 10 minutes, the engine was loaded gradually to 25% of the full load using the eddy current dynamometer.

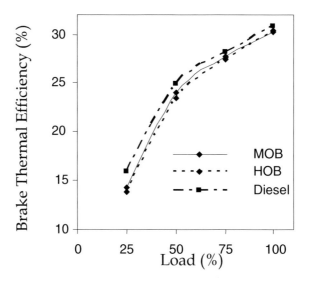

Figure 3. Effect of fuels on brake thermal efficiency at different loads.

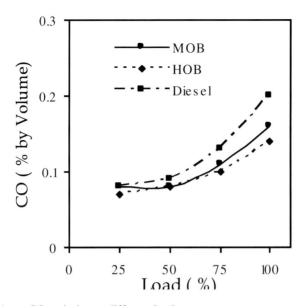

Figure 4. Effect of fuels on CO emission at different loads.

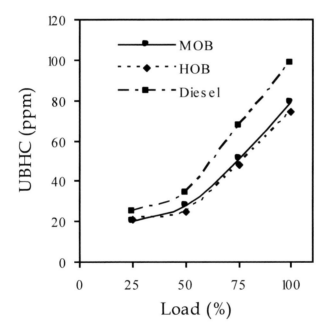

Figure 5. Effect of fuels on UBHC emission at different loads.

At this load condition, the fuel flowrate, engine speed and engine exhaust emissions were measured. Then the load was increased to 50% of the full load and the fuel flowrate, engine speed and engine exhaust emissions were measured. Similar procedure was followed for 75% of full load and full load. Then the fuel tank and fuel supply were cleaned and filled with the biodiesel. The engine test procedure followed for the diesel fuel was followed for the biodiesel.

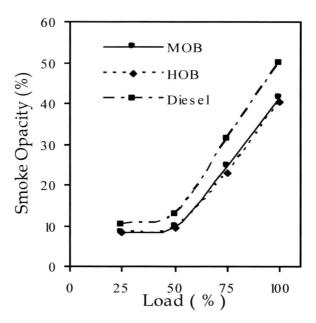

Figure 6. Effect of fuels on smoke emission at different loads.

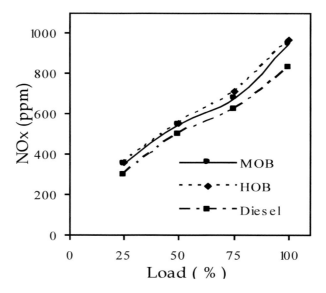

Figure 7. Effect of fuels on NOx emission at different loads.

The engine test performance with diesel, mahua oil biodiesel (MOB) and honge oil biodiesel (HOB) is discussed in the following paragraph and shown in Figure 3 to 7. During engine tests, knocking was not observed when biodiesel was used as fuel. From the Figure 3, it is observed that the brake thermal efficiency of the engine with biodiesel is lower than the diesel. This is due to lower volatility and higher flash point of the biodiesel. From the figure, it is also observed that the brake thermal efficiency of the engine with MOB is slightly higher than the HOB.

Figure 4 to 7 shows the effect of fuels on engine exhaust emissions. From the Figure 4 to 6, it is observed that the engine emissions such as carbon monoxide (CO), un-burnt hydrocarbon (UBHC) and smoke, of the biodiesel (MOB and HOB) are lower than the diesel. This is due to the presence of oxygen in the molecular structure of the engine which results in better combustion and reduces the formation of these emissions. From these figures, it is also observed that the emissions of HOB is lower than the MOB at higher loads. From the Figure 7, it is observed that the engine NOx emission with biodiesel is higher than the diesel. This is due to elevated bulk modulus of compressibility of the biodiesel and its lower volatility, which results in increase in the length of time spent at the elevated temperatures in the cylinder.

CONCLUSION

The honge and mahua oils are inedible and can be used as a raw material for the production of biodiesel. These oils are unrefined and hence, a two-step transesterification process can be used for the production of biodiesel from these oils. The properties of these biodiesel satisfy ASTM biodiesel standards. The diesel engine fuelled with the honge biodiesel and mahua biodiesel results in a slightly lower brake thermal efficiency and lower emissions such as CO, UBHC and smoke, as compared to the diesel. From this work, it is concluded that honge biodiesel and mahua biodiesel can be used as a renewable alternative substitute for the fossil diesel.

ACKNOWLEDGMENT

Authors wish to thank the Department of Science and Technology, India, for financially supporting this work (Grant No. INT/Bulgaria/B-01/08, 2009).

REFERENCES

Balat, M. (2010) Production of Biodiesel from Vegetable Oils: A Survey, *Journal of Energy Sources, Part A: Recovery, Utilization, and Environmental Effects*, Vol.29, pp. 895 -913.

Marchetti, J, M, Miguel, V,U. Errazu, A,F. (2007). Possible methods for biodiesel production, *Journal of Renewable and Sustainable Energy Reviews*, Vol.11, pp.1300–1311.

Shahriar, S.; Erkan Topal. (2009). When will fossil fuel reserves be diminished?. *Journal of Energy Policy*, Vol..37, pp. 181-189.

Subramanian, K, A. Singal, S,K. Mukesh Saxena, Sudhir Singhal., (2005). Utilization of liquid biofuels in automotive diesel engines : An Indian perspective, *Journal of Biomass and Bioenergy*, Vol. 29, pp. 65-72.

svlele, 15-76-2010, Available from http://www.svlele.com/karanj.htm

Ulf Schuchart, Ricardo Sercheli, Rogerio Matheus Vargas. (1998). Transesterification of vegetable oils: a review. *Journal of Brazilian Chemical Society,* Vol.9(1), pp.199-210.

IEO, International Energy Outlook 2008 Report, 15-7-2010, Available from http://www.eia.doe.gov/oiaf/ieo

novodboard, Report on Oilseeds and Vegetable Oils, 15-7-2010, Available from http://novodboard.com/Mahua.pdf .

In: Oil: Production, Consumption and Environmental Impact   ISBN: 978-1-61942-877-5
Editor: Shuangning Xiu   © 2012 Nova Science Publishers, Inc.

Chapter 5

OIL FROM BIOMASS: ENGINEERING PROCESS TECHNOLOGIES

Shuangning Xiu,[*] Bo Zhang and Abolghasem Shahbazi

Biological Engineering Program, School of Agriculture,
NC A&T State University, US

ABSTRACT

The development of products derived from biomass is becoming an important component for economic development in the world. Rising oil prices and uncertainty over the security of existing fossil reserves, combined with concerns over global climate change, have created the need for new transportation fuels and for the manufacture of bio products to substitute for fossil-based materials.

This overview describes the state-of-the-art in extraction and processing technologies, and recent advancements in the research and development of biomass to bio-oil (bio-crude). The technologies considered mainly include flash (fast) pyrolysis and hydrothermal liquefaction. Pyrolysis is an important thermochemical conversion process in which biomass is degraded to bio-oil, syngas and bio-chars in the absence of oxygen. Hydrothermal liquefaction refers to decomposition reactions taking place in water media at high temperature and pressure. In this review, the principles of fast pyrolysis and hydrothermal liquefaction are discussed, and the main reactors for bio-oil production reviewed. Barriers to achieving improvements are also pointed out.

1. INTRODUCTION

Ever since the shortages of petroleum resources began with the global energy crisis in the 1970s, considerable attention has been focused on the development of alternative fuels. Renewable biomass sources can be converted to fuels, and are a logical choice to replace oil. Unlike fossil fuel, biomass from plant sources removes carbon from the atmosphere while it

---

[*] Corresponding author. Tel.:+1 3363347787; fax: +1 3363347270. E-mail: xshuangn@ncat.edu.

is growing, and returns carbon when it is burned. Under sustainable management, biomass is harvested as part of a constantly replenished crop. This is achieved through woodland or management and coppicing, or as part of a continuous programme of replanting with the new growth taking up CO_2 from the atmosphere at the same time as it is released by combustion of the previous harvest. This maintains a closed carbon cycle with no net increase in atmospheric CO_2 levels.

Biomass encompasses a variety of biological materials with distinctive physical and chemical characteristics, such as woody or lignocellulosic materials, grasses and legumes, crop residues and animal wastes. Biomass can be converted to various forms of energy by numerous technical processes, depending on the raw material characteristics and the type of energy desired. As a result, a wide variety of conversion schemes have been developed. Among various technologies, thermochemical conversion such as pyrolysis or hydrothermal liquefaction offers a convenient way to produce liquid fuels. These liquid fuels, known as bio-oils, are regarded as promising candidates to replace or supplement petroleum fuels for power generation, heat, and chemicals.

Bio-oil has several environmental advantages over fossil fuels as a clean fuel. Bio-oils are CO_2 and green house gas (GHG) neutral. Therefore, they can generate carbon dioxide credits. No SOx emissions are generated, because plant biomass contains insignificant amounts of sulfur. Therefore, bio-oil would not be subjected to SOx taxes. Bio-oil fuels generate more than 50% lower NOx emissions than diesel oil in a gas turbine. In addition, renewable and locally produced bio-oil can be produced from large volumes of organic waste. Thus, bio-fuels are cleaner and cause less pollution.

This chapter comprehensively reviews the state of the art and the use and drawbacks of the processes that are used to produce bio-oil, specifically flash pyrolysis and hydrothermal liquefaction. The principles of fast pyrolysis and hydrothermal liquefaction are discussed, and the main reactors for bio-oil production reviewed. It also points out barriers to achieving future improvements to the technologies.

2. BIOMASS AND BIO-OIL

2.1. Biomass

Biomass is a renewable organic material from plant or animal sources that can be used to produce energy. These resources include aquatic or terrestrial vegetation, residues from forestry or agriculture, animal waste and municipal waste. In laymen's terms, that means biomass comes from crops, wood or manure. Producing fuel and energy from biomass is a complex procedure but the principle behind it corresponds to photosynthesis. This is a chemical reaction in which carbon dioxide and water are transformed into oxygen gas and glucose through the input of energy from the sun.

As a renewable source of energy, biomass has the following advantages over fossil fuels:

First, biomass is one of the most abundant resources in the world. By definition, it is the mass of living or recently dead plants and animals, along with their waste. This means that there is not a single square centimeter of Earth that does not contain some form of biomass.

Secondly, biomass is renewable. If people exercise proper conservation techniques, any form of biomass that is harvested to produce energy can be replaced over a period of time. How much time is required depends on the exact biomass used. For instance, trees would take much longer to replace than corn plants. Fossil fuels, on the other hand exist in finite amounts that will never be replaced.

Thirdly, biomass can easily be converted from its natural form into concentrated, high energy fuels such as alcohols or a gas that is virtually identical to natural gas. These fuels are relatively clean burning compared to the fossil fuels in use today. With management in growing, harvesting, and replacing biomass for fuel production, the amount of carbon dioxide released into the atmosphere would undergo a net decrease, as new plants absorbed it to produce energy for their own growth. This could help to slow or stop global warming and restore balance to the carbon cycle that was destroyed when man began large scale use of fossil fuels that had been absent for the carbon cycle for millions of years.

2.2. Bio-oil

Bio-oil is a liquid, typically dark red-brown to almost black – a color that depends on the chemical composition and the presence of micro-carbon (Figure 1). It is also referred to as "biomass pyrolysis oil," "pyrolysis oil," "pyrolysis liquid," and "bio-crude."

Figure 1. Pyrolysis bio-oil.

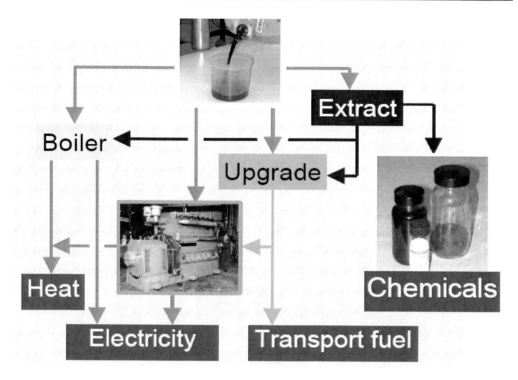

Figure 2. Application of Bio-oils.

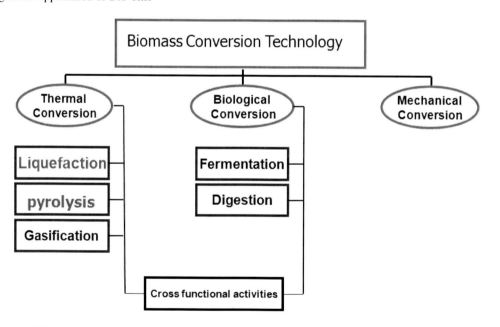

Figure 3. Biomass conversion technologies.

Bio-oil is water miscible and is composed of a very complex mixture of oxygenated hydrocarbons and water which is retained from both the original moisture and the reaction itself. Solid char may also be present. Bio-oil has the following physicochemical properties:

- Combustible,
- Not miscible with hydrocarbons,
- Heating value ~ 17 MJ/kg,
- Density~1.2 kg/L,
- Viscosity, 25~1000 cP,
- Acid, Ph~2.5,
- Smoky odor,
- "Ageing"- viscosity increases with time
- Almost no metal or sulfur compounds

Bio-oil can serve as a substitute for fuel oil or diesel in many static applications, including boilers, furnaces, engines, and turbines for electricity generation. Alternatively, the crude oil could serve as a raw material for the production of adhesives and phenol-formaldehyde-type resins. Different specialty chemicals from the hydrothermal processing oils can be obtained after further processing and separation. Figure 2 summarizes some possible uses of bio-oil.

3. Current Technologies for Conversion of Biomass to Bio-oils

3.1. Biomass Conversion Technologies

Biomass can be converted to various forms of energy by numerous technical processes. There are three typical conversion technologies for processing biomass for energy, as shown in Figure 3. These are thermal (thermochemical) conversion, biological conversion and mechanical conversion. Thermal conversion is one of the major categories, and is the subject of this discussion

Table 1. Comparison of two typical thermochemical processes for bio-oil production

Methods	Treatment conditions required	Reaction mechanism /process description	Feasibility	
			Pros.	Cons.
Flash/Fast Pyrolysis	Relatively high temperature (450-500 °C); a short residence time (~1s); atmosphere pressure; drying necessary	The light small molecules are converted to oily products through homogeneous reactions in the gas phase	High oil yield up to 80% on dry feed; lower capital cost; Commercialized already	Poor quality of fuels obtained
Hydrothermal liquefaction (HTL), also known as liquefaction or hydrothermal pyrolysis	Lower temperature (300-400 °C); longer residence time (0.2-1.0 hr.); High pressure (5-20 Mpa); drying unnecessary	Occurs in aqueous medium which involves complex sequences of reactions	Better quality of fuels obtained (High BTU, low moisture content)	Relatively low oil yield (20-60%); Need high pressure equip., thus higher capital cost

3.1.1. Thermal Conversion

Thermal conversion of biomass into energy includes three sub-categories: gasification, pyrolysis, and hydrothermal liquefaction (HTL). The two main processes for production of bio-oils are pyrolysis and HTL. During these processes, organic compounds from biomass feedstocks are converted into liquid, gas or solid. An advantage of the thermochemical process is that it is relatively simple, usually requiring only one reactor, and thus has a low capital cost. However, this process is non-selective, producing a wide range of products including a large amount of char (Huber and Dumesic, 2006).

3.1.2. Pyrolysis vs. Hydrothermal Liquefaction

Defined in its broadest sense, pyrolysis is the thermal decomposition of organic matter occurring in the absence of air or oxygen. The products of the pyrolytic process can be gaseous, liquid, and/or solid. Pyrolysis of organic materials was studied as early as the 1920's (Hurd, 1929). Pyrolysis can be further divide into slow pyrolysis and fast, or flash, pyrolysis. Slow pyrolysis is characterized by a relative low heating rate (less than 10 °C/s) and long gas and solids residence time, compared to fast pyrolysis. The primary products are tar and char. Flash pyrolysis is a rapid, moderate temperature (450-600 °C) process that produces liquids. With a fast heating rate of 100~10,000 °C/s and a short residence times (less than 2 s), the oil products are maximized over char and gas. The feedstock of pyrolysis is usually dry matter.

Hydrothermal liquefaction was historically linked to hydrogenation and other high-pressure thermal decomposition processes that employed reactive hydrogen or carbon monoxide carrier gases to produce a liquid fuel from organic matter at moderate temperatures (300 - 400 °C) under longer residence times (0.2-1.0 hr.) and relatively high operating pressures (5-20 Mpa). Contrary to flash pyrolysis and gasification processes, drying the feedstock is not necessary. This makes the hydrothermal process especially suitable for naturally wet biomass. However, a reducing gas and/or a catalyst are often included in the process in order to increase the oil yield and quality. The characteristic and technique feasibility of the two thermochemical processes for bio-oil production are compared in table 1.

3.2. Principles

The reaction mechanisms of the two processes are different, and have been studied by many investigators (Demirbaş, 2000a; Minowa et al., 1998). The hydrothermal liquefaction process occurrs in an aqueous medium and involves complex sequences of reactions including solvolysis, dehydration, decarboxylation, and hydrogenation of functional groups, etc. (Chornet and Overend, 1985). The decomposition of cellulose was studied by Minowa et al. (1998), who investigated the effects of adding a sodium carbonate catalyst, a reduced nickel catalyst, and no catalyst in the decomposition of cellulose in hot-compressed water. They found that hydrolysis can play an important role in forming glucose/oligomer, which can quickly decompose into non-glucose aqueous products, oil, char and gases (Figure 4). Without a catalyst, char and gases were produced through oil as intermediates. However, with an alkali catalyst, oil production was achieved because char production was inhibited because the oil intermediates were stabilized. Reduced nickel was found to catalyze the steam reforming reaction of aqueous products as intermediates and the machination reaction. Typical yields of liquid products from hydrothermal conversion processes were in the range of 20-60%, depending on many factors including substrate sustrate type, temperature, pressure, residence time, type of solvents, and catalysts employed (Xu and Etcheverry, 2008).

The presence of water is essential in the hydrothermal process. Aside from its role as a vehicle and catalyst carrier for the feedstock, water also serves as a solvent and reactant. The use of water as the solvent for the HTL process presents several advantages over other solvents. Water is simple to use, low cost, and environmentally friendly.

With flash pyrolysis, which depends on drying the feedstock prior to processing, the light small molecules are converted to oily products through homogeneous reactions in the gas phase. The biomass flash pyrolysis process is shown in Figure 5. Biomass is rapidly heated in the absence of air, vaporizes, and quickly condenses to bio-oil. The main product, bio-oil, is obtained in yields of up to 80% wt on dry matter base, together with char and gas byproducts (Bridgewater and Peacocke, 2000).

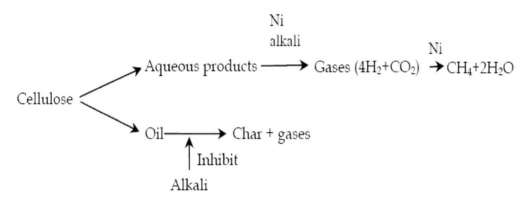

Figure 4. Reaction pathway for the hydrothermal liquefaction of cellulose.

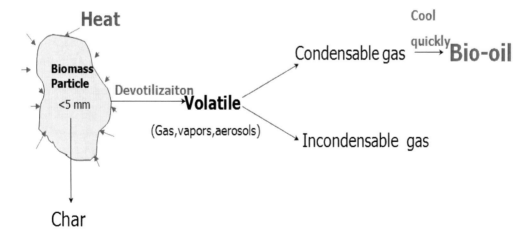

Figure 5. Reaction pathway for the biomass flash pyrolysis process.

Table 2. Typical pyrolysis reactors (Bridgewater and Peacocke, 2000)

Reactor type	Organizations
Fluid bed	Aston University, Dynamotive, Hamburg University, INETI, IWC,Leeds University,Zaragoza University, ZSW-Stuttgart University
Albative	NREL, Aston University, BBC, Castle Capital
Circulating fluid bed	CRES, CPERI, ENEL/Pasquali
Entrained flow	CTRI, Egemin
Rotating cone	Twente University, BTG/Schelde/Kara
Transported bed	Ensyn
Vacuum moving bed	Laval University/Pyrovac

4. RELATED RESEARCH DEVELOPMENTS

4.1. Flash Pyrolysis

Flash pyrolysis for the production of liquids has developed considerably since the first experiments in the late 1970s. Several pyrolysis reactors and processes have been investigated and developed to the point where fast pyrolysis is now an accepted, feasible and viable route to renewable liquid fuels, chemicals and derived products. Since the 1990s, several research organizations have successfully established large-scale fast pyrolysis plants. Bridgewater and Peacocke (2000) have intensively reviewed the key features of fast pyrolysis and the resultant liquid product, and described the major reaction systems and processes that have been developed over the last 20 years. A wide range of reactor configurations have been investigated, as summarized in Table 1 (Bridgewater and Peacocke, 2000). While a wide range of reactor configurations have been operated, fluid beds and circulating fluid beds are the most popular configurations due to their ease of operation and ready scale-up. Although a number of flash pyrolysis installations have been constructed, they all suffer from a lack of operational hours and none have proven to be economically viable yet. Industries such as heat and electricity producers, oil companies and food/feed companies are waiting for full-scale demonstrations of continuous operation (>7000 hours per year), and preferably in multiple plants on a scale of 5 to 10 tons biomass feedstock (Venderbosch and Prins, 2010).

Recently, Venderbosch and Prins (2010) reviewed fast pyrolysis technologies, and concluded that challenges for the coming years are (1) improvement of the reliability of pyrolysis reactors and processes; (2) the demonstration of the oil's utilization in boilers, engines and turbines; and (3) the development of technologies for the production of chemicals and biofuels from pyrolysis oils.

4.2. Hydrothermal Liquefaction

Unlike flash pyrolysis, technological developments in the area of HTL present new ways to turn wastes to fuel. HTL was initially developed for turning coal into liquid fuels, but recently, the technique has been applied to a number of feedstocks, including woody biomass, agricultural residues, organic wastes (e.g., animal wastes, sewage sludge), and aquatic plants.

Table 3 summarizes representative literature data of hydrothermal liquefaction of common types of biomass and the most influential operating parameters. As can be seen from Table 3, organic waste materials are more favourable than woody biomass and agricultural residues for HTL, owing to their higher oil yield and the higher heating value of their bio-oil products. This earlier work was very promising, showing that HTL can be used as an efficient method to treat different types of biomass and produce a liquid biofuel. In particular, HTL presents a unique approach to mitigate the environmental and economic problems related to disposing of large volumes of organic wastes. It not only reduces the pollutants, but also produces useful energy in the form of liquid fuel.

Compared with flash pyrolysis, HTL is at an early developmental stage, and the reaction mechanisms and kinetics are not yet fully understood. So far, the approach has been experimental to analyze the processing conditions on the oil yield and quality of the products from different types of biomass. The processing conditions include final liquefaction temperature, residence times, rate of biomass heating, size of biomass particles, type of solvent media and hydrogen donor solvents. The yield and quality of the bio-oil is significantly affected by the operating parameters. Scattered information about processing parameters has been discussed in original articles, technical notes, and review papers. Until recently, Akhtar and Amin (2011) presented a systematic overview of the effect of these parameters on the yield and composition of the liquid products. In general, most RandD work has focused on maximizing the overall oil yield without paying sufficient attention to the interaction of these parameters or their effect on the product composition and quality.

It's believed that any organic material, specifically carbohydrates, proteins, and fats could be converted into crude oil (Kruse and Gawlki, 2003; Minowa et al., 1998). However, biomass is a very heterogeneous and chemically complex resource. The characteristics of bio-oil produced through HTL is therefore affected by the type of biomass feedstock and its chemical composition and physical structure (Minowa et al., 1998). Various types of biomass used in HTL have been studied, as illustrated in Table 3. Though these results are extremely relevant in understanding both the oil yield and oil quality, limited research has been carried out to understand the effects of individual compounds and their interactions (e.g., ash, proteins) in HTL reactions. Cellulose, lignin and hemicellulose have been used as individual model compounds to study the reaction pathways and decomposition mechanism (Demirbas et al., 2005; Fang et al., 2008). This study found that the presence of high amounts of lignin leads to the formation of char residue. Hemicelluloses and cellulose are favorable for the bio-oil yield (Akhtar and Amin, 2011). However, waste materials are very complex in terms of composition. Until now, results of laboratory investigations are quite poor regarding the understanding of what is actually taking place and how the compositions of biomass affect the process. Thus, a rigorous study involving the use of combinations of different model compounds (carbohydrates, proteins, fats, mineral content and ash) to simulate a wide variety of waste feedstock may prove more useful.

Studies on HTL were predominately conducted in batch scales as described in Table 3. However, some researchers also investigated the HTL process in continuous systems. Chornet and overend (1985) compiled a list of available information on continuous biomass HTL processes. Itoh et al. (1994) developed a scale-up of hydrothermal liquefaction of sewage sludge into oils. This demonstration plant, with a capacity of 5 tons/day, was operated at a temperature of 300 °C and 10 Mpa. In 2005, the University of Illinois at Urbana-Champaign developed a small-scale continuous hydrothermal process reactor system (Ocfemia et al.,

2006), and converted fresh swine manure into bio-oil. It had a capacity to process up to 48kg of manure slurry per day. Worldwide Bioenergy, LLC has commercialized this technology and built a pilot plant with a capacity of 40 barrels/day in Houston, Texas (Figure 6). Although the operation of the early designed reactor showed satisfactory results, the design was not free of problems.

Table 3. Overview of literature on hydrothermal processing of common types of biomass

Raw Materials	Reactor Capacity	Temp. (°C)	Pressure (Mpa)	Time (min)	Oil Yield (%)	Heating Value (MJ/kg)	Reference
a) Woods							
Beech	--	277-377	--	25	13.8-28.4	27.6-31.3	Demirbaş, et al., 2005
Spruce	--	277-377	--	25	13.8-25.8	28.3-33.9	Demirbaş, et al., 2005
Sawdust	0.2 L	280	N/A		7.2	--	Karagöz et al., 2005
b) Agricultural residues							
Corn stalk	0.3 L	300	10 Mpa	30	28.3 on organic basis	29.7	Minowa et al., 1998
Rice husk	0.3 L	300	10 Mpa	30	28.8 on organic basis	30.8	Minowa et al., 1998
Rice straw	1.0 L	260-350	6-18 Mpa	3-5	13.0-38.35	27.6-35.8	Yuan et al., 2007
c) organic wastes							
Swine manure	1-L autoclave	260-340		0-90	14.9-24.2	36.1	Xiu et al., 2010a
Swine manure	Continuous mode	285-305	9-12	40-80	2.8-53.3	25.2-33.1	Ocfemia et al., 2006
Dairy manure	Batch/ continuous mode	250-380	10-34	--	50	--	Appell, et al., 1980
Sewage sludge	5 t/d	300	10	--	48	37-39	Itoh, et al., 1994
Garbage	0.3 L autoclave	250-340	6-18	6-120	27.6	36	Minowa, et al., 1995
Sewage sludge	0.3 L autoclave	150-300	--	0-180	44.5	35.7	Suzuki, et al., 1990
Sewage sludge	4.2L microwave	250-350	8-20	--	30.7	36.4	Bohlmann, et al., 1999
MSW	autoclave	260-340	13-34	--	32	46	Gharieb et al., 1995
MSW	autoclave	295-450	--	20-90	35-63.3	--	Kranich et al., 1984
Sewage sludge	20 kg/hr.	300-360	10-18	5-20	--	30-35	Goudriaan et al., 2000
c) Aquatic plants							
Duckweed	1 L autoclave	250-374	4.1-22.1	5-90	10-30.3	33.95	Xiu et al., 2010b
Algae	2 L autoclave	200-300	8.9-10.3	30-120	24-39.4	21.3-38.5	Yu et al., 2011

Figure 6. Pilot-scale continuous HTL system at Houston, Texas (Worldwide Bioenergy, LLC and UIUC).

Slurry feeding was problematic due to durability issues of the high-pressure pump. In summary, none of the research organizations or commercial entities has succeeded to a point where they have developed standardized systems that are economically viable. Furthermore, the reliability of these pilot scale systems remains unknown.

5. CLOSING REMARKS

Flash pyrolysis and HTL are interesting techniques enabling conversion of large amount of biomass into liquid oil products. This bio-oil can be used as a raw material to produce heat, transportation fuels, electricity, and chemicals. Flash pyrolysis processes are so far the only commercially piloted technology for production of bio-oil or bio-crude from biomass. A wide range of reactor configurations have been operated and demonstrated. However, flash, or fast pyrolysis is still an immature technology, of which many aspects are unknown.

HTL is a promising technology for converting biomass into liquid oils with much higher caloric values. In particular, the use of HTL with organic wastes is a promising way to not only create value, but also reduce pollutants. Compared with flash pyrolysis, HTL is at an early developmental stage, and challenges for the coming years are: 1) Improvement of oil production rate and energy efficiency of the process; 2) Understanding the reaction mechanisms and kinetics in order to achieve a desirable oil yield and quality; 3) development of pilot-scale plants, and detailed economic feasibility studies in order to assess the profitability of the process; 4) The development of technologies for the production of chemicals and biofuels from liquefied oils.

REFERENCES

Akhtar, J and Amin, N.A.S. (2011). A review on process conditions for optimum bio-oil yield in hydrothermal liquefaction of biomass. *Renewable and Sustainable Energy Reviews* 15:1615–1624.

Appell, H.R., Fu Y.C., Friedman S., Yavorsky P.M., and Wender I. (1980). Converting of organic wastes to oil: a Replenishable Energy Source. U.S. Bureau of Mines. *Report of Investigations 7560.* Washington, DC.

Bohlmann, B.J.T., Lorth C.M., Drews A., and Buchholz, R. (1999). Microwave high pressure thermochemical conversion of sewage sludge as an alternative to incineration. *Chem. Eng. Technol.* 21(5): 404-409.

Bridgwater, A.V.; Peacocke, G.V.C. (2000). Fast pyrolysis processes for biomass. *Renewable and Sustainable Energy Reviews* 4(1): 1-73.

Chornet, E., and R. P. Overend. (1985). Biomass liquefaction: an overview. In *Fundamentals of Thermochemical Biomass Conversion*, eds. R. P. Overend, T. A. Milne, and L. K. Mudge, 967-1002. New York: Elsevier Applied Science.

Demirbaş, A. (2000). Mechanisms of liquefaction and pyrolysis reactions of biomass. *Energy Conversion and Management* 41: 633-646.

Demirbaş, A.; Balat, M. and Bozbas, K. (2005). Direct and catalytic liquefaction of wood species in aqueous solution. *Energy Sources* 27(11): 271-277.

Fang Z., T. Sato, R. L. Smith Jr., H. Inomata, K. Arai, and J. A. Kozinski. 2008. Reaction chemistry and phase behavior of lignin in high-temperature and supercritical water. *Bioresource Technology* 99: 3424-3430.

Gharieb, H.K.; Faramawy, S. and Zaki, N.N. (1995). Liquefaction of cellulosic waste V. Water formation and evaluation of pyrolytic char as a byproduct of pyrolysis reaction. *Fuel Sci. Technol. Int.* 13 (7): 895–909.

Goudriaan, F., Beld B.van de, Boerefijn F.R., Bos G.M., Naber J.E., Wal S.van der, and Zeevalkink, J.A. (2000). Thermal efficiency of the HTU process for biomass liquefaction. In Proceedings of the Progress in Thermochemical Biomass Conversion Conference, pp.1312-1325.

Huber G. W. and Dumesic, J. A. (2006). An overview of aqueous-phase catalytic processes for production of hydrogen and alkanes in a biorefinery. *Catalysis Today* 111(1-2): 119-132.

Hurd, C.D.1929. The pyrolysis of carbon compounds. New York : The chemical Catalog Company, Inc.

Itoh S., A. Suzuki, T. Nakamura, and S.Yokoyama. (1994). Production of heavy oil from sewage sludge by direct thermochemical liquefaction. *Desalination*. 98:127-133.

Kranich, W.L. (1984). Conversion of sewage sludge to oil by hydroliquefaction. U.S. Enviromental Protection Agency. EPA-600/2-84-010. Cincinnati, OH Kruse, A and A. Gawlik, 2003. Biomass conversion in water at 330-410 °C and 30-50 Mpa: Identification of key compounds for indicating different chemical reaction pathways. *Industrial and Engineering Chemistry Research* 42:267-279.

Kücük, M. M. (2005). Delignification of biomass using alkaline glycerol. *Energy Sources, Part A* 27(13):1245-1255.

Minowa T., Murakami M., Dote Y., Ogi T., and Yokoyama S. (1995). Oil production from garbage by thermochemical liquefaction. *Biomass and Bioenergy* 8(2):117-120.

Minowa, T.; Kondo, T. and Sudirjo, S. T. (1998). Thermochemical liquefaction of Indonesian biomass residues. *Biomass and Bioenergy* 14(5-6):517-524.

Ocfmia, K. S.; Zhang, Y. and Funk, T. (2006). Hydrothermal processing of swine manure into oil using a continuous reaction system: Development and testing. *Transaction of the ASABE* 49(2): 533-541.

Suzuki A., Nakamura T., and Yokoyama S. (1990). Effect of operating parameters on thermochemical liquefaction of sewage sludge. *Journal of Chemical Engineering of Japan* 23(1): 6-11.

Venderbosch R.H., and Prins W. (2010). Fast Pyrolysis Technology Development. *Biofuels Bioproducts and Biorefining* 4 (2):178 – 208.

Xiu, S., Shahbazi, A., Croonenberghsa, J., Wang, L. (2010b). Oil Production from Duckweed by Thermochemical Liquefaction. *Energy Sources, Part A* 32:1293–1300.

Xiu, S.; Shahbazi, A.; Shirley, V. and Cheng, D. (2010a). Hydrothermal pyrolysis of swine manure to bio-oil: Effects of operating parameters on products yield and characterization of bio-oil. *Journal of Analytical and Applied Pyrolysis* 88(1):73-79.

Xu, J.; Jiang, J.; Sun, Y. and Lu, Y. (2008). Bio-oil upgrading by means of ethyl ester production in reactive distillation to remove water and to improve storage and fuel characteristics. *Biomas s and Bioenergy* 32(11): 1056-1061.

Yu, G., Zhang, Y., Schideman, L., Funk, T. L. and Wang, Z. (2011). Hydrothermal liquefaction of low lipid content microalgae into bio-crude oil. *Transactions of the ASABE* 54(1): 239-246.

Yuan X. Z., H. Li, G. M. Zeng, J. Y. Tong, W. Xie. (2007). Sub- and supercritical liquefaction of rice straw in the presence of ethanol-water and 2-propanol-water mixture. *Energy* 32(11):2081-2088.

In: Oil: Production, Consumption and Environmental Impact   ISBN: 978-1-61942-877-5
Editor: Shuangning Xiu   © 2012 Nova Science Publishers, Inc.

Chapter 6

OIL FROM BIOMASS: CHARACTERIZATION, UPGRADING AND APPLICATION

Shuangning Xiu,[*] Bo Zhang and Abolghasem Shahbazi

Biological Engineering Program, School of Agriculture, NC A&T State University, US

1. INTRODUCTION

Bio-oil is the liquid product made from biomass materials such as agricultural crops, algal biomass, municipal wastes, and agricultural and forestry by-products via thermo-chemical processes. As one kind of new inexpensive, clean and green bio-energies, bio-oil is considered as an attractive option instead of conventional fuel in the aspect of reducing environmental pollution.

Bio-oils are very complex mixtures of compounds. Each bio-oil typically contains more than 100 chemical compounds. The properties of bio-oil mostly depends on the type of biomass uses, the process, pyrolysis conditions (temperature, residence time, and heating rate profiles), and the liquid recovery systems used. Characterization of biomass derived oils is very important in order to utilize them directly as fuel or for further upgrading. Upgrading of bio-oils can be designed in an optimal manner by performing selected evaluations of chemical and structural features. The understanding of bio-oil's physical and chemical behaviours is important to the design and control of the upgrading parameters, produce specifications, and product storage and transportation.

The examination of biomass-derived oils requires the use of various spectroscopic and chromatographic methods owing to their complex structures. Strategies for upgrading heavy petroleum oils emphasize the difference in their properties, which in turn influences the choice of methods or combinations thereof for conversion of heavy petroleum oils to various products. Naturally, similar principles are applied to bio-oil, and the availability of processes that can be employed to convert bio-oils to usable products has increased significantly in recent years. Thus, to determine the processability of bio-oil, a series of consisitent and

[*] Corresponding author. Tel.:+1 3363347787; fax: +1 3363347270. E-mail: xshuangn@ncat.edu.

standardized characterization procedures are required. These procedures can be used with a wide variety of feedstocks to develop a general approach to predict processability.

The purpose of this chapter is to enumerate those methods and analytical techniques that are regularly applied to evaluation of biomass-derived oils. Current bio-oil upgrading techniques are also discussed in relation to the bio-oil properties.

2. Biomass-derived Oil Evaluation

In order to understand the properties and composition of bio-oil so as to use effectively, it's necessary to carry on characterization to bio-oil. In general, characterization of bio-oil is divided into two categories, including both physical properties (fuel properties) and chemical properties (chemical nature and structure). Section 2.1 and section 2.2 described those methods and analytical techniques that are regularly applied to evaluation of bio-oil physical and chemical properties, respectively.

2.1. Bio-oil Physical Properties Characterization

2.1.1. Bio-oil Physical Properties

The bio-oil from biomass is typically a dark-brown liquid with a pungent odour, and the physical properties of the bio-oil are different from conventional fossil fuels. The typical physical properties of biomass derived crude bio-oil are summarized in table 1 and compared with those of conventional fossil fuels. Bio-oils differ a great deal from petroleum-based fuels in physical properties. Bio-oil has many inferior properties, such as low heating value, high oxygen content, high water content, acidity, instability, and incompatibility with standard petroleum fuels. It cannot be used as high-quality fuels like gasoline and diesel without any treatments.

Table 1. Typical properties of biomass derived bio-oil and conventional fossil fuels

Physical properties	Bio-oil	Heavy oil	diesel	gasoline
Moisture content, wt%	20-30	0.1	0.1	0.025
Solid content, wt%	<1	0.2-2.5	<0.5	--
Ash, wt%	<1	>0.3	<0.01	--
Elemental analysis, wt% C	32-75	85	85-86	84-88
H	4.0-8.5	12.5	13-15	12-16
N	<0.4	0.2	0.1	0.1
O	15-60	1	--	--
S	0.05	>1	0.2-0.5	0.08
Stability	unstable	stable	stable	stable
Viscosity, cSt	15-35 (40°C)	20-200 (80°C)	3-8 (20°C)	0.6-0.7(40°C)
Density (15°C), kg.m^{-3}	1.1-1.3	<980	850	700-800
Flash Point, °C	40-100	<130	40-55	--
Cock yield, wt%	17-23	<20	0.1-3	--
LHV, MJ/kg	13-18	38-40	40-46	46
pH	2-3	--	--	--

Yin et al., 2010.

Table 2. Analytical Methods for Wood-Based Pyrolysis Liquids

Analysis	method	Sample size
Water content (wt %)	ASTM 203	1 g
Solids content (wt %)	Karl-Fischer titration, ASTM D1744 ethanol insolubles methanol-dichloromethane insolubles	0.03-0.05 g 30 g 30 g
Particle size distribution	microscopy + particle counter	1 g
Conradson carbon residue content (wt %)	ASTM D189	2-4 g
Ash content (wt %)	EN 7, D482-80	40 mL
CHN content (wt %)	ASTM D5291, elemental analyzer	1 mL
Sulfur and chlorine content (wt %)	capillary electrophoresis	2-10 mL
Alkali metals content (wt %)	AAS	50 mL
Metals content (wt %)	ICP, AAS	50 mL
Density at 15 °C (kg/dm3)	ASTM D4052	4 mL
Viscosity at 20 and 40 °C (cSt) Viscosity (mPa s)	ASTM D445, capillary or rotary viscometry Capillary rotational viscometry	80 mL 40 mL
Pour point (°C)	ASTM D97	80 mL
Heating value (MJ/kg)		
Calorimetric value, HHV	DIN 51900	1 mL
Effective value, LHV	DIN 51900	1 mL
Flash point (°C)	ASTM D93	150 mL
pH	pH meter	50 mL
Water insolubles content (wt %)	water addition	5 mL
Stability	80 °C for 24 h 40 °C for 1 week viscosity at 20 and 40 °C and water by Karl-Fischer titration	200 mL 200 mL

Mohan et al., 2006; Oasmaa et al., 1997, 2001.

2.2.2. Analytical Techniques for Bio-oil Physical Properties Characterization

Due to the differences between the bio-oil and petroleum-based oil, the standard fuel oil methods developed for petroleum-based oils may not be suitable as such for bio-oil. Oasmaa et al. (1997, 2001) in VTT Energy tested the applicability of standard fuel oil methods developed for petroleum-based fuels to pyrolysis liquids. In general, most of the methods can be used as such but the accuracy of the analysis can be improved by minor modifications. The various methods necessary for the characterization of bio-oil fuels and the sample sizes required for each analysis are provided in Table 2. Since bio-oil's physical properties are well documented in the literature, only a few import physical properties and their relation to the fuel application are discussed here.

Water Content

The water content of pyrolysis liquid has been typically analysed by Karl-Fischer titration. Pyrolysis liquids contain low-boiling (below 100 °C) compounds and hence any drying method cannot be used. The water content in the bio-oil is normally analyzed by Karl-Fischer titration according to ASTM D1744. The sample solvent is a mixture of chloroform and methanol (3:1 v/v) (Sipila et al., 1998), because this solvent can dissolve almost all of the component of bio-oil. In the process of experiment, a small amount of bio-oil (0.03-0.05g) was added to an isolated glass chamber containing Karl Fischer solvent. The titrations were carried out using the Karl Fischer titrant (Wildschut et al., 2009).

Bio-oil has a content of water as high as 15–30 wt% derived from the original moisture in the feedstock and the product of dehydration during the pyrolysis reaction and storage (Lu et al., 2009). Water can be found in oil either in the form of droplets or as an emulsion. The presence of water lowers the heating value and flame temperature, but on the other hand, water reduces the viscosity and enhances the fluidity, which is good for the atomization and combustion of bio-oil in the engine.

Ash Content

The determination of ash is important because it provides information as to whether or not the oil product is suitable for use in a given application. Ash is related to the mineral matter in the oil. Ash content is one of the properties that indicate the amounts of undesirable residue present in the oil. The presence of ash in the bio-oil can cause erosion, corrosion, and gumming problems in engine valves. Problem with ash content become more serious when the ash content of the fuel is greater than 0.1wt% (Peacocke et al., 1994). The ash of bio-oil is usually vary in 0.004-0.03 wt% (Oasmaa and Czernik, 1999), which is also relevant to the raw materials and reaction conditions.

The ash content of the bio-oils can be determined following the procedure outlined in ASTM D482-80 for petroleum products. In summary, the oil sample was ignited and allowed to burn completely in a furnace at 775°C, cooled and then weighed.

Elemental Analysis

The analysis of feedstocks for the percentages of carbon, hydrogen, nitrogen, oxygen, and sulfur is perhaps the first method used to examine the general nature and perform an evaluation of a feedstock. The atomic ratios of the various elements to carbon (that is, H/C, N/C, O/C, and S/C) are frequently used for indication of the overall character of the feedstock. For example, Carbon and hydrogen mainly indicate the heating value of the oil. The atomic ratio of hydrogen to carbon (H/C) gives an idea of the level of saturation of the hydrocarbons in the oil. Higher H/C ratio is desirable. It is also of value to determine the amounts of trace elements, such as vanadium and nickel, in a feedstock since these materials can have serious deleterious effects on catalyst performance during refining by catalytic processes.

The elemental compositions of the oils (C, H, O and N) can be determined using a CHN-S analyzer according to ASTM D 5291. The oxygen content can be calculated by difference. The oxygen content of the bio-oil varies in the range of 35-40% (Oasmaa and Czernik, 1999). The presence of high oxygen content is regard as the biggest differences between bio-oil and fossil oil, that's because it lead some poor properties, such as corrosiveness, viscosity, low energy density, thermal instability, and so on (Elliott et al., 2009). Of course, a certain amount of oxygen in the fuel is beneficial to improve combustion sufficiency.

Viscosity

Viscosity is the most important single fluid characteristic governing the motion of fuel and is actually a measure of the internal resistance to motion of a fluid by reason of the forces of cohesion between molecules or molecular groupings. In order to be considered as a gas turbine fuel, the bio-oil must meet certain viscosity standard. The viscosity of gas turbine oil is usually around 0.6~0.7cSt at 40 °C. Many types of instruments have been proposed for the determination of viscosity. The simplest and most used are capillary types (ASTM-D445).

pH

The pH of bio-oil can be measured by pH meter. The bio-oil has amount of diluted water and volatile acids, such as acetic and formic acid, which results in the low pH values varied in 2~3. The presence of acids in the bio-oil is the main reason to account for the property of corrosion to materials in the storage and application processes. Therefore, it requires upgrading to fulfil the requirement of fuels before application through upgrading processes.

Density

Density is the mass of unit volume of material at a specified temperature and has the dimensions of grams per cubic centimetre. The density of the oil is an important physical property because oil is typically bought and sold on that basis. If oil is bought or sold on a volume basis, it is then converted into mass basis using density measurements.

Density can be measured at 15°C using pycnometer or digital density meter by ASTM D 4052 (Sipila et al., 1998). The density of bio-oil is usually in the range of 1.1~1.3kg/m^3, which is depending on the raw materials and pyrolysis conditions. The density of bio-oil is larger than the gasoline and diesel because of the presence of a large number of water and macromolecule such as cellulose, hemicelluloses, oligomeric phenolic compounds (Oasmaa and Czernik, 1999), and so on.

Heating Value

The heating value (heat of combustion) of the fuel is the amount of heat produced when the fuel is burned completely. Heating value is divided into higher heating value (HHV) and lower heating value (LHV) depending on the water produced through hydrogen in vapour or liquid phase. HHV of bio-oil can be determined by the oxygen-bomb colorimeter in accordance to DIN 51900. In addition, the theoretical HHV of the bio-oil is also calculated using the following formula (Milne et al., 1990):

$$HHV = 338.2 \times C + 1442.8 \times (H - O/8) \ (MJ/kg) \tag{1}$$

The LHV can be determined by the HHV and the total weight percent of hydrogen (from elemental analysis) in the bio-oil according to the formula as shown below (Oasmaa et al., 1997):

$$LHV = HHV - 218.3 \times H\% \ (wt\%) \ (KJ/kg) \tag{2}$$

Bio-oil have a lower heating value (15-20 MJ/kg), compared to the conventional fossil oil (41-43 MJ/kg) (Wildschut et al., 2009). It indicated that the energy density of bio-oil is only about half of the fossil oil, which is attribute to the higher water and oxygen contents. In order to improve the heating value of bio-oil, it is necessary to reduce the contents of water and oxygen by the way of upgrading, as described in section 3.

Table 3. Major chemical components of bio-oil

Major components	Wt.%
Water	15-30
Lignin compounds	15-30
Aldehydes	10-20
Carboxylic acids	10-15
Carbohydrates	5-10
Phenols	2-5
Furfurals	1-4
Alcohols	2-5
Ketones	1-5

Flash Point

Flash point of a liquid fuel is defined as the lowest temperature for the vapor above the liquid to be ignited when exposed to a flame. It is an important parameter for fuel handling to prevent fire hazard. The flash points of bio-oils are usually measured by closed-cup testers and vary in the range of 40–70 °C or above 100 °C, depending on the contents of light organic volatiles. It is usually difficult to measure the flash points at 70–100 °C, due to the strong evaporation of water which will inhibit the ignition of the fuel vapor (Oasmaa et al., 1997).

2.2. Bio-oil Chemical Characterization

The chemical composition of a feedstock is a much truer indicator of refining behaviour. It can enable the refiner to determine the nature of the reactions. Hence, chemical composition can play a large part in determining the nature of the products that arise from the refining operations. It can also play a role in determining the means by which a particular feedstock should be processed.

2.2.1. Bio-oil Chemical Compositions

Bio-oil is a complex mixture of several hundreds of organic compounds, mainly including acids, alcohols, aldehydes, ketones, phenols, and lignin-derived oligomers. Some of these compounds are directly related to the undesirable properties of bio-oil. The major chemical components of bio-oil are summarised in Table 3.

According to Meir (1999), these components can be globally represented as: around 20 mass% water, around 40 mass% GC-detectable compounds, around 15 mass% non-volatile HPLC detectable compounds and around 15 mass% high molar mass non-detectable compounds (Figure 1). A complete analysis of bio-oils requires the combined use of more than one analytical technique. A precise description of bio-oil composition has not yet been achieved.

2.2.2. Analytical Techniques for Bio-oil Chemical Characterization

Owing to its complex nature, chemical characterization of bio-oils has been a challenging undertaking. Chemical characterization of pyrolysis oils has generally been based on the fractionation of the oils into different classes of chemical functionality. Fractionation strategies reported in the literature use differences in polarity and/or acidity as a driving force to achieve the separation of fractions (Garcia-Perez et al., 2007). In solvent extraction, the oils have been divided mainly into acidic, phenolic, basic, hydrocarbon and aqueous fractions. In adsorption chromatography, the oils have been separated into different hydrocarbon and polar classes. Fractionation methods with successive analyses of the fractions have often been quite complicated, elaborate and time consuming. The main methods of analysis used to determine the composition of oil product and its fractions are GC/MS, HPLC/LC-MS, GPC, FT-IR, NMR and TGA. The description of these techniques is described as follows.

GC/MS

Although many analytical techniques are required to obtain a complete analysis of bio-oil, the most extendedly used analyzing method for pyrolysis bio-oils is GC/MS. GC-MS is an analytical tool which uses gas chromatography and mass spectrometry in tandem. The gas chromatograph separates the volatile components of a mixture of organic compounds into pure compounds and the mass spectrometer provides the spectrum of those components that have been fully or partially separated by GC. GC-MS is used for the identification and confirmation of molecular structure of organic compounds as well as for their quantification in kinetic studies such as in bioenergetics, waste utilization, or pharmacokinetics. For identification and confirmation of the structure of organic compounds, GC-MS can provide exact molar mass of the analyte and/or fragmentation that can be interpreted for structural elucidation of the analyte. GC/MS has been the technique most widely used in the analyses the bio-oil and its fractions (Sipila et al., 1998).

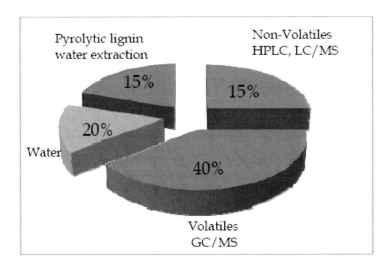

Figure 1. Bio-oil Chemical Characterization.

Overall, GC/MS has been the technique most widely used to identify and quantify individual compounds in bio-oil or its fractions. However, it is reported that the potent chemicals are simply not detected by GC-MS, as only 40% of chemicals in bio-oil are GC-

MS detectable (Meir, 1999; Booker et al., 2010). Gas chromatography requires that the compounds have a moderate boiling point (less than 280 °C for most of the instrumental set-up), but bio-oil contains quite amounts of larger compounds in non-volatiles fraction (Figure 1) and thus do not reach the detector.

HPLC/ LC-MS

High-performance liquid chromatography (HPLC), is a chromatographic technique that can separate a mixture of compounds and is used in biochemistry and analytical chemistry to identify, quantify and purify the individual components of the mixture. HPLC has been used to quantify some water-soluble species in the bio-oil. In addition, Aqueous HPLC can be used to quantify acetic acid, acetol, and levoglucosan because of difficulty quantifying these compounds by GC/MS. Liquid chromatography with mass spectrometry detection (LC-MS) is a powerful technique in the analysis of the active bio-oil fraction. LC-MS with a softer ionization detection technique will be very useful in analyzing bio-oil fraction with larger compounds with higher boiling point. LC-MS does not yet have a comprehensive database for identifying compounds, which makes this technique a more complex analysis tool compared to GC-MS (Booker et al., 2010).

GPC (Molecular Weight)

Gel permeation chromatography is an attractive technique for the determination of the number average molecular weight (Mn) and the weight average molecular weights (Mw) distribution of oil fractions, especially the heavier constituents, and petroleum products.

For wood pyrolysis oil, the typically reported data fall in the range of wood pyrolysis oils, which typically fall in the range of Mn ≈330-380 andMw≈420-550 (Ingram et al., 2008). GPC was also used to evaluate the stability of the bio-oils. Instability is a result of the fact that bio-oil undergoes a number of reactions during storage that increases their average molecular weight and viscosity (Ingram et al., 2008; Fahmi et al., 2008; Mullen et al., 1010).

Tetrahydrofuran (THF) has been extensively used as eluent and polystyrene as standard in most of bio-oil GPC analyses reported in the literature (Scholze et al., 2001; Williams and Taylor, 1994). The use of THF to characterize the molar mass distribution of bio-oils presents however some limitations. For example, high molar mass compounds and some poly-sugars are partially or totally insoluble in THF. Dimethyl-formamide (DMF) on the other hand is reported to be one of the most effective organic solvent to dissolve lignins (Johnson et al., 1988; Himmel et al., 1988) over a wide range of molar masses. DMF is also effective for sugars and polar heavy compounds.

FT-IR (Functional Groups)

Fourier transform infrared spectroscopy (FT-IR) is a technique which is used to obtain an infrared spectrum of absorption, emission, photoconductivity or Raman scattering of a solid, liquid or gas. FT-IR is regarded as a fast, cheap, reliable, accurate, and nondestructive analytical technique which allows the qualitative determination of the characteristic vibrational mode of each molecular group in samples (Xu et al., 2011).

FTIR spectroscopic analysis methods are rapidly becoming a workhorse technique for providing data on bio-oil main organic components (e.g., monomeric alcohol, phenol, ketones, aldehydes, carboxylic acid) analysis based on the peaks of the functional groups present (Kumar et al., 2010; Zou et al., 2010; Xiu et al., 2010b). Kumar et al. (2010) used Perkin-Elmer Fourier transformed infrared spectrophotometer to obtain the FT-IR of the pyrolysis oil of eucalyptus wood obtained at different temperatures. FTIR was used to monitor the thermal deterioration process of bio-oil samples in thermal treatment and/or during long-term storage at ambient temperatures (Xu et al., 2011). FTIR spectroscopy was also used to observe the changes in functional groups of the bio-oil/biodiesel mixtures over time (Jiang and Ellis, 2010).

NMR (Functional Groups, Bonds)

Nuclear magnetic resonance (NMR) is a powerful technique because it allows for different components to be identified. When analyzing complex hydrocarbons, it is useful to know how many carbons are present in an aromatic or aliphatic way. Classical analysi by means of NMR is commonly used and it is called the "the direct ^{13}C" method. It is possible to identify of aromatic and aliphatic carbons with this method. Aromatic carbons are found by integration of the chemical shif area between 160 and 100ppm, whereas aliphatic carbons (CH, CH_2, CH_3, quaternary aliphatic carbon) are found at 70 to 0 ppm. Some researchers have used ^1H and ^{13}C NMR as a means of obtaining approximate ratios of the chemical environments of protons and carbon atoms of the oil and determined the approximate aromatic: aliphatic ratios (Schnitzer et al., 2007; Özbay et al., 2008).

Additionally, distortionless Enhancement Polarization Transfer (^{13}C DEPT) spectra were integrated and used to quantify carbon atoms in the bio-oils on the basis of attached protons and chemical environment. This method not only provides the percentages of carbons in different chemical functional groups (based on chemical shift), but also provides information on the substitution numbers of those carbon atoms. In this way, NMR can be used as an assay to determine which feedstocks and pyrolysis conditions produce bio-oil with particular desired characteristics (such as presence of functional groups, degrees of branching or saturation, aromatic content) for downstream production of fuels or chemicals.

Unlike the other techniques mentioned above, NMR has the potential of being able to examine nearly the entire, intact, bio-oil rather than a selected fraction of it (Mullen et al., 2009; Cao et al., 2011).

In conclusion, by combing structural information obtained by NMR, functional group analysis which obtained by FTIR, it is possible to derive hypothetical average structures for bio-oil molecules.

TGA (Thermal Characteristics)

Thermogravimetric analysis (TGA) is one of the most commonly used analytical techniques for measuring the thermal characteristics of carbonaceous materials. It can determine the decomposition weight loss, combustion analysis, and temperature stability of oil samples.

The most direct application of bio-oil is as boiler fuel oil (Li et al., 2009). Therefore, a deeper study of bio-oil combustion characteristics will contribute to the design, operation and maintenance of the boilers and improve combustion efficiency and reduce environmental pollution.

Table 4. Brief description, treatment condition, and technical feasibility of the current techniques used for upgrading bio-oil

Upgrading methods	Treatment condition/ requirement	Reaction mechanism/process description	Technique Feasibility	
			Pros.	Cons.
Hydrotreating /hydrofining	Mild conditions (~500°C /low pressure), chemical needed: H_2/CO, catalyst (e.g., CoMo, HDS, NiMo, HZSM-5)	Hydrogenation without simultaneous cracking (eliminating N, O and S as NH_3, H_2O and H_2S)	Cheaper route, Commercialized already	High coking (8-25%) and poor quality of fuels obtained
Hydro-cracking/ hydrogenolysis/ catalytic cracking	Severe conditions (>350 °C, 100~2000 Psi), chemical needed: H_2/CO or H_2 donor solvents, catalyst (e.g., Ni/Al$_2$O$_3$-TiO$_2$)	Hydrogenation with simultaneous cracking Destructive(resulting in low molecular product)	Makes large quantities of light products	Need complicated equipment, excess cost, catalyst deactivation, reactor clogging
Sub-/Supercritical fluid	Mild conditions, organic solvents needed such as alcohol, acetone, ethyl acetate, glycerol	Promotes the reaction by its unique transport properties: gas-like diffusivity and liquid-like density, thus dissolved materials not soluble in either liquid or gaseous phase of solvent	Higher oil yield, better fuel quality (lower oxygen content, lower viscosity)	Solvent is expensive
Solvent addition(direct add solvent or esterification of the oil with alcohol and acid catalysts)	Mild conditions, polar solvents needed such as water, methanol, ethanol, and furfural	Reduces oil viscosity by three mechanisms: (1) physical dilution (2) molecular dilution or by changing the oil microstructure; (3) chemical reactions like esterification and acetalization	The most practical approach (simplicity, the low cost of some solvents and their beneficial effects on the oil properties)	Mechanisms involved in adding solvent are not quite understand yet
Emulsification /Emulsions	Mild conditions, need surfactant (e.g. CANMET)	Combines with diesel directly. Bio-oil is miscible with diesel fuels with the aid of surfactants	Simple, less corrosive	Requires high energy for production
Steam Reforming	High temperature(800-900 °C), need catalyst (e.g. Ni)	Catalytic steam reforming + water-gas shift	Produces H_2 as a clean energy resource	Complicated, requires steady, dependable, fully developed reactors
Chemical extracted from the bio-oils	Mild conditions	Solvent extraction, distillation, or chemical modification	Extract valuable chemicals	Low cost separation and refining techniques still needed

Xiu et al., 2011.

Combustion is the thermal decomposition of biomass in presence of excess air or oxygen. Several researchers have done research on the combustion characteristics of bio-oil via TGA (Xiu et al., 2010a; Li et al., 2009; Aprameya et al., 2006). In addition, the combustion properties of the bio-oil can be tested by the biomass fuels combustion system, which consists of a droplet generator, a laminar flow reactor, and a video imaging system (Wornat, et al., 1994). The device can observe the combustion behaviors of bio-oil droplets directly.

This technique also has been used to compare the evaporation and cracking behavior of different bio-oils and their fractions (Hallett et al., 2003; Vitolo and Ghetti, 1994).

3. UPGRADING OF BIO-OIL

Considering the above discussion on the properties of bio-oils, it is obvious that the fuel quality of bio-oils is inferior to that of petroleum-based fuels. So, an upgrading process by reducing the oxygen content is required before its application. There have been intensive studies on bio-oil upgrading research and various technologies have been developed for bio-oil upgrading. The recent upgrading techniques are summarized in table 4. The detail description of these upgrading techniques can be found in literatures (Xiu et al., 2011).

In summary, over the years various technologies have been developed for bio-oil upgrading, including hydrotreating, hydrocracking, supercritical fluids extraction, solvent addition/esterification, emulsification, steam reforming, and chemical extraction. Solvent addition (esterification) appears to be the most practical approach due to simplicity, the low cost of some solvents and their beneficial effects on the oil properties. However, none of these bio-oil upgrading techniques has been commercialized due to low biofuel efficiency and their limitations. Upgrading of bio-oil through emulsification with diesel oil is relatively simple. It provides a short-term approach to the use of bio-oil in diesel engines. The emulsions showed promising ignition characteristics, but fuel properties such as heating value, cetane and corrosivity were still unsatisfied. Moreover, this process required high energy for production. Design, production and testing of injectors and fuel pumps made from stainless steel or other materials are required. Therefore, novel integrated refinery processes are needed to systematically upgrade bio-oils into transportation fuels that have desirable qualities, while producing other value-added co-products to make the economics work.

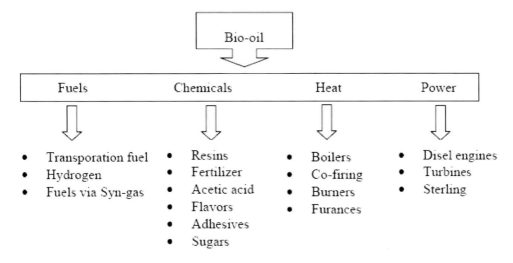

Figure 2. Bio-oil Application.

4. APPLICATIONS OF BIO-OIL

As a renewable liquid fuel, bio-oil can be readily stored and transported. It can serve as a substitute for fuel oil or diesel in many static applications including boilers, furnaces, engines, and turbines for electricity generation. Alternatively, the crude oil could serve as a raw material for the production of adhesives, phenol-formaldehyde-type resins, wood flavors: etc. Different specialty chemicals form the bio-oils are also possible after further processing and separation. Figure 2 summarized some industrial uses of bio-oil.

5. CLOSING REMARKS

Bio-oils are low-grade liquid fuels when compared with petroleum fuels. The poor fuel properties include the complex chemical structures, high contents of oxygen, water, solids and ash, low heating values, high viscosity, chemical and thermal instability, low pH values, and poor ignition and combustion properties. Bio-oil's physical properties are well documented in the literature. Complete chemical characterization of bio-oil is difficult due to the complex chemical nature of bio-oil. Traditional analytical techniques have been tailored to study the chemical properties of bio-oil. Using these techniques, researchers have developed a much more fundamental understanding of the chemical properties of the bio-oil. There have been intensive studies on bio-oil upgrading research and various technologies have been developed for bio-oil upgrading. However, none of these bio-oil upgrading techniques has been commercialized due to low biofuel efficiency and their limitations. Therefore, novel refinery processes are needed to systematically upgrade bio-oils into transportation fuels that have desirable qualities, while producing other value-added co-products to make the economics work.

REFERENCES

Aprameya, A., M. Nader and F. Norman. 2006. Thermogravimetric studies on pyrolysis and combustion behavior of a heavy oil and its asphaltenes. *Energy and Fuel*, 20:560-5.

Booker C.J. et al. 2010. Bioenergy II: Characterization of the Pesticide Properties of Tobacco Bio-Oil. *International Journal of Chemical Reactor Engineering* 8: article 26.

Cao, X., K.S. Ro, M. Chappell,Y. Li, and J. Mao. 2011. Chemical Structures of Swine-Manure Chars Produced under Different Carbonization Conditions Investigated by Advanced Solid-State 13C Nuclear Magnetic Resonance (NMR) Spectroscopy. *Energy Fuels* 25: 388–397.

Catalytic Hydroprocessing of Biomass Fast Pyrolysis Bio-oil to Produce Hydrocarbon Products. *Environmental Progress and Sustainable Energy,* 28 (3):441-449.

Characterization of bio-oils in chemical families. *Biomass and Bioenergy*, 31(4):222-242.

Elliott, D. C., Hart, T. R., Neuenschwander, G. G., Rotness, L. J. and Zacher, A. H. 2009.

Fahmi, R., Bridgwater, A.V., Donnison, I., Yates, N., Jones, J.M. 2008. The effect of lignin and inorganic species in biomass on pyrolysis oil yields, quality and stability. *Fuel*, 87: 1230-1240.

Garcia-Pereza, M., A. Chaalac, H. Pakdela, D. Kretschmerb, and C. Roy. 2007.

Hallett WLH, Clark NA, White M. 2003. Evaporation of biomass pyrolysis oil droplets-II. Combustion Inst. *Canadian Section, Spring Meeting*, p. 41.1–41.6.

Himmel ME, Tatsumoto K, Oh K, Grohmann K, Johnson DK, Li CH. 1988. Molecular weight distribution of Aspen lignins estimated by universal calibration. in: Glasser WG, Sarkanen S, editors. Lignin, properties and materials. *ACS Symposium Series 397*, p. 82.

Ingram, L., Mohan, D., Bricka, M., Steele, P., Strobel, D.,Crocker, D., Mitchell, B., Mohamma, J., Cantrell, K., Pittman, C. U. 2008. Pyrolysis o wood and bark in auger reactor: physical properties and chemical analysis of the produced bio-oil. *Energy Fuel* 22: 614–625.

Jiang, X. and N. Ellis. 2010. Upgrading Bio-oil through Emulsification with Biodiesel: Thermal Stability. *Energy Fuels* 24: 2699–2706.

Johnson DK, Li CH, Hyatt JA. 1988. Molecular weight distribution studies using lignin model compounds. in: Glasser WG, Sarkanen S, editors. Lignin, properties and materials, *ACS Symposium Series 397*, p. 109.

Kumar,G., Panda, A.K., and R.K. Singh. 2010. Optimization of process for the production of bio-oil from eucalyptus wood. *Journal of Fuel Chemistry and Technology* 38(2): 162-167.

Li, C., Y.Yamanoto, M.Suzuki, D.Hirabayashi, and K.Suzuki. 2009. Study on the combustion kinetic characteristics of biomass tar under catalysts. *J.Therm. Anal.Cal.*, 95: 991-7.

Lu, Q., Li, W. and Zhu, X. 2009. Overview of Fuel Properties of Biomass Fast Pyrolysis Oils. *Energy Conversion and Management,* 50(5):1376-1383.

Meir, D. 1999. New Methods for chemical and physical characterization and round robin testing, A. Bridgwater, Editor, et al.*Fast pyrolysis of biomass: a handbook*, CPL Press, Newbury, UK, pp. 92–101.

Milne, T. A., Brennan, A. H. and Glenn, B. H. 1990. *Source Book of Methods of Analysis for Biomass and Biomass ConVersion Processes.* Elsevier Applied Science Publishers Ltd,ISBN 1-85166-527-7, London, England.

Mohan, D., C.U. Pittman, Jr., and P.H. Steele. 2006. Pyrolysis of Wood/Biomass for Bio-oil: A Critical Review. *Energy and Fuels* 20: 848-889.

Mullen, C., G.D. Strahan, and A.A. Boateng. 2008. Characterization of Various Fast-Pyrolysis Bio-Oils by NMR Spectroscopy. *Energy and Fuels* 23: 2707–2718.

Mullen, C.A., Akwasi A. Boateng, K. B. Hicks, N.M. Goldberg, and R. A. Moreau. 2010. Analysis and Comparison of Bio-Oil Produced by Fast Pyrolysis from Three Barley Biomass/Byproduct Streams. *Energy Fuels* 24: 699–706.

Oasmaa, A. and Czernik, S.1999. Fuel Oil Quality of Biomass Pyrolysis Oils State of the Art for the End Users. *Energy and Fuels,* 13(4): 914-921.

Oasmaa, A., Leppamaki, E., Koponen, P., Levander, J. and Tapola, E. 1997. *Physical Characterisation of Biomass-based Pyrolysis Liquids: Application of Standard Fuel Oil Analyses.* VTT Publications 306, Espoo, Finland.

Oasmaa, A., Peacock, C. A. 2001. Guide to Physical Property Characterization of Biomass DeriVed Fast Pyrolysis Liquids. Technical Research Centre of Finland, Espoo, Finland, 2001, *VTT Publication No. 450.*

Özbay, N., Apaydin-Varol, E., B.B. Uzun, and A.E. Pütün. 2008. Characterization of bio-oil obtained from fruit pulp pyrolysis. *Energy* 33:1233-1240.

Peacocke, G. V. C., Russell, P. A., Jenkins, J. D. and Bridgwater, A. V. 1994. Physical properties of flash pyrolysis liquids. *Biomass and Bioenergy*, 7(1-6):169 – 177.

Schnitzer, M. I., Monreal, C. M., Facey, G. A., and Fransham, P. B. 2007. The conversion of chicken manure to biooil by fast pyrolysis. I. Analyses of chicken manure, biooils and char by ^{13}C and ^{1}H NMR and FTIR spectrophotometry. *J. EnVir. Sci. Health B* 42:71–77.

Scholze, B., C. Hanser and D. Meier. 2001. Characterization of the water-insoluble fraction from fast pyrolysis liquids (pyrolytic lignin): Part II. GPC, carbonyl goups, and 13C-NMR. *Journal of Analytical and Applied Pyrolysis*, 58-59: 387–400.

Sipila, K., Kuoppala, E., Fagernas, L. and Oasmaa, A. 1998. Characterization of Biomass based Flash Pyrolysis Oils. *Biomass and Bioenergy,* 14(2): 103-113.

Vitolo, S. and P. Ghetti. 1994. Physical and combustion characterization of pyrolytic oils derived from biomass material upgraded by catalytic hydrogenation. *Fuel*, 73(11):1810–1812.

Wildschut, J., Mahfud, F. H., Venderbosch, R. H. and Heeres, H. J. 2009. Hydrotreatment of Fast Pyrolysis Oil Using Heterogeneous Noble-Metal Catalysts. *Industrial andEngineering Chemistry Research,* 48(23): 10324-10334.

Williams, P.T. and D.T. Taylor. 1994. Molecular weight range of pyrolytic oils derived from tyre waste. *Journal of Analytical and Applied Pyrolysis*, 29:111–128.

Wornat, M. J., Porter, B. G. and Yang, N. Y. C. (1994). Single Droplet Combustion of Biomass Pyrolysis Oils. *Energy and Fuels,* 8(5):1131-1142.

Xiu S., Shahbazi A., V.B.Shirley, M.R. Mims, C.W. Wallace. 2010b. Effectiveness and mechanisms of crude glycerol on the biofuel production from swine manure through hydrothermal pyrolysis. *Journal of Analytical and Applied Pyrolysis*, 87:194-198.

Xiu S., Zhang, B., Shahbazi A. 2011. Biorefinery Processes for Biomass Conversion to Liquid fuel. In: *Biofuel's Engineering Process Technology* ISBN 978-953-307-480-1, InTech.

Xiu, S., H. K. Rojanala , A. Shahbazi , E. H. Fini, and L. Wang. 2010a. Pyrolysis and combustion characteristics of Bio-oil from swine manure. *J.Therm. Anal.Cal.* DOI: 10.1007/s10973-011-1604-8.

Xu, F., Xu, Y., Lu, R., Sheng, P., and Yu, H. 2011. Elucidation of the Thermal Deterioration Mechanism of Bio-oil Pyrolyzed from Rice Husk Using Fourier Transform Infrared Spectroscopy. *J. Agric. Food Chem.* 59: 9243–9249.

Yin, Q., S.Wang, X. Li, Z. Guo, and Y. Gu. 2010. Review of Bio-oil Upgrading Technologies and Experimental Study on Emulsification of Bio-oil and Diesel. *2010 International Conference on Optoelectronics and Image Processing*, 343-347.

Zou, S., Wu Y., Yang, M., Imdad, K, Li, C., and Tong, J. 2010. Production and characterization of bio-oil from hydrothermal liquefaction of microalgae Dunaliella tertiolecta cake. *Energy* 35(12): 5406-5411.

In: Oil: Production, Consumption and Environmental Impact   ISBN: 978-1-61942-877-5
Editor: Shuangning Xiu   © 2012 Nova Science Publishers, Inc.

Chapter 7

FACTORS INFLUENCING FAST PYROLYSIS

*Hui Wang**

Department of Agricultural and Biological Engineering,
Mississippi State University, MS State, MS, US

ABSTRACT

Pyrolysis is an important way to convert biomass to biofuesl and bioproducts. Lots of factors influence the progress of pyrolysis and result in different yield and composition. In this chapters, factors, including composition of biomass and operational parameters, are discussed to clarify their ways to influence the pyrolysis.

1. INSTRUCTION

1.1. Biomass Pyrolysis

Pyrolysis is the thermal decomposition of materials in the absence of oxygen or when significantly less oxygen is present than required for complete combustion. It is important to differentiate pyrolysis from gasification. Gasification decomposes biomass to syngas by carefully controlling the amount of oxygen present. Pyrolysis is difficult to precisely define, especially when applied to biomass. The older literature generally equates pyrolysis to carbonization, in which the principal product is a solid char. Today, the term pyrolysis often describes processes in which oils are preferred products. [1]

The general features that occur during pyrolysis are enumerated below.

(1) Heat transfer from a heat source, to increase the temperature inside the fuel;
(2) The initiation of primary pyrolysis reactions at this higher temperature releases volatiles and forms char;

---

* E-mail: hwang@abe.msstate.edu.

(3) The flow of hot volatiles toward cooler solids results in heat transfer between hot volatiles and cooler unpyrolyzed fuel;

(4) Condensation of some of the volatiles in the cooler parts of the fuel, followed by secondary reactions, can produce tar;

(5) Autocatalytic secondary pyrolysis reactions proceed while primary pyrolytic reactions (item 2, above) simultaneously occur in competition; and

(6) Further thermal decomposition, reforming, water gas shift reactions, radicals recombination, and dehydrations can also occur, which are a function of the process's residence time/temperature/pressure profile.

1.2. Type of Biomass Pyrolysis

Pyrolysis may be conventional or fast pyrolysis, depending on the operating conditions that are used.

1.2.1. Conventional Pyrolysis

Conventional slow pyrolysis has been applied for thousands of years and has been mainly used for the production of charcoal. In slow wood pyrolysis, biomass is heated to 500 °C. The vapor residence time varies from 5 min to 30 min. [2, 3] Vapors do not escape as rapidly as they do in fast pyrolysis. Thus, components in the vapor phase continue to react with each other, as the solid char and any liquid are being formed. The heating rate in conventional pyrolysis is typically much slower than that used in fast pyrolysis.

1.2.2. Fast Pyrolysis

Fast pyrolysis is a high-temperature process in which biomass is rapidly heated in the absence of oxygen. [4,5] Biomass decomposes to generate vapors, aerosols, and some charcoal-like char. After cooling and condensation of the vapors and aerosols, a dark brown mobile liquid is formed that has a heating value that is about half that of conventional fuel oil. Fast pyrolysis processes produce 60-75 wt % of liquid bio-oil, 15-25 wt % of solid char, and 10-20 wt % of noncondensable gases, depending on the feedstock used. No waste is generated, because the bio-oil and solid char can each be used as a fuel and the gas can be recycled back into the process.

Fast pyrolysis uses much faster heating rates than traditional pyrolysis. Advanced processes are carefully controlled to give high liquid yields. There are four essential features of a fast pyrolysis process. [6] First, very high heating and heat transfer rates are used, which usually requires a finely ground biomass feed. Second, a carefully controlled pyrolysis reaction temperature is used, often in the 425-500 °C range. Third, short vapor residence times are used (typically <2 s). Fourth, pyrolysis vapors and aerosols are rapidly cooled to give bio-oil.

Heating rates of 1000 °C/s, or even 10000 °C/s, at temperatures below 650 °C have been claimed. At higher fast pyrolysis temperatures, the major product is gas. Many researchers have attempted to exploit the complex degradation mechanisms by conducting pyrolysis in unusual environments. The main pyrolysis variants 55 are listed in Table 1.

Table 1. Pyrolysis Methods and Their Variants

pyrolysis technology	residence time	heating rate	temperature (°C)	products
carbonization	days	very low	400	charcoal
conventional	5-30 min	low	600	oil, gas, char
fast	0.5-5 s	very high	650	bio-oil
flash-liquid	<1s	high	<650	bio-oil
flash-gas	<1s	high	<650	chemicals, gas
ultra	<0.5s	very high	1000	chemicals, gas
vacuum	2-30 s	medium	400	bio-oil
hydro-pyrolysis	<10 s	high	<500	bio-oil
methano-pyrolysis	<10 s	high	>700	chemicals

Over the last two decades, fundamental research on fast or flash pyrolysis has shown that high yields of primary, nonequilibrium liquids and gases, including valuable chemicals, chemical intermediates, petrochemicals, and fuels, could be obtained from carbonaceous feedstocks. Thus, the lower value solid char from traditional slow pyrolysis can be replaced by higher-value fuel gas, fuel oil, or chemicals from fast pyrolysis. [2]

1.3. Bio-oil

Bio-oil is a complex mixture of oxygenated hydrocarbons that may be burned in a furnace, or with some modification, combusted in industrial turbines for power generation. [7] It is obtained in yields of up to 80 wt% in total (wet basis) on dry feed, together with by-product char and gas which are, or can be, used within the process so there are no waste streams. [8] Further upgrading bio-oil in a "bio-refinery" to produce valuable chemicals for purposes other than combustion is an ongoing research concern [9] and may have strong economic potential. Raw bio-oil has a number of unique characteristics, including high density (specific gravity of 1.2), low pH (2.5), a moderate heating value (18 MJ/kg), and a high water content (15-30%). For reference, heavy fuel oil, the nearest market analogue, has a lower density (specific gravity of 0.94), very low water content (0.1%), and substantially higher heating value (40 MJ/kg). [7] A further drawback relating to its high water content is that bio-oil will not form a stable emulsion with other hydrocarbon fuels without the addition of an emulsifier. [10] Thus, it cannot be easily blended with other petroleum fuels.

Typical properties and characteristics of wood-derived bio-crude oil are presented in Table 5. Bio-oil has many special features and characteristics. These require consideration before any application, storage, transport, upgrading or utilization is attempted. These features are summarized in Table 2. [11]

2. FACTORS INFLUENCING FAST PYROLYSIS

2.1. Type of Feedstock

Biomass is mainly composed of cellulose, hemicelluose, lignin, mineral and ash. The detailed composition depends on the variety, producing area and planting conditions. Table 3 and Table 4 show the chemical composition, element composition and mineral composition of several types of biomass. Cellulose content in wood and corn straw is almost half of the organic content, while it is a little bit less in wheat straw and rice straw. Hemicellulose and lignin content are about 30% and 20% respectively.

Table 2. Typical Properties and Characteristics of Wood Derived Crude Bio-oil

property	characteristics
appearance	From almost black or dark red-brown to dark green, depending on the initial feedstock and the mode of fast pyrolysis. Varying quantities of water exist, ranging from _15 wt % to an upper limit of _30-50 wt % water, depending on production and collection.
miscibility	Pyrolysis liquids can tolerate the addition of some water before phase separation occurs. Bio-oil cannot be dissolved in water. Miscible with polar solvents such as methanol, acetone, etc., but totally immiscible with petroleum-derived fuels.
density	bio-oil density is _1.2 kg/L, compared to _0.85 kg/L for light fuel oil
viscosity	viscosity (of as-produced bio-oil) varies from as low as 25 cSt to as high as 1000 cSt (measured at 40 °C) depending on the feedstock, the water content of the oil, the amount of light ends that have collected, the pyrolysis process used, and the extent to which the oil has been aged
distillation	it cannot be completely vaporized after initial condensation from the vapor phase at 100 °C or more, it rapidly reacts and eventually produces a solid residue from _50 wt % of the original liquid
ageing of pyrolysis liquid	it is chemically unstable, and the instability increases with heating it is always preferable to store the liquid at or below room temperature; changes do occur at room temperature, but much more slowly and they can be accommodated in a commercial application causes unusual time-dependent behavior properties such as viscosity increases, volatility decreases, phase separation, and deposition of gums change with time

Table 3. Chemical composition and ultimate analysis of several biomass samples (wt%, dry basis) [12, 13]

Biomass	Chemical composition analysis				Ultimate element analysis			
	cellulose	hemicellulose	Lignin	ash	C	H	O	N
Wheat straw	30.5	28.9	16.4	11.2	47.5	5.4	35.8	0.1
Rice straw	37.0	22.7	13.6	19.8	36.9	5.0	37.9	0.4
Corn straw	42.7	23.6	17.5	6.8	41.9	5.3	46.0	0
Poplar wood	42.3	31.0	16.2	0.4	49.6	6.1	43.7	0.6

Mineral content varies with the variety and planting condition of biomass. Mineral in the biomass includes K, Ca, Na, Mg, Si and other elements, of which content of Si, K and Ca is the highest. Basically, ash content of straws is much higher than woods. Rice straw has the highest ash content among the straws. By comparing corn straw and woods, it is found that the content of cellulose, hemicellulose and lignin is similar. On the other hand, Mg, Al and Na content in corn straw is much higher than woods.

Table 4. Composition of mineral in biomass (wt%, dry basis)

Biomass	Ash	Composition of mineral						
		Al_2O_3	CaO	Fe_2O_3	MgO	Na_2O	K_2O	SiO_2
Wheat straw	10-15	1.7	10	1.9	2.5	1.2	25	46
Corn Straw	5-10	6	14	1.4	18	20	0.6	40
Poplar wood	2-3	1	47	0.5	4.4	0.2	20	2.6
Deal wood	2-3	4.5	49	3.5	0.5	0.4	2.6	32.5
Maple wood	3-5	4	56	2	20	–	6	10

Table 5. Comparison of the composition of bio-oil of hardwood and corn straw [14]

Pyrolysis	Poplar wood (500-510°C)	Corn straw (480-500°C)
Gas	9-13	23-24
Char	12-15	18-21
Water	9-12	
Bio-oil	63-68	42-52
Acetic acid	5.4-6.3	13
Acids	8.4-11.4	15.8
Methanol and aldehydes	1.5-4.0	11.7
Hydroxyacealdedhyde	6.5-10.0	–
Pyrolysis lignin	16-25	–

As a result, the yield and composition of pyrolysis products are different. As shown in Table 5, the yield of fast pyrolysis bio-oil is 60-70% for woods, higher than 50-60% for straws. For example, yield of fast pyrolysis bio-oil for poplar wood is 10% higher than corn straw. Besides, content of acids and low molecule products is much less than corn straw. The composition of cellulose, hemicellulose and lignin is similar in poplar wood and corn straw (Table 3). So, the difference in yield and composition of bio-oil is probably due to the diversity in structure and ash content.

2.2. Composition of Feedstock

2.2.1. Cellulose

Cellulose, as the main component of plant cell wall, is the most widely distributed polysaccharose. Cellulose is a highmolecular-weight (10^6 or more) linear polymer of ß-$(1{\rightarrow}4)$-D-glucopyranose units in the $^4C_1$ conformation. The fully equatorial conformation of ß-linked glucopyranose residues stabilizes the chair structure, minimizing flexibility.

Glucoseanhydride, which is formed via the removal of water from each glucose, is polymerized into long cellulose chains that contain 5000-10000 glucose units. The basic repeating unit of the cellulose polymer consists of two glucose anhydride units, called a cellobiose unit. [15]

Cellulose degradation occurs at 240-350 °C to produce anhydrocellulose and levoglucosan. When cellulose is pyrolyzed at a heating rate of 12 °C/min under helium in DTA experiments, an endothermal reaction is observed at 335 °C (temperature of maximum weight loss). The reaction is complete at 360 °C.[16] Levoglucosan is produced when the glucosan radical is generated without the bridging oxygen from the preceding monomer unit..[17] Pakhomov also proposed that intermediate radicals form and degradation occurs through one of two biradicals. Specifically, a hydroxy group in radical I is transformed from C-6 to C-4, which occurs during the C-1 to C-6 oxygen bridge formation. [18]

The content of cellulose has a great influence on the biomass pyrolysis. In the biomass feedstock with higher content of cellulose, more volatile component and higher bio-oil are produced. The composition of pyrolysis bio-oil is mainly levoglucosan and other components, like glycollic aldehyde, acetol, methanol, acetic acid. [8]

2.2.2. Hemicellulose

Hemicellulose is the second major chemical constituent in biomass, which is also known as polyose. Hemicellulose is a mixture of various polymerized monosaccharides such as glucose, mannose, galactose, xylose, arabinose, 4-O-methyl glucuronic acid and galacturonic acid residues. Hemicelluloses exhibit lower molecular weights than cellulose. The number of repeating saccharide monomers is only 150, compared to the number in cellulose (5000-10000). Cellulose has only glucose in its structure, whereas hemicellouse has a heteropolysaccharide makeup and some contains short side-chain "branches" pendent along the main polymeric chain.

Hemicellulose decomposes at temperatures of 200-260 °C, giving rise to more volatiles, less tars, and less chars than cellulose. [19] Most hemicelluloses do not yield significant amounts of levoglucosan. Much of the acetic acid liberated from biomass during pyrolysis is attributed to deacetylation of the hemicellulose. Hardwood hemicelluloses are rich in xylan and contain small amounts of glucomannan. Softwood hemicelluloses contain a small amount of xylan, and they are rich in galactoglucomannan.

The onset of hemicellulose thermal decomposition occurs at lower temperatures than crystalline cellulose. The loss of hemicellulose occurs in slow pyrolysis of wood in the temperature range of 130-194 °C, with most of this loss occurring above 180 °C. [20] However, the relevance of this more rapid decomposition of hemicellulose versus cellulose is not known during fast pyrolysis, which is completed in few seconds at a rapid heating rate.

2.2.3. Lignin

The third major component of biomass is lignin, which is an amorphous cross-linked resin with no exact structure. It is the main binder for the agglomeration of fibrous cellulosic components while also providing a shield against the rapid microbial or fungal destruction of the cellulosic fibers. Lignin is a three-dimensional, highly branched, polyphenolic substance that consists of an irregular array of variously bonded "hydroxy-" and "methoxy-"substituted phenylpropane units. [21] These three general monomeric phenylpropane units exhibit the p-coumaryl, coniferyl, and sinapyl structures. In lignin biosynthesis, these units undergo radical dimerization and further oligomerization, and they eventually polymerize and cross-link. The resonance hybrids of the radical formed on oxidation of coniferyl alcohol illustrates the positions where radicals dimerizations occur during lignin formation.

The physical and chemical properties of lignin differ, depending on the extraction or isolation technology used to isolate them. Because lignin is inevitably modified and partially degraded during isolation, thermal decomposition studies on separated lignin will not necessarily match the pyrolysis behavior of this component when it is present in the original biomass. Lignin decomposes when heated at 280-500 °C. [19] Lignin pyrolysis yields phenols via the cleavage of ether and carbon-carbon linkages. Lignin is more difficult to dehydrate than cellulose or hemicelluloses. Lignin pyrolysis produces more residual char than does the pyrolysis of cellulose. In differential thermal analysis (DTA) studies at slow heating rates, a broad exothermic plateau extending from 290 °C to 389 °C is observed, followed by a second exothermic, peaking at 420 °C and tailing out to beyond 500 °C. [22] Lignin decomposition in wood was proposed to begin at 280 °C and continues to 450-500 °C, with a maximum rate being observed at 350-450 °C. [23]

2.2.4. Inorganic Minerals

Biomass also contains a small mineral content that ends up in the pyrolysis ash. Table 6 shows some typical values of the mineral components in wood chips, expressed as a percentage of the dry matter (DM) in the wood. Inorganic minerals have a great influence on the pyrolysis, although their content in the biomass is very little. The effects are expressed in three different ways:

Table 6. Typical Mineral Components of Plant Biomass

element	percentage of dry matter
potassium, K	0.1
sodium, Na	0.015
phosphorus, P	0.02
calcium, Ca	0.2
magnesium, Mg	0.04

a) Pyrolysis Feature

Raveendran investigated effect of inorganic minerals on pyrolysis of 13 types of biomass. He found that the inorganic minerals decreased the activation energy and reaction temperature. [12]

b) Distribution of Pyrolysis Products

Ash and added inorganic minerals in biomass decrease the volatile components of pyrolysis products, thus decreasing the yield of bio-oil and increasing the yield of char and gas. Scott investigated the relationship between ash content and bio-oil yield based on 8 types of biomass. He found the maximum bio-oil yield significantly decreased with the increase of ash content. The maximum bio-oil yield went up to 80 wt% when the ash was removed. [24]

c) Composition of Bio-oil

Inorganic minerals increase the low molecule components in the bio-oil, like glycollic aldehyde and decrease the evoglucosan content. Gray reduced the ash content by pretreatment. It was found that the low molecule components in bio-oil, such as formic acid, acetic acid, methanol and acetone, were decreased and the bio-oil yield were increased. [25]

2.3. Operation Conditions of Pyrolysis

2.3.1. Pyrolysis Temperature

Pyrolysis temperature is an important factor influencing the composition of pyrolysis products. Basically, low temperature, slow heating rate and long residence time facilitates the production of char. Fast pyrolysis with high temperature reduces the char and increase the incondensable gas. There exists a maximum value of bio-oil yield when the pyrolysis temperature is increased. Optimum temperature for the maximum bio-oil yields of woods and non-wood feedstocks is very close, 450~550°C. However, the maximum bio-oil yield differs from 50~60% for straws to 60-70% for woods. So, the optimum temperature is the primary factor to optimize the pyrolysis process.

2.3.2. Particle Size

The particle size is one of the most important variables affecting the pyrolysis. Several investigators studied the effect of the particle size on the oil yield and weight loss. The size of the particles has a direct impact on the nature of the reactions of biomass decomposition. In the literature, significant particle size effects were observed in the pyrolysis of coal and oil shales. [26] In contrast to coal and oil shale, the pyrolysis yield are fairly independent of particle size for biomass sample. These results suggest that mass transfer restrictions to the volatile evolution and escape of the evolved volatiles from the inside of particle are much less important for rapeseed compared to coals and oil shales. [27] In Şensöz's study, the pyrolysis product yields were fairly independent of particle size for rapeseed. [28]. Islam also found the similar result for palm shell. [29] They obtained the maximum oil yield with a relatively large particle size. This suggested that there was no significant effect of the particle size on the pyrolysis oil yield for biomass feed stock. It might because mass transfer restrictions to the volatile evolution and escape of the evolved volatiles from the inside of particle were much less important.

2.3.3. Residence Time

Solid particles break into smaller particles and decompose into volatile material when the feedstocks are heated. Volatile materials will occur secondary cracking and producing the incondensable gas, thus reducing the bio-oil yield. Residence time of volatile components is very important for the yield and composition of the bio-oil. Very short residence times result in incomplete depolymerisation of the lignin due to random bond cleavage and inter-reaction of the lignin macromolecule resulting in a less homogenous liquid product, while longer residence times can cause secondary cracking of the primary products, reducing yield and adversely affecting bio-oil properties.

2.3.4. Heating Rate

Low heating rate facilitates the production of char and reduce the bio-oil. High heating rate inhibits the secondary cracking of the gas and can improve the bio-oil yield to more than 70%. Heating rates of 1000 °C/s, or even 10000 °C/s, at temperatures below 650 °C have been used. [6] Rapid heating and rapid cooling produced the intermediate pyrolysis liquid products, which condense before further reactions break down higher-molecular-weight species into gaseous products. High reaction rates minimize char formation. Under some conditions, no char is formed. [30] At higher fast pyrolysis temperatures, the major product is gas.

2.3.5. Pressure

Pressure can influence the residence time of volatile materials, thus affecting the extent of the secondary cracking. As a result, the molecule distribution will also be affected. Researchers found that yields of bio-oil and char of cellulose are 19.1% and 34.2% at $300^{\circ}C$, nitrogen and 1 atm, while yields of 55.8% and 17.8% at 200Pa. Low pressure can facilitate removal of volatile gas from the surface of the feedstock and reduce the opportunity of secondary reaction, improving the bio-oil yield.

2.3.6. Pretreatment

Feedstock pretreatment has become an important tool to increase cellulosic ethanol production yields. Pretreatment processes break down lignin and disrupt the crystalline structure of cellulose, rendering it more accessible to enzymes to allow more ready fermentation to sugars. [31] Numerous pretreatment methods for cellulosic ethanol production have been investigated, including physical, [32] chemical, [32] and a combination of both. [34] For example, steam explosion, [35] hot compressed water treatments, [36] and applications of dilute acids [37] or bases [38] have been utilized. These pretreatment processes could have potential to be used prior to fast pyrolysis to improve bio-oil characteristics, produce useful selected chemicals, and increase the yield of sugars. [39, 40]

Hassan investigated six chemical pretreatments: dilute phosphoric acid, dilute sulfuric acid, sodium hydroxide, calcium hydroxide, ammonium hydroxide, and hydrogen peroxide. Bio-oils were produced from untreated and pretreated 10-year old pine wood feed stocks in an auger reactor at 450 °C. Results showed that the physical and chemical characteristics of the bio-oils produced from pretreated pine wood feed stocks were influenced by the biomass pretreatments applied. Acid pretreated pine wood produced bio-oils with lower pH, higher acid values, and viscosity compared to the bio-oils of untreated and alkaline pretreated pine wood. The HHV for all bio-oils ranged from 19.7 to 24.4 MJ/kg except that, for the bio-oil of hydrogen peroxide pretreatment, the HHV was 7.28 MJ/kg due to very high water content (24%). The average molecular weights for the bio-oils of acid pretreated pine wood were higher than for untreated and alkaline pretreated pine wood. GC/MS chemical characterization showed also that the chemical concentrations for most bio-oil components that arise from the degradation of hemicelluloses, cellulose, and lignin were lower than that in the bio-oil of untreated pine wood. Calcium hydroxide pretreatment increased the concentration of laevoglucose and other anhydrosugars in the produced bio-oil. FTIR spectra indicated that most bio-oils had similar chemical compositions with the possibility of increased hydrocarbon compounds in the bio-oil of calcium hydroxide, sodium hydroxide, and hydrogen peroxide pretreated pine wood. [41]

REFERENCES

[1]   Dinesh Mohan, Charles U. Pittman, Jr., and Philip H. Steele, Pyrolysis of Wood/Biomass for Bio-oil: A Critical Review, *Energy and Fuels* 2006, 20, 848-889.

[2]   Bridgwater A. V.; Czernik, S.; Piskorz, J. An overview of fast pyrolysis. In *Progress in Thermochemical Biomass Conversion,* Volume 2; Bridgwater, A. V., Ed.; Blackwell Science: London, 2001, pp 977-997.

[3]   Bridgwater, A. V. Appl. Catal., A 1994, 116, 5-47)(Bridgwater, A. V. *Biomass* 1990, 22 (1-4), 279-290.

[4]   Boucher, M. E.; Chaala, A.; Pakdel, H.; Roy, C. *Biomass Bioenergy* 2000, 19, 351-361.

[5]   Bridgwater, A. V.; Kuester, J. L. *Research in Thermochemical Biomass Conversion;* Elsevier Science Publishers: London, 1991.) (Bridgwater, A. V. *Catal. Today* 1996, 29 (1-4), 285-295.

[6]   Bridgwater, A. V. *Chem. Eng. J.* 2003, 91, 87-102.

[7]   Czernik, S. and A.V. Bridgwater, Overview of Applications of Fast Pyrolysis Bio-oil, *"Energy and Fuels",* Vole 18, 2004

[8]   An overview of fast pyrolysis of biomass. A.V. Bridgwater a,*, D. Meier b, D. Radlein, *Organic Geochemistry* 30 (1999) 1479-1493.

[9]   Magrini-Blair, K., S. Czernik, R. French, Y. Parent, M. Ritland, E. Chornet, Fluidizable Catalysts for Producing Hydrogen by Steam Reforming Biomass Pyrolysis Liquids, *"Proceedings of the 2002 U.S. DOE Hydrogen Program Review",* 2002.

[10]   Bridgwater, A.V., S. Czernik, and J. Piskorz, *Status of Biomass Fast Pyrolysis, "Fast Pyrolysis of Biomass: A Handbook",* Vol 2, CPL Press, 2002.

[11]   Bridgwater A. V. *J. Anal. Appl. Pyrolysis* 1999, 51, 3-22.

[12]   Raveendran k, Ganesh A, Khilart K C. Influence of Mineral Matter on Biomass Pyrolysis Characteristics. *Fuel*, 1995, 74(12): 1812-1822.

[13]   Scott D S, Piskorz J. The continuous flash pyrolysis of biomass. *The Canada Journal of Chemical Engineering*, 1984, 62 (6): 404-412.

[14]   Piskorz J, Majerski P, Radlein D. Composition of oils obtained by fast pyrolysis of different woods, in: Pyrolysis oils from biomass. *ACS symposium series* 376, 1988: 167-178.

[15]   Rowell, R. M. The Chemistry of Solid Wood; American Chemical Society: Washington, DC, 1984.

[16]   Zugenmaier, P. *Prog. Polym. Sci.* 2001, 26, 1341-1417.

[17]   Modorsky, S. L.; Hart, V. E.; Stravs, S. J. *Res. Natl. Bur. Stand.* 1956, 54, 343-354.

[18]   Pakhomov, A. M.; Akad-Nauk, I.; Otdel, S. S. S. B. *Khim. Nauk*, 1957, 1457-1449

[19]   Soltes, E. J.; Elder, T. J., Pyrolysis. In Organic Chemicals from Biomass; Goldstein, I. S., Ed.; CRC Press: Boca Raton, FL, 1981; pp 63-95.

[20]   Runkel, R. O. H.; Wilke, K.-D. *Holzals Rohund Werkstoff* 1951, 9, 260-270.

[21]   McCarthy, J.; Islam, A. Lignin chemistry, technology, and utilization: a brief history. In Lignin: Historical, Biological and Materials PerspectiVes; Glasser, W. G., Northey, R.

A., Schultz, T. P., Eds.; *ACS Symposium Series* 742; American Chemical Society: Washington, DC, 2000; pp 2-100.

[22] Berkowitz, N. *Fuel* 1957, 36, 355-373.

[23] Kudo, K.; Yoshida, E. *J. Tap. Wood Res. Soc.* 1957, 3 (4), 125-127.

[24] Scott D S, Piskorz J, Radlein D. Liquid products from the continuous flash pyrolysis of biomass. *Ind. Eng. Chem. Process Des. Dev*, 1985, 24, 581~588.

[25] Gray M R, Corcoran W H, Gavalas G R. Pyrolysis of a wood-drived material: effect of moisture and ash content. *Ind. Eng. Chem. Process. Des. Dev*, 1985, 24, 646~651.

[26] Gavalas GR, In: Anderson LL, editor. *Coal science and technology* 4; Coal pyrolysis. Amsterdam: Elsevier Science, 1982. p. 92-93.

[27] Ekinci E, Putun A E, Ctroglu M, Love G D, Laerty CJ, Snape CE. International Conference on Coal Science, Newcastle upon Tyne, 1991. p. 520-523.

[28] Şensöz, S., Angin, D., Yorgun, S., 2000. Influence of particle size on the pyrolysis of rapeseed (Brassica napus L.): fuel properties of bio-oil. *Biomass andBioenergy.* 19, 271-279.

[29] Islam, M.N., Zailani, R., Ani, F.N., 1999. Pyrolytic oil from fluidised bed pyrolysis of oil palm shall and its characterization. *Renewable Energy.* 17: 73-84].

[30] Demirbas, A. *J. Anal. Appl. Pyrolysis* 2005, 73, 39-43.

[31] Mosier, N., Wyman, C., Dale, B., Elander, R., Lee, Y.Y., Holtzapple, M., Ladisch, M., 2005. Features of promising technologies for pretreatment of lignocellulosic biomass. *Bioresource Technology.* 96, 673-686.

[32] Mandels, M., Hontz, L., Nystrom, J., 1974. Enzymatic hydrolysis of waste cellulose. *Biotechnology and Bioengineering.* 16, 1471–1493.

[33] Yang, Y., Sharma-Shivappa, R., Burns, J.C., Cheng, J., Dilute Acid Pretreatment of Oven-dried Switchgrass Germplasms for Bioethanol Production. Energy Fuels, 2009, 23 (7), 3759–3766 Sun, Y., Cheng, J., 2002. Hydrolysis of lignocellulosic materials for ethanol production: a review. *Bioresource Technology*, 83, 1–11.

[34] Sun, Y., Cheng, J., 2002. Hydrolysis of lignocellulosic materials for ethanol production: a review. *Bioresource Technology*, 83, 1–11.

[35] Kaar, E., Gutierrez, C.V., Kinoshita, C.M., 1998. Steam explosion of sugarcane bagasse as a pretreatment for conversion to ethanol. *Biomass and Bioenergy.* 14, 277–287.

[36] Mok, W.S.L., Antal, Jr., M, J., 1992. Uncatalyzed solvolysis of whole biomass hemicellulose by hot compressed liquid water. *Industrial and Engineering Chemistry Research.* 31, 1157–1161.

[37] Nguyen, Q.A., Tucker, M.P., Keller, F.A., Eddy F P., 2000. Two-stage dilute-acid pretreatment of softwoods. *Applied Biochemistry and Biotechnology*, 84-86, 561–576.

[38] Kim, T.H., Kim, J.S., Sunwoo, C., Lee, Y.Y., Pretreatment of corn stover by aqueous ammonia. 2003. *Bioresource Technology*, 90, 39–47.

[39] Piskorz, J., Radlein, D., Scott, D.S., Czernic, S., 1989. Pretreatment of wood and cellulose for production of sugars by fast pyrolysis. *Journal of Analytical and Applied Pyrolysis,* 16, 127–142.

[40] Dobele, G., Dizhbite, T., Rossinskaja, G., Telysheva, G., Meie, D., Radtke, S., Faix, O.J., 2003. Pre-treatment of biomass with phosphoric acid prior to fast pyrolysis: A promising method for obtaining 1, 6-anhydrosaccharides in high yields. *Journal of Analytical and Applied Pyrolysis.* 68-69, 197–211.

[41] Hassan, M.E., Steele, P., Ingram, L, 2009. Characterization of Fast Pyrolysis Bio-oils
      Produced from Pretreated Pine Wood. *Appl. Biochem. Biotechnol.* 154, 182–192]

In: Oil: Production, Consumption and Environmental Impact   ISBN: 978-1-61942-877-5
Editor: Shuangning Xiu   © 2012 Nova Science Publishers, Inc.

Chapter 8

MICROWAVE-ASSISTED PYROLYSIS OIL: PROCESS, CHARACTERIZATION, AND FRACTIONATION

Bo Zhang, *Shuangning Xiu and Abolghasem Shahbazi*

Biological Engineering Program, North Carolina Agricultural and Technical State
University, 121 Sockwell Hall, 1601 E Market Street
Greensboro, NC 27411, US

1. INTRODUCTION

There have recently been increasing concerns of the environmental problems (such as global climate change, greenhouse gases concentration), the energy demand, and the price and the security of fossil fuels. Biomass, as a clean and renewable source of energy, has received more attention since the middle of the 20th century. A number of biorefinery processes have been developed to produce biofuels and chemicals from the initial biomass feedstock (Figure 1). There are two primary biorefinery platforms: the biological conversion route and the thermochemical route. In the thermochemical route, biomass is converted into syngas through gasification or bio-oils through pyrolysis and catalytic hydrothermal treatment, which can be further upgraded to liquid fuels and other chemicals, such as menthol, gasoline, diesel fuel, and biodegradable plastics. While the biological route is based on the breakdown of biomass into aqueous sugars using chemical and biological means. The fermentable sugars can be further processed to ethanol or other advanced biofuels [1]. The conversion of biomass into the bio-oil using pyrolysis technologies is one of the most promising alternatives under study today to convert biomass into useful products and energy [2]. The pyrolysis is the thermal degradation of biomass by heat in the absence of oxygen, which results in the production of charcoal (solid residues), bio-oils (liquid) and gaseous products. Depending on the heating rates and other operating parameters, the pyrolysis process can be divided into three categories: 1. Conventional Pyrolysis; 2. Fast Pyrolysis; 3.

---

* E-mail:bzhang@ncat.edu.

Flash Pyrolysis. The range of the main operating parameters for pyrolysis processes are summarized in Table 1 [3]. So far, the preferred pyrolysis technology is fast or flash pyrolysis at high temperatures with very short residence time [4].

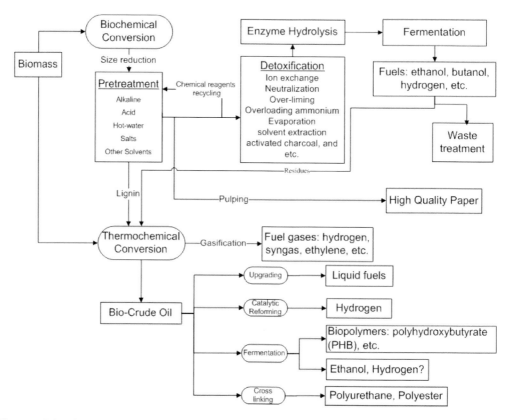

Figure 1. Biorefinery options.

Table 1. The main operating conditions of conventional, fast and flash pyrolysis processes

	Conventional	Fast	Flash
Reaction temperature (K)	550–950	850–1250	1050–1300
Heating rate (K/s)	0.1–1	10–200	>1000
Particle size (mm)	5–50	<1	<0.2
Residence time (s)	450–550	0.5–10	<0.5

2. MICROWAVE-ASSISTED PYROLYSIS PROCESS

2.1. Microwave Heating

Microwaves are electromagnetic waves in the radio frequency portion of the electromagnetic spectrum, which are generated from electrical energy. As all electromagnetic waves, they are a sinusoidal perpendicular electric and magnetic field. They span frequencies from 0.3 to 300 GHz and correspondingly wavelengths from approximately 1000 to 1 mm.

The mechanism of microwave heating is called "dialectric heating", whereby polar molecules (such as water molecules) are caused to vibrate and rotate as they attempt to align themselves to the shifting incoming microwave radiation frequencies. Typically household microwave ovens are 64% efficient at converting incoming electricity into microwave radiation, the rest of it is lost as heat mostly in the magnetron and the device, which transforms high voltage electricity into microwave radiation [5]. During the heating-up process, the efficiency with which the targeted material actually absorbs the microwave radiation depends significantly on the moisture content of the material. If there is too few water polar molecules, little to no heating will occur; whereas if there is a significant amount of excess water polar molecules, an excessive amount of time and energy is required to heat the material. Efficiency is also determined by the extent to which microwave radiation can pass through the material. If the material is too large or impenetrable by microwave radiation, differential heating is likely to occur.

2.2. Microwave-assisted Pyrolysis Process

Microwave-assisted pyrolysis is a gentle and medium speed pyrolytic process, which belongs to either conventional pyrolysis or fast pyrolysis. Microwave pyrolysis is one of the many ways of converting biomass into higher value products such as oils, gases, charcoal and chemicals. The conversion of oil palm [6], wood [7-9], microalgae [10], distillers dried grain(DDG) [11], corn stover [12] and sewage sludge [13] are among the recent studies in the fields of microwave pyrolysis and bioenergy. Increased process yield, environmental compatibility, savings in process time and low requirements for space and capital equipment are among the advantages reported regarding to microwave processing of materials [14].

Biomass size reduction is always required by conventional pyrolysis. Conventional pyrolysis oil and char yields were found to be largely dependent on the particle size of the biomass feedstock [15]. In a conventional pyrolysis process, biomass particles with larger size are difficult to be agitated and processed in the fluidized bed reactor, as particles tend to settle to the bottom of the bed, thus the heat transfer and the efficiency of thermal conversion are reduced. Larger particles also have a negative effect on the efficiency of production of bio-oil.

It's found that the bio-oil yields increased when the particle size was reduced. Fine particles can increase overall heat transfer in the pyrolysis process, but also require substantial amount of energy and effort for grinding, pre-processing and screening of biomass feedstocks. Otherwise, thermochemical conversion reactions can take place rapidly in large-sized biomass materials by using microwave irradiation. Very fine feedstock grinding required by conventional pyrolysis is not necessary for microwave pyrolysis process, resulting in substantial energy savings.

2.2.1. Bench-Top Process

A typical bench-top microwave-assisted pyrolysis process may be done in a commercial microwave oven of 600-1300 watts at the microwave frequency of 2450 MHz. Approximately 50-250 g biomass samples could be placed in a 500 ml quartz flask, which in turn was placed inside the microwave cavity (Figure 2). The oven was purged with nitrogen gas at a flow rate 200 mL/min for 2 min before microwave treatment to create an oxygen-free gas background. The temperature of the sample during the experiments was immediately monitored by a K-type thermocouple after microwave heating finished. The final mean temperature of the pyrolysis is within the range of 450 to 500°C. The volatile pyrolyzates were condensed after passing a water-cooling column, and then collected in the collection vials. This fraction is called a pyrolytic liquid (bio-oil). The solid char residue was allowed to cool to room temperature before it was weighed. The condensates adhering to the interior wall of the quartz flask were washed with ethanol into the pyrolytic liquid collection bottle. All liquid collected was concentrated at 40°C using a rotovap to a constant weight, and the weight was recorded. The weight of syngas product was calculated using following equation:

Weight of syngas = initial biomass − pyrolytic liquid mass − char residue mass

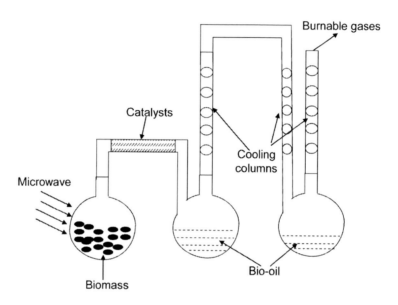

Figure 2. Schematic diagram of the microwave-assisted pyrolysis system.

2.2.2. Pilot Scale Continuous Process

The Bioenergy Laboratory of Department of Mathematical Sciences and Technology at the Norwegian University of Life Sciences has been actively researching and developing the microwave pyrolysis process together with X-Waste International AS since 2000. During 2005, the first pilot-scale microwave pyrolysis reactor was constructed and tested at the Bioenergy Laboratory (Figure 3). The Center for Biorefining of Bioproducts and Biosystems Engineering at the University of Minnesota collaborated with Norwegian University of Life Sciences on the microwave pyrolysis technology. The second prototype pilot-scale microwave pyrolysis reactor was successfully constructed at the Center for Biorefining of Bioproducts and Biosystems Engineering of the University of Minnesota during 2008 [16].

The pilot-scale microwave pyrolysis reactor by Norwegian University of Life Sciences and X-Waste International AS has 4.5 kW power and 10 Kg/hr feeding rate. A various input materials could be feed into the air tight hopper system, which has a 1 m³ capacity. The auger transport system was used to push the feedstock through the pyrolysis chamber. The second generation pilot-scale microwave pyrolysis reactor at the University of Minnesota, which has a larger capacity of 15 Kg/hr, is two-stage processes. The biomass first pyrolysized in the first reactor around 300-450 °C, then the biomass further gasified in the second reactor around

650-700 °C to maximize the production of fuel gases. Both two pilot systems have the bio-oil distillation columns built in to further refine the bio-oil.

Figure 3. Pilot-scale continuous microwave-assisted pyrolysis system at Norwegian University of Life Sciences.

For a continuous system, the exit of the vaporous products to the distillation column is pressure driven. The pressure is partially from the vaporization of the volatile components and partially by the feeding of reused, dry, reheated pyrolysis gas. The flow rate of reused pyrolysis gas is one of the key variables in regulating the process [17].

3. CHARACTERIZATION

3.1. Characterization

Understanding the physical and chemical properties of the pyrolysis bio-oil is very important to the design and control of microwave pyrolysis processing parameters, product specifications, and product storage and transportation.

3.1.1. GC-MS Analysis

Chemical compositions of the pyrolysis bio-oil were identified using a HP 6890 GC/mass spectrometer with a DB-5 capillary column. The GC was programmed at 40°C for 0.5 minute and then increased at 10 °C/min to 300°C and finally held with an isothermal for 10 minutes. The injector temperature was 300°C and the injection size was 1 µL. The flow rate of the carrier gas (Helium) was 0.6 ml/min. The ion source temperature was 230°C for the mass selective detector. The compounds were identified by comparison with library of NIST Mass Spectral.

3.1.2 FTIR

The FTIR spectroscopy of oil samples was achieved by using Nicolet MAGNA-IR 750 model Fourier Transform Infrared Spectrophotometer (Thermo Electron Corporation, Madison, WI, USA).

3.1.3. Other Methods

The following methods were performed to characterize the chemical and physical properties of oil.

Density: Density was determined according to ASTM D1298 standard method.

Water content: The water content of oil was found by Karl Fisher method according to ASTM D1744.

Viscosity: The kinematic viscosity was determined by using a Brookfield viscometer.

3.2. Physical and Chemical Properties of the Bio-oils

Properties of the bio-oils mainly depend on the starting materials. Only bio-oils from lignocellulosic feedstock will be discussed in this chapter. Following is an example of the bio-oil produced from corn stover. The bio-oils from a microwave prolysis process are dark brown viscous liquid. The gross heating value of the corn stover bio-oil is 17.51 MJ/kg. It is similar to the gross heating values of bio-oils produced by other pyrolysis processes (15 -19 MJ/kg), but lower than that of petroleum fuels (42 MJ/kg). The heating value of the bio-oils from microwave pyrolysis is approximately 41.7% of a petroleum fuel oil [12].

As shown in Table 2, some physical and chemical properties of the bio-oils from corn stover are summarized. These properties were similar to bio-oils from conventional pyrolysis processes, but significantly different from those of petroleum derived diesels.

The ash content in this bio-oil is 0.04 wt%, and the solid content is 0.22 wt%. Problems associated with ash content become more serious when the ash content of the fuel is greater than 0.1 wt% [18]. Solid particles may wear the fuel system, block the filter and clog the fuel nozzle [19]. Thus the solid content of a bio-oil is important with respect to the particulate emissions during the combustion process. The metal contents of the bio-oils were found to be: 3 ppm K, 2 ppm Na and 7 ppm Ca. They are lower than those of the bio-oils generated by other conventional pyrolysis processes. One way to reduce the alkali metal and calcium concentration in bio-oils is using the organic solvent dilution. By doing this, the fuel quality will be improved, and this method is simple and cost-effective. The pH value of this corn stove bio-oil by microwave pyrolysis is 2.9. Most pyrolysis bio-oils have a pH in the range of 2.0-3.8, because of the presence of organic acids, such as acetic acid and formic acid [20]. The acids in the bio-oils are corrosive to common construction materials such as carbon steel and aluminum, especially under elevated temperature and increasing water content. However, bio-oils are not corrosive to stainless steels. The water content in the bio-oils from microwave pyrolysis of corn stove is 15.2% wt. The water is likely from two sources: the moisture in the raw corn stover and the water produced as a result of the dehydration reactions occurring during the pyrolysis. Therefore, the water content of the pyrolysis bio-oil may vary in a wide range (15-30%) depending on the feedstock and process conditions [21]. At this concentration, water is usually miscible with the oligo-cellulosic derived components, because of the solubilizing effect of other polar hydrophilic compounds (acids, alcohols, hydroxyaldehydes, and ketones) mostly originating from the decomposition of carbohydrates. The presence of water has both negative and positive effects on the oil properties. Obviously, it lowers its heating value, contributes to the increase in ignition delay and the decrease in combustion rate compared to other engine fuels. On the other hand, it reduces the oil viscosity and improves its flow characteristics, which is beneficial to combustion. The dynamic viscosity of the bio-oils of corn stover was 185 mPa · s at 40°C (or 148 cSt @ 40°C, calculated by the dynamic viscosity of bio-oils divided by the density), which is can not be used directly for gas turbine. The viscosity of gas turbine oils is usually around 2.5 - 30 cSt at 40°C. Further processing is necessary to reduce viscosity. The GC-MS results of the bio-oil from corn stover are given in Table 3. With a GC-MS analysis, the liquid products from microwave-assisted pyrolysis were identified to be mainly composed of polycyclic aromatic hydrocarbons, ketones, aldehydes, carboxylic acids, esters, nitrogenated compounds, and their derivatives (Table 3). The percentage values indicate the proportions of individual compounds in the liquid and do not represent the actual concentration of these compounds.

Table 2. Physicochemical properties of bio-oils of corn stover

Properties	Units	Bio-oil	Conventional bio-oils
pH		2.87	2.0-3.8
Moisture	wt%	15.2	15-30
Density at 20°C	g/ml	1.25	1.1-1.4
Dynamic viscosity at	mPa · s		
20°C		1270	
40°C		185	
50°C		60	
80°C		34	
Gross heating value (HHV)	MJ/ kg	17.51	15-19
Elemental composition	wt%		
C		60.66	55.3-63.5
H		7.70	5.2-7.0
N		2.02	0.07-0.39
S		0.15	0.00-0.05
Ash content	wt %	0.04	0.03-0.30
Solid content	wt %	0.22	< 1

Table 3. The composition (% area) of the main pyrolysis liquid compounds obtained from corn stover using 300 watt power supply

Retention time (min)	Possible Chemical Name	Possible Chemical Formula	Percentage
6.0	Furan, 3-pentyl-	C9H14O	2.5
7.8	Styrene	C8H8	2.1
11.4	Phenol	C6H6O	4.2

Table 3. (Continued)

Retention time (min)	Possible Chemical Name	Possible Chemical Formula	Percentage
11.7	Benzofuran	C_8H_6O	0.1
13.4	Benzene, 1-propynyl-	C_9H_8	2.4
14.0	Acetic acid, 4-methylphenyl ester	$C_9H_{10}O_2$	0.8
14.7	6-Nonynoic acid, methyl ester	$C_{10}H_{16}O_2$	0.1
14.8	Phenol, 3-methyl-	C_7H_8O	2.3
14.9	Phenol, 2-methoxy-	$C_7H_8O_2$	15.9
17.7	Phenol, 4-ethyl-	$C_8H_{10}O$	20.5
18.1	Naphthalene	$C_{10}H_8$	10.9
18.4	Phenol, 3,4-dimethyl-	$C_8H_{10}O$	0.5
19.3	Benzofuran, 4,7-dimethyl-	$C_{10}H_{10}O$	0.2
19.4	2-Propenoic acid, 3-(2-hydroxyphenyl)-, (E)-	$C_9H_8O_3$	12.3
19.9	Benzenamine, 2,4-dimethyl-	$C_8H_{11}N$	0.8
20.9	Phenol, 4-ethyl-2-methoxy-	$C_9H_{12}O_2$	7.1
21.5	1H-Indene, 1-ethylidene-	$C_{11}H_{10}$	0.8
22.0	Benzeneacetaldehyde	C_8H_8O	6.1
22.0	2-Propanone, 1-phenoxy-	$C_9H_{10}O_2$	0.1
23.1	Phenol, 3,4-dimethoxy-	$C_8H_{10}O_3$	4.8
25.8	Acenaphthylene	$C_{12}H_8$	0.2
32.6	1-Dodecanol, 3,7,11-trimethyl-	$C_{15}H_{32}O$	0.5

4. CATALYST SELECTION

4.1. Directly Mixed with the Biomass

A number of catalysts have studied to improve the bio-oil quality. Moen et al. studied chlorides, nitrates and metal-oxides catalysts [8]. By adding catalysts of 2% of the aspen mass (air dry aspen pellet weight basis), chlorides in particular were found to favor liquid yield, especially the yield of water phase residue.

Average liquid yield with adding chloride catalysts was 41% wt of the total biomass input, compared to 35% wt without any catalyst. Metal-oxides were found to favor pyrolysis heavy oil, and thus total oil yield. Nitrates were found to favor pyrolysis gas production.

In another study, the effects of catalysts metal oxides, salts, and acids including $K_2Cr_2O_7$, Al_2O_3, KAc, H_3BO_3, Na_2HPO_4, $MgCl_2$, $AlCl_3$, $CoCl_2$, and $ZnCl_2$ on product selectivity of microwave-assisted pyrolysis of corn stover and aspen wood were evaluated [22]. Following catalysts KAc, Al_2O_3, $MgCl_2$, H_3BO_3, and Na_2HPO_4 were found to increase the bio-oil yield by either suppressing charcoal yield or gas yield or both. These catalysts may function as a microwave absorbent to speed up heating or participate in so-called ''in situ upgrading'' of pyrolytic vapors during the microwave-assisted pyrolysis of biomass. GC–MS analysis of the bio-oils found that chloride salts promoted a few reactions while suppressing most of the other reactions observed for the control samples. At 8 g $MgCl_2$/100 g biomass level, the GC–MS total ion chromatograms of the bio-oils from the treated corn stover or aspen show only one major furfural peak accounting for about 80% of the area under the spectrum. It's concluded that some catalysts tested here improve bio-oil yields, and chloride salts in particular simplify the chemical compositions of the resultant bio-oils and therefore improve the product selectivity of the pyrolysis process.

4.2. Catalysts for Pyrolysis Vapors

The effect of the following catalysts: MS (Molecular sieve) 4A, Fe_2O_3/MS 4A, CoO/MS 4A, NiO/MS 4A, MgO/MS 4A, PtO/MS 4A, Al_2O_3/MS 4A, La_2O_3/MS 4A, Cl^-/MS 3A, SO_4^{2-} /MS 3A, Na_2O/MS 3A, CaO/MS 3A, K_2O/MS 3A, CoO/ZrO_2, NiO/ZrO_2, La_2O_3/ZrO_2, NiO/CaO $ZrO2$, Cl^-/ZrO_2, SO_4^{2-} /ZrO_2, Na_2O/ZrO_2, CaO/ZrO_2, and MgO/ZrO_2, on chemical profile of the products from microwave-assisted pyrolysis of biomass was studied [23]. A microwave oven with a frequency of about 2.4 gigahertz, and a power of about 1–1.3 kilowatt was used to pyrolyze aspen (*Populus tremuloides*).

The steam that evolved was removed from the oven and passed to a catalyst column where the temperature was controlled at about 350–600°C, and the converted vapors were then condensed to bio-oils. The chemical profiles of the bio-oils were determined using gas chromatography-mass spectrometry. Solid acids were proved to be effective catalysts to decompose pyrolysis vapors, while solid alkaline and other catalysts do not seem to affect the composition of the liquid products from microwave-assisted pyrolysis. The chemicals of pyrolysis vapors were mainly converted to 1,1-dimethoxyhexane when using a solid acid as the catalyst, such as Cl^-/ZrO_2 or SO_4^{2-} /ZrO_2. Increasing the temperature of the catalyst bed and the ratio of catalysts to biomass adversely affected the liquid yield.

Another study performed similar research on fast pyrolysis of poplar wood followed with catalytic cracking of the pyrolysis vapors using analytical pyrolysis-gas chromatography/mass spectrometry (Py-GC/MS) [24]. This study provided more candidates of the catalysts that may work for pyrolysis vapors. These catalysts: nano MgO, CaO, TiO_2, Fe_2O_3, NiO and ZnO displayed different catalytic capabilities towards the pyrolytic products. Using the catalyst of CaO significantly reduced the levels of phenols and anhydrosugars, and eliminated the acids, while it increased the formation of cyclopentanones, hydrocarbons and several light compounds. ZnO was found to be a mild catalyst, as it only slightly altered the pyrolytic products.

The usage of other four catalysts decreased the linear aldehydes, and increased the ketones and cyclopentanones. The catalysis by Fe_2O_3 resulted in the formation of various hydrocarbons. Only catalyst CaO was able to greatly reduce the acid production.

5. FRACTIONATION

Bio-oil from thermochemical conversion of biomass is a complex mixture of polar and non-polar compounds, and can not be directly used as a combustion engine fuel due to its low heating value, high viscosity, chemical instability, and incomplete volatility. In the previous section, we discussed how the catalysts may affect and improve the bio-oil. The methods of solvent mixing and extraction will be discussed below.

Blending bio-oils with burnable solvents such as methanol and ethanol is a practical approach to the improvement of the bio-oil shelf stability and performance. It has been reported that the presence of methanol or ethanol in the bio-oil provides a simple method for controlling the viscosity of the bio-oil, facilitating combustion, improving homogeneity, and enhancing stability [25]. Adding methanol and/or ethanol to the corn stover bio-oils reduced the viscosity and slowed down the increase in viscosity and water content during the storage. Blending of methanol or ethanol with the bio-oils may be a simple and cost-effective approach to convert the pyrolytic bio-oils into a stable gas turbine or home heating fuels.

Up to date, many methods have been studied to upgrade the bio-oil for a suitable liquid fuel such as emulsification [26], hydrotreating [27], and catalytic cracking [28] etc. The drawbacks of emulsification include the cost of surfactants, the high energy required and unwanted carbon residue after combustion. Hydrotreating of bio-oil normally is carried out at high temperature, high hydrogen pressure, and in the presence of catalysts. Hydrotreating results in elimination of oxygen as water, and the process is economical deficiency. A number of catalysts have been used for production of hydrocarbon fuels from the bio-oil; however catalytic cracking may raise problems such as catalyst coking and deactivation, and high cost of processing. Therefore, the methods above should be further developed and improved.

Bio-oil fractionation of solvent extraction has been proposed as a simple method for refining bio-oil [29]. Many studies concentrated on the separation of chemicals from bio-oil or the analysis of bio-oil fractions obtained by the multi-step extraction method. It's well known that the bio-oil contains oily and hydrophilic components including aliphatic and aromatic hydrocarbons, oxygenated compounds such as phenols, aldehydes, acids and sugars etc. An effective separation approach was developed to achieve for extracting fuel from oily components of bio-oil and chemicals from hydrophilic and acidic components of bio-oil by using simple solvent extraction [30]. A simple scheme of bio-oil fractionation for light oil is shown in Figure 4.

A 200-mL of bio-oil was first emulsified by mixing with water (1:1 volume ratio) at the temperature of $40^{o}C$, and then separated in a separation funnel. The top emulsion phase containing alkenes and low molecular lignin and heavy oil was precipitated in the bottom layer. The emulsion phase (light oil rich) was further extracted three times with a pentane-mix-solvent immediately after separation. The solvents of extract phase were evaporated at $40^{o}C$ under vacuum, and then recycled. The extraction process yields 20-30% of light oil based on bio-oil.

The effects of inorganic salts including NaCl, $CaCl_2$ and $ZnCl_2$, and number of extraction were investigated. $ZnCl_2$ promoted higher yield of light oil than NaCl and $CaCl_2$. This suggests a stronger salting-out effect of $ZnCl_2$ on the extraction of light oil from bio-oil emulsion phase.

By a GC-MS analysis, heavy oil was found to be mainly composed of high molecular weight phenols with different methoxy, and ethoxy groups etc. Light oil is as a mixture of several macro-families including polycyclic aromatic hydrocarbons (PAHs), phenols, esters, furan derivatives, aliphatic hydrocarbons, some acids, benzenemethanol, etc. TGA analysis showed that how that no carbon residue was left after light oil combustion, but heavy oil combustion results in over 25% carbon residue. The light oil, which is generated by the two-step fractionation procedure, could be a good alternative fuel for engines. The new approach would be economic for full utilization of bio-oil.

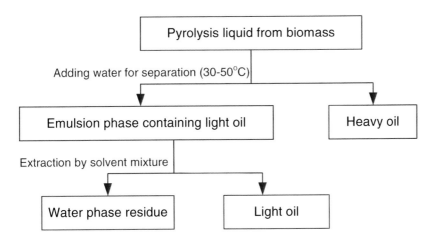

Figure 4. Separation scheme of bio-oil fractionation.

6. CLOSING REMARKS

Mobile or decentralized microwave pyrolysis systems have been proposed as an option for farmers and industry in converting agricultural wastes or energy crops into higher values, less bulky products. Liquid bio-oils are collected and brought to central refineries (modified oil refineries) for upgrading to fuels and valuable chemicals. The gaseous products may be burned directly in a gas turbine engine to generate electricity on site for running the pyrolysis system, or they may be further refined to liquid fuels, for example using the Fischer-Tropsch process. The charcoal, containing most of the minerals from the biomass, will be put back to the fields as a fertilizer, a soil remediation agent or a medium for carbon sequestration. Pyrolysis chars also have the potential for being modified to activated carbon. In summary, microwave-assisted pyrolysis is a promising solution for the complete utilization of biomass. Application of this novel technology may boost rural economy, and explore future market for biomass refining.

REFERENCES

[1]   Zhang B, Shahbazi A. Recent Developments in Pretreatment Technologies for Production of Lignocellulosic Biofuels. *J. Pet. Environ. Biotechnol.* 2011;2:108.

[2]   Demirbas A. Current Technologies for the Thermo-Conversion of Biomass into Fuels and Chemicals. *Energy Sources* 2004;26:715.

[3]   Maschio G, Koufopanos C, Lucchesi A. Pyrolysis, a promising route for biomass utilization. *Bioresource Technology* 1992;42:219.

[4]   Elliott DC, Beckman D, Bridgwater AV, Diebold JP, Gevert SB, Solantausta Y. Developments in direct thermochemical liquefaction of biomass: 1983-1990. *Energy and Fuels* 1991;5:399.

[5]   Gaunt J. Low-temperature slow pyrolysis offers an energetically efficient strategy for bioenergy production. http://biocharfarms.org/ biochar_production_energy/.

[6]	Salema AA, Ani FN. Microwave induced pyrolysis of oil palm biomass. *Bioresource Technology* 2011;102:3388.

[7]	Robinson JP, Kingman SW, Barranco R, Snape CE, Al-Sayegh H. Microwave Pyrolysis of Wood Pellets. *Industrial and Engineering Chemistry Research* 2009;49:459.

[8]	Moen J, Yang C, Zhang B, Lei H, Hennessy K, Wan Y, et al. Catalytic microwave assisted pyrolysis of aspen. *Int. J. Agric. and Biol. Eng.* 2009;2:70.

[9]	Wang X-H, Chen H-P, Ding X-J, Yang H-P, Zhang S-H, Shen Y-Q. Properties of gas and char from microwave pyrolysis of pine sawdust. *BioResources* 2009;4:946.

[10]	Du Z, Li Y, Wang X, Wan Y, Chen Q, Wang C, et al. Microwave-assisted pyrolysis of microalgae for biofuel production. *Bioresource Technology* 2011;102:4890.

[11]	Lei H, Ren S, Wang L, Bu Q, Julson J, Holladay J, et al. Microwave pyrolysis of distillers dried grain with solubles (DDGS) for biofuel production. *Bioresource Technology* 2011;102:6208.

[12]	Yu F, Deng S, Chen P, Liu Y, Wan Y, Olson A, et al. Physical and chemical properties of bio-oils from microwave pyrolysis of corn stover. *Applied Biochemistry and Biotechnology* 2007;137-140:957.

[13]	Menéndez JA, Inguanzo M, Pis JJ. Microwave-induced pyrolysis of sewage sludge. *Water Research* 2002;36:3261.

[14]	National Research Council. Microwave processing of materials, National Academy Press, Washington, D.C.; 1994.

[15]	Sensöz S, AngIn D, Yorgun S. Influence of particle size on the pyrolysis of rapeseed (Brassica napus L.): fuel properties of bio-oil. *Biomass and Bioenergy* 2000;19:271.

[16]	Pilot Microwave Assisted Pyrolysis System http://biorefining.cfans. umn.edu/ component/content/article/13-news-gneral/36-pilot-microwave-assited-pyrolysis

[17]	Tunheim AIM. Destructive Distillation of Corn Stover by Microwave Pyrolysis for the Production of Biofuels. Master Dissertation, Department of Mathematical Sciences and Technology, Norwegian University of Life Sciences, 2007.

[18]	Peacocke GVC, Russell PA, Jenkins JD, Bridgwater AV. Physical properties of flash pyrolysis liquids. *Biomass and Bioenergy* 1994;7:169.

[19]	Boucher ME, Chaala A, Roy C. Bio-oils obtained by vacuum pyrolysis of softwood bark as a liquid fuel for gas turbines. Part I: Properties of bio-oil and its blends with methanol and a pyrolytic aqueous phase. *Biomass and Bioenergy* 2000;19:337.

[20]	Elliott DC. Water, alkali and char in flash pyrolysis oils. *Biomass and Bioenergy* 1994;7:179.

[21]	Oasmaa A, Czernik S. Fuel Oil Quality of Biomass Pyrolysis OilsState of the Art for the End Users. *Energy and Fuels* 1999;13:914.

[22]	Wan Y, Chen P, Zhang B, Yang C, Liu Y, Lin X, et al. Microwave-assisted pyrolysis of biomass: Catalysts to improve product selectivity. *Journal of Analytical and Applied Pyrolysis* 2009;86:161.

[23]	Zhang B, Yang C, Moen J, Le Z, Hennessy K, Wan Y, et al. Catalytic Conversion of Microwave-assisted Pyrolysis Vapors. *Energy Sources, Part A: Recovery, Utilization, and Environmental Effects* 2010;32:1756.

[24]	Lu Q, Zhang Z-F, Dong C-Q, Zhu X-F. Catalytic Upgrading of Biomass Fast Pyrolysis Vapors with Nano Metal Oxides: An Analytical Py-GC/MS Study. *Energies* 2010;3:1805.

[25] Boucher ME, Chaala A, Pakdel H, Roy C. Bio-oils obtained by vacuum pyrolysis of softwood bark as a liquid fuel for gas turbines. Part II: Stability and ageing of bio-oil and its blends with methanol and a pyrolytic aqueous phase. *Biomass and Bioenergy* 2000;19:351.

[26] Czernik S, Bridgwater AV. Overview of Applications of Biomass Fast Pyrolysis Oil. *Energy and Fuels* 2004;18:590.

[27] Bridgwater AV. Catalysis in thermal biomass conversion. *Applied Catalysis A: General* 1994;116:5.

[28] Williams PT, Horne PA. Characterisation of oils from the fluidised bed pyrolysis of biomass with zeolite catalyst upgrading. *Biomass and Bioenergy* 1994;7:223.

[29] Mohan D, Pittman CU, Steele PH. Pyrolysis of Wood/Biomass for Bio-oil: A Critical Review. *Energy and Fuels* 2006;20:848.

[30] Yang C, Zhang B, Moen J, Hennessy K, Liu Y, Lin X, et al. Fractionation and characterization of bio-oil from microwave-assisted pyrolysis of corn stover. *Int. J. Agric. and Biol. Eng.* 2010;3:54.

In: Oil: Production, Consumption and Environmental Impact   ISBN: 978-1-61942-877-5
Editor: Shuangning Xiu   © 2012 Nova Science Publishers, Inc.

Chapter 9

THE EFFECT OF BIOMASS ON BIO-OIL PRODUCTION VIA HYDROTHERMAL CONVERSION

J. Gan[1] and W. Yuan[2,]*

[1]Department of Biological and Agricultural Engineering,
Kansas State University, KS, US
[2]Department of Biological and Agricultural Engineering,
North Carolina State University, NC, US

ABSTRACT

Bio-oil production from lignocellulosic biomass and high moisture content biomass via hydrothermal conversion (HTC) was studied widely. Lignocellulosic biomass is made of cellulose, hemicellulose and lignin. High-moisture content generally is composed with crude protein, crude fat, crude fiber, non-fibrous carbohydrate or neutral detergent fiber. The yield and quality of bio-oil produced by biomass HTC were significantly affected by the biomass chemical compositions. The problems existed in biomass HTC and the effect of these chemical compositions on bio-oil production from biomass HTC was reviewed in this paper.

Keywords: Hydrothermal Conversion, Bio-oil Production, Lignocellulosic Biomass, High-moisture Content Biomass, Chemical Composition

1. INTRODUCTION

The United States currently consumes more than 140 billion gallons of transportation fuels annually. Conversion of grain or cellulosic biomass (e.g., corn starch and corn stover) to biofuels offers major economic, environmental, and strategic benefits. DOE and USDA projected that the U.S. biomass resources could provide approximately 1.3 billion dry tons of

---
[*]Phone: 919-515-2694, E-mail: wyuan2@ncsu.edu.

feedstock for biofuels, which would meet about 40% of the annual U.S. fuel demand for transportation [1].

As shown in Figure 1, there are two primary routes in such a projection, the sugar platform and the thermochemical platform. Corn starch based ethanol and cellulosic ethanol fall into the sugar platform, wherein biomass is hydrolyzed to fermentable sugars which are further processed to ethanol or chemicals.

In the thermochemical platform, biomass is converted into synthesis gas through gasification or bio-oils through pyrolysis and hydrothermal conversion (HTC), which can be further upgraded to liquid fuels (e.g., gasoline and diesel fuel) and other chemicals. Among these technologies, HTC of biomass possesses some special features and advantages. HTC is also called hydrothermal/direct liquefaction or hydrothermal upgrading/ depolymerization, which is conducted under elevated pressure (50~200atm) and temperature (200~400°C) to keep water in either liquid or supercritical state.

The use of water as a solvent obviates the need to dry biomass and permits reactions to be carried out at lower temperatures in comparison with other thermo-chemical technologies. The primary product of HTC is an oily organic liquid, called bio-oil or bio-crude, and the main byproducts are the solid residue, bio-char, and water containing soluble organic compounds.

Bio-oils can be used as a fuel for diesel engines, boilers or turbines [3]. They may also serve as a starting material for valuable petroleum-based fuels (e.g., gasoline and diesel) and products such as polymers, aromatics, lubricants and asphalt [4, 5].

It is well known that the yield and quality of bio-oils from biomass HTC are significantly affected by the feedstock [6-9]. However, little information is available to relate biomass type and characteristics to HTC performance. In this article, the effect of chemical compositions of lignocellulosic biomass and high moisture content biomass on bio-oil yield and quality are reviewed.

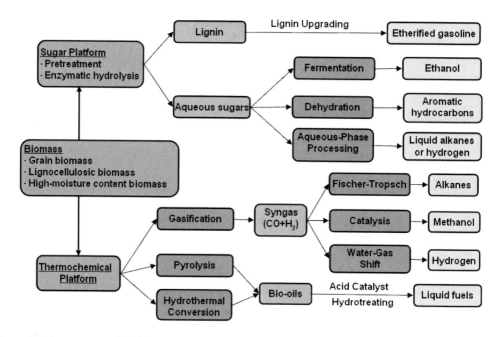

Figure 1. Primary routes for biofuels conversion [2].

2. HTC OF VARIOUS BIOMASS FEEDSTOCKS

HTC is a chemical reforming process, in which organic matters are depolymerized and reformed to bio-oil, gases, char, and water-soluble matters in a heated, pressurized, and oxygen-absent enclosure [10]. Chemical reactions in HTC process include hydrolysis, solvolysis, cracking, depolymerization, hydrogenation, decarboxylation, condensation, and repolymerization etc. [11, 12]. However, the mechanisms and kinetics of HTC process are not well understood yet.

2.1. Bio-Oil Yield and Quality

Bio-oil yield and quality are the two most important performance indicators of biomass HTC. Bio-oil quality is mainly characterized by the molar ratios of O/C and H/C, and the heating value of the oil. Oils with H/C molar ratio higher than 1.5, O/C molar ratio less than 0.06, and heating value higher than 40 MJ/kg, containing mainly alkanes, cycloalkanes and aromatic hydrocarbons are desired [13]. Many types of biomass feedstocks, including lignocellulosic biomass such as wood, straws, stalks, shells, and husks, and naturally high moisture content biomass such as sewage sludge, ethanol fermentation stillage, animal manures, and algae, have been successfully converted into bio-oils through HTC. Table 1 summarizes the yield and quality of bio-oils from some common types of biomass feedstocks. Yield spatially ranged from 6.5% to 60%, while H/C ratio and O/C ratio were in the range of 0.96 to 1.70 and 0.07 to 0.72, respectively. Large variances of bio-oil yield and quality indicate that either biomass type or operating conditions, or both, significantly affect biomass HTC. However, it is still not clear which factor is dominant and how they affect the process.

Table 1. Hydrothermal conversion of common types of biomass

Raw material	T(^{o}C)	RT (min)	Catalyst	Oil Yield (%)	O/C	H/C	Heating value (kJ/g)	Reference
Corn stalk	300	30	5% Na_2CO_3	28.3	0.21	1.01	29.7	[8]
Rice husk	300	30	5% Na_2CO_3	28.8	0.22	1.12	30.8	[8]
Rice straw	280	15	No	6.5	-	-	-	[14]
	300	30	5% Na_2CO_3	22.5	0.17	1.20	29.8	[8]
	260-340	3 or 5	No	10-40	0.11-0.72	1.14-1.45	27.55-37.17	[15, 16]
Beech wood	277-377	25	No	16.8-28.4	0.19	0.96	27.6-31.3	[17]
Spruce wood	277-377	25	No	13.8-25.8	0.19	0.97	28.3-33.9	[18]
Sawdust	280	15	No	7.2	-	-	-	[14]
Sewage sludge	250-340	0[a]	5% Na_2CO_3	25.3-51.8	0.23-0.27	1.25-1.66	28.7-32.7	[19]
Stillage	250-340	0[a] or 120	0-20% Na_2CO_3	15-60	0.1-0.16	1.4-1.7	33-37	[20]
Algae	250-340	5 or 60	0 or 5% Na_2CO_3	30.9-43.8	0.07-0.14	1.32-1.55	33.3-37.8	[7]

[a]After temperature reached the set point, the reactor was cooled down immediately to the room temperature.

2.2. Product Separation Procedures

Biomass HTC has been studied by many researchers, however, it is usually difficult to compare research results because different researchers use different organic solvents and/or separation procedures to obtain HTC products. General procedures for HTC product separation are shown in Figure 2.

First of all, gaseous products are vented or collected in sampling bags for analysis. If no floating bio-oil is produced, the solid and liquid products are collected from the reactor and separated by filtration.

Subsequently, liquid products are extracted with organic solvents, such as acetone, dichloromethane, diethyl ether, and esters [14]. The solvent soluble fraction is then evaporated to remove the solvent and obtain water soluble oils, whose yield and chemical properties are greatly related to the organic solvent used.

The solid product is usually extracted by acetone [8, 21] and sometimes by tetrahydrofuran (THF) [16]. The solvent soluble portion is then evaporated in a rotary evaporator to remove solvent, and the remaining product is water insoluble heavy oil. The solvent insoluble portion is dried to obtain residual solid, called bio-char. If floating heavy bio-oil is generated, the oil can be decanted before the separation of residual solids and liquid products. The following separation process is the same as that without floating bio-oil.

The definitions of bio-oil and yield measurement methods are also different. Sometimes liquefaction rate is used, while in other cases water soluble light oil, water insoluble heave oil, or free floating oil, or their combinations are taken into account. In order to compare research results more scientifically, the word "bio-oil" in this paper refers to water insoluble heavy oil or floating oil when applicable.

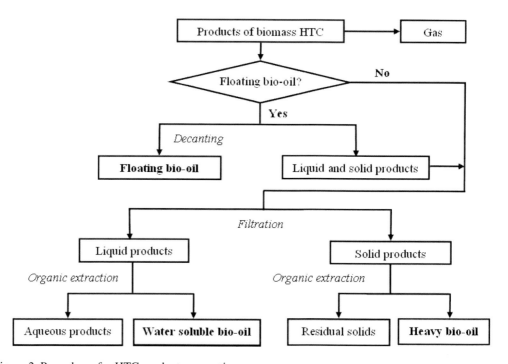

Figure 2. Procedures for HTC products separation.

3. HTC OF LIGNOCELLULOSIC BIOMASS

Lignocellulosic biomass are mainly composed of cellulose (40-60 wt%), hemicellulose (20-40 wt%) and lignin (10-25%). Decomposition behaviors of the three components are different in HTC processes because of their different chemical structure, thermal stability, and alkali resistance etc. Consequently, bio-oil production from lignocellulosic biomass HTC is affected by the type of biomass due to their different chemical compositions and physical structures.

3.1. Effects of Cellulose Content on Bio-Oil Production at Neutral Conditions

Cellulose is a long linear chain polymer of glucose, which was strung together by ß-glycosidic linkages. The high degree of hydrogen bonding between cellulose chains makes cellulose more stable and resistant to chemical attack in comparison with hemicellulose. Correlations between cellulose content and bio-oil yield at different reaction temperatures are shown in Figure 3. Research data [17, 18] showed that at neutral conditions, bio-oil yield generally increased with increasing cellulose content. However, correlation coefficient R^2 of the linear regressions were low, ranging from 0.66 to 0.87 indicating that there must have some factors other than cellulose content affecting bio-oil yield. It is also evident from Figure 3 that reaction temperature had significant positive effect on bio-oil production in HTC. As reaction temperature increased from 277°C to 377°C, bio-oil yield generally increased from 12% to 28% depending on the type of biomass.

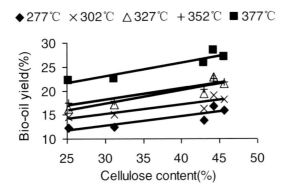

Figure 3. Effect of cellulose content on bio-oil yield at neutral conditions. (Data were adopted from [17, 18]; spruce wood, beech wood, hazelnut shell, tea waste, and *quersus pedunculate* were used as the HTC feedstock in the temperature range of 277°C to 377°C without catalyst).

3.2. Effect of Lignin Content on Bio-Oil Yield at Neutral Conditions

Lignin is composed of paracoumaryl alcohol, confieryl alcohol and shinapyl alcohol. These three components are cross-linked by ethers [22]. Compared to cellulose, lignin content has opposite effect on bio-oil production. Research results showed that bio-oil yield decreased with increasing lignin content without catalyst [9, 17, 18, 23], which are shown in Figure 4 by correlations between lignin content and bio-oil yield. The correlation coefficients were in the range of 0.84 to 0.96, indicating a strong negative correlation between lignin content and bio-oil yield. In addition, Zhong and Wei [23] found that the yield of bio-oil produced from woody biomass HTC generally decreased with increasing lignin content in the temperature range of 280°C to 340°C without catalyst. Bhaskar et al., [9] also found that cherry with higher lignin content produced less bio-oil than cypress with lower lignin content at 280°C without catalyst. The above analyses indicate that cellulose rather than lignin in lignocellulosic biomass dominates bio-oil production at neutral conditions. When pure cellulose was used as HTC feedstock without catalyst, it was found to decompose quickly between 240 and 270° C. The formation of bio-oil from cellulose HTC started at 240° C, and bio-oil yield reached the highest at 300° C, but then decreased as temperature further increased [24].

Lignin is difficult to be converted into bio-oil at neutral conditions due to its thermal stability and complex structure. Lignin is physically and chemically stable until high temperatures above 350°C [22], which was also confirmed by some other researchers that the decomposition of lignin or lignin rich biomass in HTC was relatively less than cellulose or cellulose rich biomass [9, 14].

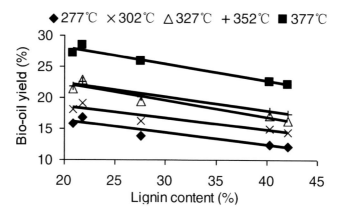

Figure 4. Effect of lignin content on bio-oil yield at neutral conditions. (Data were adopted from [17, 18]. Beech wood, spruce wood, quersus pedunculate, hazelnut shell and tea waste used as feedstock in the temperature range of 277°C to 377°C without catalyst).

3.3. Effect of Cellulose Content on Bio-Oil Yield at Alkaline Conditions

At alkaline conditions, the effect of cellulose content on bio-oil yield becomes more complex as compared to that at neutral conditions. The relationship between bio-oil yield and cellulose content depends on the type of biomass feedstock. At low cellulose contents (30%~40%), bio-oil yield decreased with increasing cellulose content. In contrast, bio-oil yield increased as cellulose content increased for high cellulose content biomass (40%~55%). Correlations between bio-oil yield and cellulose contents are shown in Figure 5. Although general trends seem clear, R^2 of linear regressions were low (0.52 and 0.64 for low cellulose and high cellulose content biomass feedstocks, respectively), indicating that there must have some other factors affecting bio-oil yield.

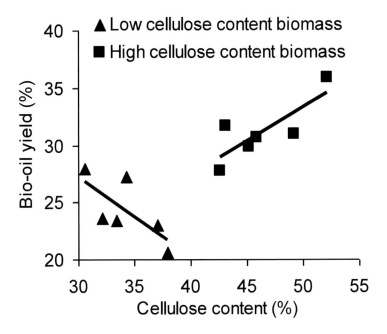

Figure 5. Effect of cellulose content on bio-oil yield at alkaline conditions. (Data were adopted from [8]. All experiments were operated at 300°C with 5% sodium carbonate).

3.4. Effects of Lignin Content on Bio-Oil Yield at Alkaline Conditions

At alkaline conditions, the relationship between lignin content and bio-oil yield is totally different from that at neutral conditions. A study showed that bio-oil yield increased with increasing lignin content at alkaline conditions [8], which is presented in Figure 6. The high values of R^2 (about 0.95) indicate a strong positive correlation between lignin content and bio-oil yield. This was also confirmed by others. For example, Zhong and Wei [23] found that the maximum bio-oil yields of four kinds of woody biomass generally increased as lignin content increased with 10wt% catalyst over 280°C. Bhasker et al. [9] found that cherry with higher lignin content produced more bio-oil than cypress with lower lignin content at 280°C with alkali catalyst.

It can also be seen from Figure 6 that bio-oil yields obtained from high-cellulose content biomass were higher than those from low-cellulose content biomass at the same lignin content, which cannot be explained by the sole effect of cellulose content. This is possibly due to the difference in the physical structure of the two categories of biomass feedstocks. Low-cellulose biomass (e.g., leaves) may have a cellulose-lignin structure that is difficult to be broken up at alkaline conditions for bio-oil formation.

They may also contain cellulose and/or lignin that are not appropriate for bio-oil production. Vice versa, high-cellulose biomass (e.g., hard wood) may have a physical structure or cellulose/lignin that are suitable for bio-oils. More investigations are needed to understand these phenomena.

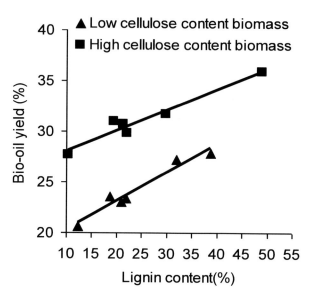

Figure 6. Effect of lignin content on bio-oil yield at alkali conditions. (Data were adopted from [8]. All experiments were operated at 300°C with 5% sodium carbonate).

3.5. Combined Effect of Cellulose and Lignin on Bio-Oil Yield at Alkaline Conditions

With a multiple linear regression analysis, the combined effects of cellulose and lignin contents on bio-oil yield are represented by Equations (1) and (2) for low-cellulose and high cellulose feedstocks, respectively.

$$Y_{bio-oil, low} = 21.42 + 0.26 C_{lignin} - 0.10 C_{cellulose} , R^2 = 0.96 \tag{1}$$

$$Y_{bio-oil, high} = 18.52 + 0.17 C_{lignin} + 0.18 C_{cellulose} , R^2 = 0.98 \tag{2}$$

In both equations, C_{lignin} and $C_{cellulose}$ are the content of lignin and cellulose in the feedstock, and $Y_{bio-oil, low}$ and $Y_{bio-oil, high}$ are the bio-oil yield of low- and high-cellulose content feedstock, respectively. P-values for lignin content are lower than 0.01, while for cellulose content are greater than 0.1. It is evident that lignin content has significant positive effect on bio-oil yield from lignocellulosic biomass at alkaline conditions. Alkali catalysts can cleave ether bonds in lignin to enable bio-oil formation, although the conversion pathways are still unclear [22].

Statistically, cellulose content does not significantly affect bio-oil yield due to the high P-values. However, based on Equations (1) and (2), cellulose also contributes to bio-oil formation, either positively or negatively depending on the type of biomass.

In addition to the effect of physical structure described in Section 3.4, another possible explanation may be that cellulose in low-cellulose feedstocks inhibits bio-oil formation. Cellulose is hydrolyzed to glucose in the first step. Then, glucose is decomposed to organic acids (i.e. acetic acid, formic acid, lactic acid, levulinic acid), aldehydes and aromatic chemicals by Lor de Bruyn-Alberda van Ekenstein transformation, Retro Aldol reaction, Dehydration, Benzilic acid rearrangement and hydration [25-35].

Some of these chemicals may inhibit or promote bio-oil formation from lignin. Lignin was known to first decompose to p-hydroxybenzoic acids and then to phenols, aldehyde and methanol, etc. Meanwhile, aldehyde and methanol react with phenol and other intermediates to form char duo to their reactive properties.

Aromatic chemicals, especially phenol derivatives are major products of lignin HTC [22]. Thus, interactions between cellulose-derived chemicals and lignin-derived chemicals are important in terms of bio-oil yield and compositions.

4. HTC OF HIGH-MOISTURE CONTENT BIOMASS

High-moisture content biomass are significantly different from lignocellulosic biomass. Their main chemical compositions are measured by crude proteins, crude fat, and non-fiber carbohydrates (NFC). Sewage sludge, manure, ethanol fermentation stillage, and algae are the major high-moisture biomass feedstocks that have been used in HTC for bio-oil production. In this section, effects of their chemical compositions on bio-oil yield are discussed as follows.

4.1. Effects of Crude Protein and Crude Fat in Swine Manure and Stillage on Bio-Oil Yield

Crude protein and fat are two major compositions in swine manure and ethanol fermentation stillage. Fresh swine manures include about 23% to 27% protein and 7% to 22% crude fat [36]. Ethanol fermentation stillages contain about 25% to 56% protein and 2% to 22% crude fat [20, 37].

As presented in Figure 7, strong positive linear relationships exist between bio-oil yield and the sum of crude protein and crude fat contents in stillage and swine manure. Protein is made of amino acids, which are linked together by peptide bonds. Protein is readily hydrolyzed into amino acids, such as alanine and glycine etc. [38]. Then, these intermediates are decomposed to methylamine, ethylamine, diketopiperazine, formaldehyde, lactic acid, and glycolic acid etc. via decarboxation and deamination reactions in HTC [39]. Fats are tri-esters of glycerol and fatty acids, which are generally soluble in organic solvents but insoluble in water.

Researchers reported that biomass with higher crude fat content produced more bio-oil at the same operating conditions. Fats were found to be able to directly dissolve in dichloromethane and had similar properties as bio-oil [20, 40]. In HTC processes, fats were first hydrolyzed into free fatty acids and glycerol, which were then converted into long chain hydrocarbons via decarboxylation and dehydration, such as carboxylic acids, alcohols, ketones, and aldehydes [41-44].

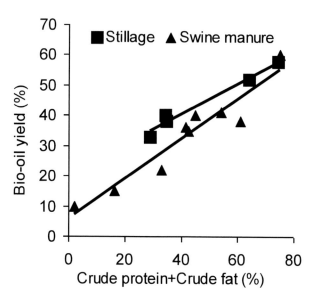

Figure 7. Linear correlation between bio-oil yield and the sum of crude protein and crude fat contents in feedstock (Data were adopted from [20, 36, 37]).

4.2. Effects of Crude Fiber and NFC in Stillage on Bio-Oil Yield

Crude fiber and NFC were used to measure the compositions of stillages [20, 37]. NFC is made up of starch, simple sugars, and soluble fibers. Crude fiber and NFC are both proved to be negative factors for bio-oil production from stillage HTC, which are shown in Figure 8. Although, it does not mean that they make no contribution to bio-oil production when other biomass is used as HTC feedstock, which will be discussed later in section 4.3.

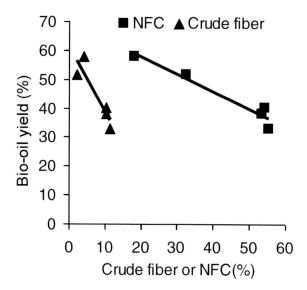

Figure 8. Relationship between bio-oil yield and the crude fiber or NFC content in Stillages (Data were adopted from [20, 37]).

4.3. Bio-Oil Yield of Sewage Sludge HTC

Compared with stillage and swine manure, sewage sludge is a special high moisture biomass, which is usually biologically treated. Sewage sludge is the by-product of municipal wastewater treatment, including digested sludge, raw waste activated sludge, and raw primary sludge. A strong linear relationship between bio-oil yield and the chemical compositions of sewage sludge was observed via multiple-linear regression [40], which is presented in Equation (3).

$$Y_{bio-oil} = -13.00 + 0.44C_{Protein} + 1.15C_{Fat} + 0.63C_{Fiber} + 0.57C_{NFC} \tag{3}$$

where $Y_{bio-oil}$ is bio-oil yield, %; $C_{Protein}$, C_{Fat}, C_{Fiber} and C_{NFC} were the weight percentage of crude protein, crude fat, crude fiber and NFC, respectively. All data were on a volatile solid basis.

The R^2 of the regression is 0.97 and P-values for all parameters in Equation (3) are less than 0.05, which indicate a strong positive correlation between the four compositions and bio-oil yield. It is also evident that crude fat had the most significant effect on bio-oil yield, showing by its largest slop in Eq. (3). The effect of crude fat on bio-oil yield in sewage sludge is similar to that in swine manure and stillage, however, fibers and NFC contents showed different trends in different feedstocks. They were found to inhibit bio-oil formation in stillages and swine manure, but positively contribute to bio-oil yield in sewage sludge. This might be explained by the special characteristics of sewage sludge, which usually is pretreated biologically and contains some catalytic inorganic components, like calcium salts, which can enhance bio-oil formation [40].

4.4. Bio-Oil from Algae HTC

Algae are a special kind of high moisture biomass, which may contain high levels of oils, proteins, and carbohydrates. Some algae are rich in oil with an oil content up to 70% to 80% on a dry weight basis [45, 46].

Oil production from algae has received great attention due to their extraordinary potential of oil productivity. However, high harvesting, drying, and oil extraction costs are some of the limiting factors for commercialization of algae-based oils [47]. It is therefore not surprising to use wet algae for bio-oil production through HTC to avoid the costly drying and oil extraction processes.

Yields of bio-oil from algae HTC vary with the species of algae. *Botryococcus braunii* achieved 64% bio-oil yield at 300°C for 1h, regardless of catalyst loading [49]. The obtained bio-oil had a high heating value of 50MJ/kg and low viscosity of 79 mPas [48]. Bio-oil obtained from *Botryococcus braunii* HTC with 5% sodium carbonate at 300°C was found to be comprised of three fractions: low molecular hydrocarbons (C17-22), botryococcenes, and polar substances (C14-20 fatty acids) [50].

The high bio-oil yield from *Botryococcus braunii* is related to its special chemical composition. *Botryococcus braunii* is known to accumulate oily straight-chain hydrocarbons (called botryococcenes, C30-36), which are structurally similar to crude oil and can be readily converted to bio-oils [49]. HTC bio-oil yield from another species, Microsystis viridis, was 33% at the optimum condition (340°C for 30min, 5wt% catalyst), and the bio-oil heating value was 31 kJ/kg.

The bio-oil mainly contained n-alkane of C17-C18 hydrocarbon [50]. *Dunaliella tertiolecta* was another alga used as HTC feedstock, which contained 10% glycerol [51]. The maximum bio-oil yield from *Dunaliella tertiolecta* HTC was 43.8% on an organic basis at 300°C without using catalyst, but the oil had high viscosity of 14,000 mPas. However, when temperature increased to 340°C, the viscosity significantly decreased to 150 mPas with a 40.4% bio-oil yield [7].

Evidently, bio-oil yield and quality from algae HTC is strongly dependent on the species. No sufficient data is available to correlate each chemical composition to bio-oil yield like we did for lignocellulosic biomass or other high moisture feedstocks.

However, based on the analysis in previous sections, it is expected that species with high oil content can generate more bio-oil since oils/lipids are relatively easier to be converted to bio-oils. It is also expected that algae cell-wall structure may have a significant impact on the HTC process. More investigations are needed in this area.

SUMMARY AND CONCLUSIONS

Yield and quality of bio-oil produced by biomass HTC were found to be significantly affected by biomass chemical compositions. For lignocellulosic biomass at neutral conditions, bio-oil yield increased with increasing cellulose content, but decreased with increasing lignin content.

At alkaline condition, lignocellulosic biomass should be separated into two groups: low cellulose content (< 40%) biomass and high cellulose content (>40%) biomass. For low cellulose content biomass, bio-oil yield generally decreased as cellulose content increased, but increased with increasing lignin content. For high cellulose content biomass, both cellulose and lignin positively contribute to bio-oil yield, although cellulose showed not as significant effect on bio-oil yield as lignin content. It was expected that in addition to their chemical compositions, the physical structure of the biomass and/or the intermediates of cellulose HTC could also affect bio-oil yield and compositions. Swine manure, ethanol fermentation stillage, sewage sludge, and algae are the major high-moisture biomass feedstocks that have been used in HTC for bio-oil production. The effects of their chemical compositions on bio-oil production also vary with the kind of biomass. It was found that crude fat had similar positive effect on bio-oil yield in all the three types of biomass, however, fibers and NFC contents showed different trends in different feedstocks. They were found to inhibit bio-oil formation in stillages and swine manure, but positively contribute to bio-oil yield in sewage sludge. Bio-oil yield and quality from algae HTC was strongly dependent on the species, with *Botryococcus braunii* showing the most promise.

ACKNOWLEDGMENT

This work was supported by the US Department of Transporation and South Central Sun Grant (Grant number SC11S034) and the US Department of Energy (Grant number DE-EE0000620).

REFERENCES

[1]   Perlack RD, Wright LL, Turhollow AF, Graham RL, Stokes BJ, Erback DC. Biomass as feedstock for bioenergy and bioproducts industry: Technical feasibility of a billion-ton annual supply. Sponsored by USDOE and USDA 2005.

[2]   Huber GW, Dumesic JA. An overview of aqueous-phase catalytic processes for production of hydrogen and alkanes in a biorefinery. *Catalysis Today* 2006; 111:119-132.

[3]   Shaw M. Pyrolysis of Lignocellulosic Biomass to Maximize Bio-oil Yield: An Overview. The Canadian Society of Bioengineering Paper #: 06-105. 2006.

[4]   Zhang Q, Chang J, Wang T, Xu Y. Review of biomass pyrolysis oil properties and upgrading research. *Energy Conversion and Management* 2007; 48:87-92.

[5]   Peterson AA, Vogel F, Lachance RP, Fröling M, Antal Jr. MJ, Tester JW. Thermochemical biofuel production in hydrothermal media: a review of sub- and supercritical water technologies. *Energy and Environmental Scie*nce 2008; 1:32-65.

[6]   Minowa T, Murakami M, Dote Y, Ogi T, Yokoyama S. Oil production from garbage by thermochemical liquefaction. *Biomass and Bioenergy* 1995; 8: 117-120.

[7]   Minowa T, Yokoyama S, Kishimoto M, Okakurat T. Oil production from algal cells of *Dunaliella tertiolecta* by direct thermochemical liquefaction. *Fuel* 1995; 12:1735-1738.

[8]   Minowa T, Kondo T, Sudirjo S. Thermochemical liquefaction of Indonesian biomass residues. *Biomass and Bioenergy* 1998; 14: 517-524.

[9]   Bhaskar T, Sera A, Muto A, Sakata Y. Hydrothermal upgrading of wood biomass: Influence of the addition of K2CO3 and cellulose/lignin ratio. Fuel 2008; 87:2236-2242.

[10]   Ocfmia KS, Zhang Y. Funk T. Hydrothermal processing of swine manure into oil using a continuous reaction system: Development and testing. *Transaction of the ASABE* 2006; 49:533-541.

[11]   Chornet E, Overend RP. Biomass liquefaction: An overview. In: Fundamentals of thermochemical biomass conversion. Overend RP, Milne TA, Mudge LK (Eds). New York: Elsevier Applied Science 1985; 96-1002.

[12]   Zhang Y, Riskowski G, Funk T. Thermochemical conversion of swine manure to produce fuel and reduce waste. Illinois Council on Food and Agricultural Research, December, University of Illinois, Urbana, IL, 1999.

[13]   Wang C, Pan J, Li J, Yang Z. Comparative studies of products produced from four different biomass samples via deoxy-liquefaction. *Bioresource Technology* 2008; 99:2778-2786.

[14] Karagöz S, Bhaskar T, Muto A, Sakata Y. Comparative studies of oil compositions produced from sawdust, rice husk, lignin and cellulose by hydrothermal treatment. *Fuel* 2005; 84:875-884.

[15] Li H, Yuan X, Zeng G, Tong J, Yuan Y, Cao H, Wang L, Cheng M, Zhang J, Yang D. Liquefaction of rice straw in sub- and supercritical 1,4-dioxane-water mixture. *Fuel Processing Technology* 2009; 90:657-663.

[16] Yuan X, Li H, Zeng G, Tong J, Xie W. Sub- and supercritical liquefaction of rice straw in the presence of ethanol-water and 2-propanol-water mixture. *Energy* 2007; 32:2081-2088.

[17] Demirbaş A, Balat M, Bozbas K. Direct and catalytic liquefaction of wood species in aqueous solution. *Energy Sources* 2005; 27:271-277.

[18] Demibaş A. Thermochemical conversion of biomass to liquid products in the aqueous medium. *Energy Sources* 2005; 27:1235-1243.

[19] Yokoyama S, Suzuki A, Murakamit M, Ogi T, Koguchi K, Nakamura E. Liquid fuel production from sewage sludge by catalytic conversion using sodium carbonate. *Fuel* 1987; 66: 1150-1155.

[20] Minowa T, Murakami M, Dote Y, Ogi T, Yokoyama S. Effect of operating conditions on thermochemical liquefaction of etanol fermentation stillage. *Fuel* 1994; 73:279-582.

[21] Xu C, Lancaster J. Conversion of secondary pulp/paper sludge powder to liquid oil products for energy recovery by direct liquefaction in hot-compressed water. *Water Research* 2008; 42:1571-1582.

[22] Bobleter O. Hydrothermal degradation of polymers derived from plants. Progress in Polymer Science (Oxford) 1994; 19:797-841.

[23] Zhong C, Wei X. A comparative experimental study on liquefaction of wood. *Energy* 2004; 29:1731-1741.

[24] Minowa T, Zhen F, Ogi T. Cellulose decomposition in hot-compressed water with alkali or nickel catalyst. *The Journal of Supercritical Fluids* 1998; 13:253-259.

[25] Antal Jr MJ, Mok WSL, Richards GN. Four-carbon model compounds for the reactions of sugars in water at high temperature. *Carbohydrate Research* 1990; 199:111-115.

[26] Kabyemela BM, Adschiri T, Malaluan RM, Arai K. Glucose and fructose decomposition in subcritical and supercritical water: Detailed reaction pathway, mechanisms, and kinetics. *Industrial and Engineering Chemistry Research* 1999: 38:2888-2895.

[27] Srokol Z, Bouche AG, Van Estrik A, Strik RCJ, Mashmeyer T, Peters JA. Hydrothermal upgrading of biomass to biofuels; studies on some monosaccharide model compounds. *Carbohydrate Research* 2004; 339:1717-1726.

[28] Kabyemela BM, Adschiri T, Malaluan RM, Arai K. Kinetics of glucose epimerization and decomposition in subcrtical and supercritical water. *Industral and Engineering Chemistry Research* 1997; 36:1552-1558.

[29] Aida TM, Tajima K, Watanabe M, Saito Y, Kuroda K, Nonaka T, Hattori H, Smith Jr RL, Arai K. Reaction of d-fructose in water at temperatures up to 400°C and pressures up to 100 MPa. *Journal of Supercritical Fluids* 2007; 42:110-119.

[30] Takeuchi Y, Jin F, Tohji K, Enomoto H. Acid catalytic hydrothermal conversion of carbohydrate biomass into useful substances. *Journal of Materials Science* 2008; 43:2472-2475.

[31] Kabyemela BM. Degradation kinetics of dihydroxyacetone and glyceraldehydes in subcritical and supercritical water. *Industrial and Engineering Chemistry Research* 1997; 36:2025-2030.

[32] Kishida H, Jin F, Yan X, Moriya T, Enomoto H. Formation of lactic acid from glycolaldehyde by alkaline hydrothermal reaction. *Carbohydrate Research* 2006; 341:2619-2623.

[33] Girisuta B, Janssen LPBM, Heeres HJ. A kinetic study on the decomposition of 5-hydroxymethylfurfural into levulinic acid. *Green Chemistry* 2006; 8: 701-709.

[34] Luijkx GCA, Van Rantwijk F, Van Bekkum H. Hydrothermal formation of 1,2,4-benzenetriol from 5-hydroxymethyl-2-furaldehyde and D-fructose. *Carbohydrate Research* 1993; 242:131-139.

[35] Antal Jr MJ, Mok WSL, Richards GN. Mechanism of formation of 5-(hudroxymethyl)-2-furaldehyde from d-fructose and sucrose. *Carbohydrate Research* 1990; 199:91-109.

[36] Wang Z, Zhang Y. Christianson L, Funk T. Minarick M, Dong R, Yu G. Effect of swine manure source and storage time on bio-crude oil conversion using hydrothermal process. *An ASABE Meeting Presentation Paper* #:096586. 2009.

[37] Yakayama S, Suzuki A, Murakami M, Ogi T, Koguchi K. Liquid fuel production from ethanol fermentation stillage. *Chemistry Letters* 1986; 649:652.

[38] Rogalinski T, Herrmann S, Brunner G. Production of amino acids from bovine serum albumin by continuous sub-critical hydrolysis. *Journal of Supercritical Fluids* 2005; 36: 49-58.

[39] Klingler D, Berg J, Vogel H. Hydrothermal reactions of alanine and glycine in sub-and supercritical water. *The Journal of Supercritical Fluids* 2007; 43:112-119.

[40] Suzuki A, Nakamura T. Conversion of sewage sludge to heavy oil by direct thermochemical liquefaction. *Journal of Chemical Engineering of Japan* 1988; 21:288-293.

[41] King JW, Holliday RL, List GR. Hydrolysis of soybean oil in a subcritical water flow reactor. *Green Chemistry* 1999; 261-264.

[42] Holliday RL, King JW, List GR. Hydrolysis of vegetable oil in sub- and supercritical water. *Industrial and Engineering Chemistry Research* 1997; 36:932-935.

[43] Watanabe M, Iida T, Inomata H. Decomposition of a long chain saturated fatty acid with some additives in hot compressed water. *Energy Conversion and Management* 2006; 47:3344-3350.

[44] Li L, Coppola E, Rine J, Miller JL, Walker D. Catalytic hydrothermal conversion of triglycerides to non-ester biofuels. *Energy Fuels* 2010; 24:1305-1315.

[45] Patil V, Tran KQ, Giselrod HR. Toward sustainable production of biofuels from microalge. *International Journal of Moleular Sciences* 2008; 9:1188-1195.

[46] Christi Y. Biodiesel from microalgae. *Biotechnology Advances* 2007; 25:294-306.

[47] Shen Y. Yuan W, Pei ZJ, Wu Q. Mao E. Microalgae mass production methods. *Transaction of the ASABE* 2009; 54:1275-1287.

[48] Dote Y, Sawayama S. Inoue S, Minowa T, Yokoyama S. Recovery of liquid fuel from hydrocarbon-rich microalgae by thermochemical liquefaction. *Fuel* 1994; 1855-1857.

[49] Inoue S, Sawayama S, Ogi T. Components of oil derived from liquefaction of hydrocarbon-rich microalgae. Preprints of papers, American Chemical Society. *Division of Fuel Chemistry* 1996; 41:24-28.

[50] Yang YF, Feng CP, Inamori Y, Maekawa T. Analysis of energy conversiór characteristics in liquefaction of algae. *Resources Conservation and Recycling* 2004: 43: 21-33.

[51] Kishimoto M, Okakura t, Nagashima H, Minowa T, Yokoyama S, Yamaberi K. CO_2 fixation and oil production using micro-algae. *Journal of Fermentation and Bioengineering* 1994; 6:479-482.

In: Oil: Production, Consumption and Environmental Impact   ISBN: 978-1-61942-877-5
Editor: Shuangning Xiu   © 2012 Nova Science Publishers, Inc.

Chapter 10

HYDROTHERMAL LIQUEFACTION - A CORE TECHNOLOGY FOR THE PRODUCTION OF ENVIRONMENT-ENHANCING ENERGY (E²-ENERGY)

*Zhichao Wang**

Center for Transportation Research, Argonne National Laboratory, Argonne, IL , US

1. INTRODUCTION

Hydrothermal liquefaction (HTL), also called hydro-pyrolysis, hydrothermolysis, hydrothermal pyrolysis, hydroliquefaction, hydrothermal upgrading (HTU), or hydrothermal processing (HTP) by some researchers, is one of the thermochemical conversion processes. In this process, organic materials are converted into complicated products (of which a viscous and dark water-immiscible liquid is usually the major intended product known as bio-oil) in pressurized sub- or supercritical water.

Research on HTL can date back to the 1930s when Berl (1934) reported the production of "proto product" containing aliphatic, naphthenic, and aromatic substances from cellulose and other carbohydrates in hot water with sufficient alkaline materials. Later he suggested that cornstalks, corn cobs, sugar cane and any other "carbohydrate-containing materials" could be turned into a petroleum-like product by a controlled internal combustion (Berl, 1944). Researches thereafter have confirmed Berl's conclusion using a wide range of biomass feedstocks, including livestock manure, sewage sludge, municipal wastes, woody biomass, agricultural residue and algae.

Over the past several decades, due to the unsustainability of fossil fuels, researchers have been developing various technologies for alternative energy production. HTL can treat high moisture content biomass without energy-intensive dewatering or drying processes. This advantage makes HTL especially suitable for converting the bio-wastes fraction of biomass (e.g. livestock manures, sewage sludge and food wastes) and algae since they often contain high moisture content. After the HTL of biomass, a fraction of carbon, nitrogen, phosphorous

---

*E-mail: zwang42@illinois.edu, Phone:1-217-493-2297.

and other elements remains in the aqueous product, which could be utilized to produce algae together with the CO_2 generated in this process or from other sources. Subsequently, the algal biomass produced could be further converted to bio-oil via HTL. In doing so, this approach can enhance the environment at the same time when producing renewable fuel. The energy produced in this way is therefore called Environment-Enhancing Energy (E^2-Energy). This concept was first raised by a research group in University of Illinois at Urbana-Champaign, IL, USA. Figure 1 is a conceptual diagram of E^2-Energy (Yu et al., 2011a).

The potential of E^2-energy from bio-wastes and algae is enormous. In U.S., annual biomass resource potential from forest and agricultural resources was estimated to be over 1.3 billion dry tons, and the amount of biomass currently available for bioenergy and bioproducts was about 194 million dry tons per year (Perlack et al., 2005). The amount of manure generated in the U.S. at animal feeding operations (AFOs) and concentrated animal feeding operations (CAFOs) was estimated to exceed 335 million tons of dry matter per year (USDA, 2006).

Considering the majority of the manure are being used as fertilizer, the amount of manure currently available for bioenergy production is considered as 35 million tons per year (Perlack et al., 2005). Also in the U.S., approximately 5-7 million dry tons of biosolids from over 13,000 publicly owned treatment works are produced annually (Meeroff, 2001). Conservatively assuming 30% of the 40 million tons of manure and biosolids could be converted into bio-oil and the density of bio-oil is $1,000 kg/m^3$, 75.5 million barrels of bio-oil could be produced annually just from livestock manure and biosolids. And this amount equals 1.1 % of the total liquid fuels consumption of U.S. in 2009, compared to the biofuel which supplied 4% of the total liquid fuels consumption of U.S. in 2009 (USEIA, 2011). Large-scale commercialized production of algae has the potential to further amplify this number.

Based on the estimation of total bio-wastes produced in the United States (ASABE, 2005; USEPA, 2008) and the potential for algae growth (NREL, 1998) in wastewater, it could produce enough bio-oil to meet the entire national need for transportation fuel, approximately 1.2 billion tons of crude oil per year in 2007. Since algae have many advantages over terrestrial lignocellulosic biomass for renewable biofuel production, they are widely regarded as one of the best future sources of biofuel (Miao and Wu, 2004; Patil et al., 2008).

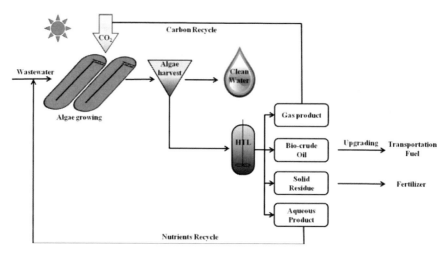

Figure 1. Concept of Environment-Enhancing-Energy (E^2-Energy) technology.

2. FEEDSTOCKS

As mentioned in section 1, many kinds of biomass could be and have already been converted to produce bio-oil using HTL process, as long as the major components in the feedstock are organic materials.

Much of the pioneering HTL work was done by Appell and co-workers at the Pittsburgh Energy Research Center in the 1970s with organic wastes as feedstock (Appell et al., 1980; Appell et al., 1970; Fu et al., 1974). Their work was later demonstrated at a pilot plant in Albany, Oregon. But the research was halted by the U.S. Department of Energy in the early 1980s as the price of petroleum began to drop and national interests shifted towards oxygenated fuel additives, such as ethanol (Peterson et al., 2008).

Eighteen kinds of agricultural and forest residues in Indonesia were hydrothermally liquefied by Minowa et al. (1998a). Tests were run in a 300 ml stainless steel autoclave at 300°C temperature and 30 min residence time. Bio-oil yields were in the range of 21-36%, depending on the species and parts of feedstock. Obtained bio-oils had similar properties: C ~70%, H ~7%, N <1%, O~20%, calorific value around 30 MJ/kg and viscosity >105 mPa.s.

Various kinds of sewage sludge were also converted to bio-oil via HTL (Suzuki et al., 1988). The reaction proceeded satisfactorily without adding any catalyst. A demonstration plant with a capacity for processing up to 5 t/d dewatered sludge was operated at 300°C, 10 MPa, (feedstock moisture content ~80%, volatile solid content ~80%). As a result, 48% (m.a.f.-moisture and ash free) of the organic materials in the sludge were converted into heavy oil. Energy balance analysis showed the treatment of sewage sludge by this method could be sufficiently profitable. (Itoh et al., 1994)

Dote et al. (1994) were among the earliest researches who studied the HTL of algae. They liquefied a strain of micro-algae and were able to yield 64% (mass basis) bio-oil from it at 300°C with Na_2CO_3 as catalyst. Ross et al. (2010) recently investigated the hydrothermal conversion of microalgae (*Chlorella vulgaris*) and cyanobacteria (*Spirulina*) in a batch reactor at 300°C and 350°C. Bio-oil yields (m.a.f.) of 11.6-20.0% and 19.1-27.3% were obtained from *Spirulina* and *Chlorella vulgaris* respectively, when different species of catalysts were added (Na_2CO_3, KOH, HCOOH, CH_3COOH). The higher heating values (HHV) of bio-oil ranged from 33.4 to 39.9 MJ/kg. *Chlorella pyrenoidosa*, a common fast-growing green microalga species with low lipid content was also converted to bio-oil via HTL by Yu et al. (2011b). The effects of key operating parameters (e.g. initial pressure, reaction temperature, and residence time) on the bio-oil yield were investigated. The highest bio-oil yield was 39.4% ±1.2% of the total dry mass of the algal feedstock, which was achieved at 280°C reaction temperature with 120 min residence time. A later study by Yu et al. (2011b) investigated the energy recovery and the distribution of nitrogen and carbon in the products. The carbon, nitrogen and energy recovered in the bio-oil all increased with the increase of reaction temperature as well as the residence time. The highest energy recovery of bio-oil (65.4%) was obtained at 280°C with 120 minutes residence time. About 65-70% of the nitrogen and about 35-40% of the carbon in the original material were converted into water soluble compounds when reaction temperature was higher than 220°C and residence time was longer than 10 minutes. The differences of the yields between the above researches were probably due to the differences in feedstocks, reaction conditions and the definition and collection methods of bio-oil. Livestock manure, a typical representative of bio-wastes has also been converted as feedstock via HTL. It has been proven that hydrothermal treatment of swine manure not only produces bio-oil but can be an efficient way to reduce COD (chemical oxygen demand) and pollutants in the manure. Previous research on hydrothermal treatment of swine manure investigated the effects of feedstock pH, total solids content, initial CO process gas addition, operating temperature, residence time and alternative process gases. The bio-oil product was characterized by analyzing the elemental contents, benzene solubility, viscosity and heating values; COD reduction efficiency was also studied (He et al., 2000a; He et al., 2000b; He et al., 2001a; He et al., 2001b; He et al., 2001c). A continuous reactor system was also developed and tested, demonstrating raw bio-oil yields ranging from 62.0%-70.4% (Ocfemia et al., 2006). Dong et al. (2009) proposed a hypothesis to explain the mechanism of the bio-oil formation from swine manure based on the experimental observation/facts. It was believed that the formation of oil was directly related to the original compositions of swine manure rather than the intermediates such as sugars derived from decomposition of swine manure under the hydrothermal conditions. The experimental results implied that the lipid component is favorable for oil formation during the hydrothermal conversion of swine manure. HTL tests of swine manure at transient temperatures (180-240°C) and residence times of 0-60 min showed that the release of fatty acids, the hydrolysis of hemicellulose and proteins, and the Maillard reactions were the major reactions happened at temperatures lower than 240°C. Similar product distribution could be obtained at higher temperature and shorter residence time, or vice versa. (Wang, 2011) To summarize, bio-oil could be generated from various kinds of feedstocks and it usually has a heating value of 30-40 MJ/kg, and the bio-oil yield could range from 10-60% depending on the different definition and extraction methods used by different researchers.

In addition to the real biomass, researchers have also used model compounds, such as glucose, microcrystalline cellulose, amino acids, triacylglycerides, lignin, etc., to investigate the HTL process. Peterson et al. (2008) made a thorough review on the HTL of these model compounds. Although it seems to be questionable if the results of simple model substances can be transferred and used for real biomass (Kruse and Gawlik, 2003), these researches shed light on the study of real biomass and the further development of HTL process. Although the HTL process has been investigated and developed for several decades, currently no large scale commercialized plants are available yet. In the 1980s, Shell developed a hydrothermal liquefaction process known as Hydrothermal Upgrading, or the HTU process. It was concluded that for high HTU conversion, selectivity and yield, essential conditions are: temperature>300°C, liquid water present and reaction time>5min. (Goudriaan and Peferoen, 1990). Unfortunately the oil company abandoned the process in 1989. However, later on in 1995 a technical and economic feasibility study was carried out by Stork Comprimo (now Stork Engineers and Contractors) to investigate the perspectives for the future of HTU. The results of the study led to the formation of a Dutch consortium which resumed the study in 1997. Main purpose of the research and development that would run till mid-2000 was the validation of the HTU Process on 20 kg (dry matter) biomass/hr pilot plant scale and the development of the necessary design data for the first commercial applications. Good preliminary results in the conversion of biocrude from HTU with hydrodeoxygenation were reported (Goudriaan et al., 2001). Changing World Technologies Inc., founded in 1997, tried to develop and commercialize the HTL process (which they called thermal conversion process). A plant in Carthage, Missouri opened in 2004, mainly treating turkey wastes. However, according to the media report, it was closed in 2009. Up to the finish of this book, no other commercialized plant has been reported using the HTL process to produce large amount of bio-oil.

3. REACTION PARAMETERS

In general, HTL conditions range from 280-380°C, 7 to 30 MPa pressure with liquid water, 10 to 60 min residence time, often with catalysts present (which are generally alkaline), and sometimes with reducing gases such as CO or H_2 (Peterson et al., 2008). The influences of several key reaction parameters are discussed in this section.

3.1. Temperature

Temperature is believed to be one of the most important reaction parameters for the HTL process. Generally, in sub-critical water (<374°C), as the temperature increases, the bio-oil yield increases and the solid residue decreases. This trend has been demonstrated by many researchers. (Dong et al., 2009; Karagoz et al., 2004; Murakami et al., 1990; Wang, 2011; Xiu et al., 2010) He et al. (2000a) reported that when swine manure was hydrothermally converted, no substantial oil product yield was achieved unless the temperature reached 285°C or above. Later on, Dong et al. (2009) also used swine manure as feedstock and with a new analytical method for the products they concluded that the toluene soluble oil has already formed at temperature as low as 240°C, although the bulk of the non-aqueous product did not appear like oil or tar yet. Wang (2011) further discovered that a toluene soluble oil yield of 18% could be obtained with swine manure even at 180°C, and the major components in the oil product were fatty acids. In this series of study on HTL of swine manure, the same trend was observed that the oil yield increases with the increase of temperature. Also in the study of Dong et al. (2009), they investigated the transition of the feedstock from slurry to separated product streams including bio-oil, aqueous phase, solid residues and gaseous products. At shorter reaction times, the raw oil product appeared to consist of numerous small spherical particles of a homogeneous size. As temperature and time increased, the sphere particles disappeared and became a tar-like fluid with an estimated pour point higher than 80°C. The spherical particles were believed to indicate primary oil formation resulting from partial depolymerization of the biopolymers even while well-defined biomass structures are still present (Boocock and Kosiak, 1988). When the temperature is higher than a certain value (usually higher than 300°C but depends on the specific feedstock), the bio-oil could decay or decompose to form other products, leading to the decrease of the oil yield. For example, Murakami et al. (1990) observed that the bio-oil yield peaked at 300°C when they hydrothermally liquefied the activated sludge from cornstarch industry in the temperature range of 225-350°C. Temperature can not only impact the products of HTL but also have a profound impact on the reaction pathways. When temperature is over the critical temperature of water, the formation of gaseous products becomes more and more favorable. And instead of hydrothermal liquefaction, hydrothermal gasification becomes the target for most researchers in this temperature range (Kruse et al., 2005; Kruse et al., 2007; Matsumura and Minowa, 2004; Minowa and Inoue, 1999; Modell, 1980; Waldner and Vogel, 2005). A detailed review of hydrothermal gasification could be found in the work of Peterson et al. (2008), and will not be further discussed in this chapter.

3.2. Residence Time

Residence time is another important reaction factor which could greatly influence the HTL process. At a given temperature in the low temperature range (180-280), only a certain amount of swine manure could be solubilized and a barrier (likely a needed critical temperature to cause chemical conversion) exists which prevents the further solubilization even with prolonged retention time. And the bio-oil yield tended to level off after the residence time reached 15min and above (Dong et al., 2009; Wang, 2011). In the study of Xiu et al. (2010), they also stated that the liquefaction was completed within 15 min at 340°C. However, a decay of bio-oil and an increase of solid residue with the increase of residence time were observed at this relatively high temperature. The result suggested the conversion of bio-oil to solid residue at longer residence time. Most researchers agree that excessive residence time can decompose and/or condensate bio-oil to low molecular chemicals and solid char. Murakami et al. (1990) and Karagoz et al. (2004)) also found similar decrease of bio-oil yield with activated sludge and sawdust as feedstock, respectively. Funazukuri et al. (1990) studied the HTL of lignin sulphonate with both subcritical and supercritical water. At 673K, the oil decomposed rapidly as the residence time increased, from 25% at 3 min to below 10% at 10min. A longer residence time enhances the degradation rate of converted hydrolysis products with glucose as feedstock (Kumar and Gupta, 2008). Generally, longer residence time may cause the formation of more complex compounds.

3.3. Pressure

Usually during the HTL, an initial pressure is needed to prevent the water from boiling at high temperature in order to avoid the energy-consuming phase change of water. Some early researches stated that reducing gas could increase the bio-oil yield. However, the University of Illinois team found that a similarly high oil yield could be achieved with inert gases, such as CO_2, N_2, or air; without clarifying the role of reducing gases in this liquefaction process. (He et al., 2001a) Xiu et al. (2010) observed when swine manure was converted at 340°C, 15min, the initial N_2 pressure could influence the bio-oil yield and the highest oil yield was obtained at 100 psi in the range of 0-150 psi. However, in the study of Yu et al. (2011b) with algae as feedstock, the initial pressure provided by nitrogen had little effect on oil yield. Currently, the functions and effects of initial pressure provided by the gas are still unclear.

3.4. Catalyst

Researchers previously have concluded that alkaline catalysts have profound effects on the HTL of cellulose and cellulosic biomass. The major effects include the increased oil yield and decreased solid residue yield (Minowa et al., 1998a; Yokoyama et al., 1984). In the recent study of Wang (2011), he compared the product distribution of HTL tests of several model compounds with and without Na_2CO_3 as catalysts (Figure 2). It can be seen that the addition of Na_2CO_3 did not show profound effects on the HTL of protein based on the product distribution.

However, significant distribution changes occurred for cellulose, glucose and xylose. And the trends of changes are rather similar for these three compounds. In this study, the addition of 5% Na_2CO_3 significantly reduced the yield of solid residue, increased the yield of gas and aqueous product yield. On the other hand, no significantly positive effect was found for the oil formation, which is quite different from the results of previous researches. The difference of bio-oil yield change may be due to the different solvent used in the studies and sometimes the different definition of "oil". Toluene, a solvent considered non-polar has a much lower ability to dissolve polar molecules than acetone does. Therefore, more polar products could be extracted using acetone. According to Nelson et al. (1984), the confirmed components in cellulose oil they listed were all polar compounds.

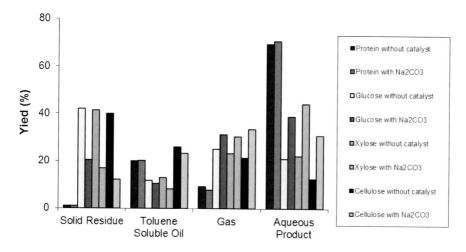

Figure 2. Effects of Na_2CO_3 (wt 5%) on the product distribution after the HTL of model compounds.

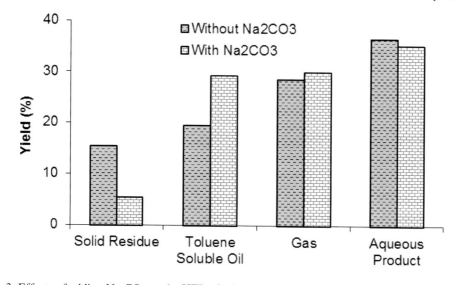

Figure 3. Effects of adding Na_2CO_3 on the HTL of mixture of protein and cellulose.

When 5% Na_2CO_3 was added to the mixture of protein and cellulose (1:1), it showed different effects on the product distribution than it did on protein and cellulose individually. A significant decrease of solid residue yield and a significant increase of toluene soluble oil yield were observed. Alkali acts as a catalyst for hydrolysis of cellulose into small fragments and for prevention of undesirable reactions, such as polymerization. Ammonia could be generated from protein and functions as a basic catalyst and prevent the occurrence of undesirable reactions (Inoue et al., 1999).

When additional Na_2CO_3 was added here, the solid residue was further reduced and the toluene soluble oil yield increased about 10%. This observation showed that to obtain maximum bio-oil yield using the mixture of cellulose and protein under current conditions, the ammonia generated during the reaction itself was probably not sufficient and certain amount of catalyst was necessary. This finding also agreed with previous researches in which alkaline catalyst could profoundly increase the bio-oil yield when using real biomass.

A widely accepted reaction mechanism describing the catalytic effects of sodium carbonate with the presence of CO was proposed by Appell (1967):

$$Na_2CO_3 + 2CO + H_2O \rightarrow 2HCOONa + CO_2$$
$$-CH(OH)-CH(OH)- \rightarrow -CH=C(OH)- \rightarrow CH_2-CO-$$
$$HCOO^- + -CH_2-CO- \rightarrow -CH_2-CH(O^-)- + CO_2$$
$$-CH_2-CH(O^-)- + H_2O \rightarrow -CH_2-CH(OH)- + OH-$$
$$OH^- + CO \rightarrow HCOO^-$$

However, even without the presence of injected CO, sodium carbonate was also widely found to catalyze the HTL reaction. And usually, no significant amount of CO was found in the gas product after HTL. It was possible that the CO was formed during the HTL and then consumed. It is hard to conclude if this proposed reaction mechanism of sodium carbonate is the major one or not. Further study is still needed to understand the functionality of alkaline catalysts.

Heterogeneous catalysts have also been investigated by some researchers, but mainly in the area of hydrothermal gasification. Minowa et al.(1998b) studied the decomposition of microcrystalline cellulose in the hot-compressed water from 200-350 °C, using a sodium carbonate catalyst, a reduced nickel catalyst or catalyst-free. They reported that the nickel catalyst catalyzes the steam reforming reaction of aqueous products and the methanation reaction. Jena and Das (2009) used nickel oxide (NiO) in the HTL of both a single (Spirulina platensis) and mixed algae (from open ponds with wastewater) at 350 °C. The added NiO decreased oil yields which could be due to more conversion of carbon into gaseous products.

Duan and Savage (2011) studied the HTL of microalga Nannochloropsis sp. via reactions at 350 °C in the presence of six different heterogeneous catalysts (Pd/C, Pt/C, Ru/C, Ni/SiO2-Al2O3, CoMo/γ-Al2O3 (sulfided), and zeolite) under inert (helium) and high-pressure reducing (hydrogen) conditions. In the absence of added H_2, all of the catalysts tested produced higher yields of bio-oil, but the elemental compositions and heating values of the crude oil (about 38 MJ/kg) were largely insensitive to the catalyst used. The development of inexpensive and efficient heterogeneous catalysts for the HTL process could be a decisive factor for the future application of this technology.

4. PRODUCTS

Typically, after the HTL process, four streams of products are obtained: gas, solid residue, aqueous products and bio-oil. Usually bio-oil is the intended product because of the possibility of replacing fossil fuels with it. However, the definition of bio-oil itself is difficult and somewhat chaotic between researchers. Bio-oil was called biocrude, biocrude oil, or simply oil in different cases. Researchers usually use an organic solvent to extract the water-insoluble fraction of the product and define the extracted solvent-soluble product as bio-oil.

However, the organic solvent used could be acetone, toluene, tetrahydrofuran (THF), dichloromethane (DCM), dimethyl ether, benzene, etc., and the usage of different solvent makes the bio-oil yields not comparable in most cases. Usually the composition of bio-oil is very complicated, even with a feedstock as simple as pure glucose (Catallo et al., 2010). GC-MS is an important and one of the commonly-used methods to investigate the bio-oil composition in many researches. FTIR, NMR and other analytical methods are often used to identify the characteristics of bio-oil. Vardon et al. (2011) investigated the properties of bio-oil obtained from the HTL of Spirulina algae, swine manure and digested anaerobic sludge and found the composition of the feedstock could greatly impact the composition of the bio-oil. The high protein content of Spirulina produced bio-oil that contained a high percentage of nitrogenous compounds, similar to findings by Biller and Ross (2011). The swine manure feedstock, with a more balanced distribution of bulk carbohydrates and crude lipids, produced bio-oil that contained a mix of phenolic- and lipid-derived compounds, similar to findings by Xiu et al. (2010). The digested anaerobic sludge feedstock, which was mainly comprised of ADF (acid detergent fiber, mainly consists of cellulose and lignin) and crude protein, resulted in bio-oil containing a high percentage of ester, phenolic and nitrogenous compounds. GC-MS analysis result for the toluene soluble oil product from the HTL of swine manure at 300°C, 30min is shown in Figure 4. Major compounds identified which have an area of more than 1% of the total area are listed in Table 1. Large amount of cycloalkanes and their derivatives were found at shorter elusion time. Alkanes such as heptane, nonane, and their derivatives with side-chains were also found. These alkanes were probably the decarboxylation product of fatty acids. Fatty acids (C16:0, C18:0) and their amides were in the far-end of the elution. Large amount of phenols and derivatives were also found.

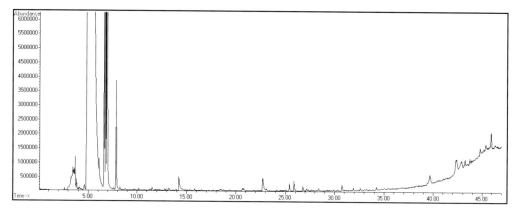

Figure 4. GC-MS chromatogram of toluene soluble oil from the HTL of swine manure at 300°C, 30min.

Table 1. Major compounds in the toluene soluble oil from the HTL of swine manure

#	Retention time	Name	Area (%)
1	3.27	Cyclohexane, 1,3-dimethyl-, cis-	5.2
2	3.44	Cyclohexane, 1,2-dimethyl-,-cis-	8.0
3	3.58	Heptane, 3-ethyl-	3.9
4	3.70	Cyclohexane, ethyl-	5.6
5	3.84	Nonane	1.4
6	4.64	Nonane, 4-methyl-	1.6
7	14.23	Acetic Acid	5.8
8	22.73	Hexanoic Acid	4.9
9	25.42	Phenyl-β-D-glucoside	1.5
10	25.88	Phenol, 4-ethyl-2-methoxy-	1.8
11	30.76	Phenol, 2,4-bis (1,1-dimethylethyl)	1.4
12	39.66	n-Hexadecanoic Acid	5.1
13	42.38	Octadecanoic Acid	9.4
14	43.25	Hexadecanamide	1.3
15	45.94	Octadecanamide	4.0
Total			60.9

Usually, the composition of the aqueous product after HTL is also very complicated. Figure 5 shows the GC-MS chromatogram of the aqueous phase product from HTL of swine manure at 240°C, 60min. The major compounds identified are listed in Table 2. A large amount of organic acids (C2-C6) were found in the aqueous product, especially acetic acid which accounts 14.98% of the total peak area. N-containing chemicals, such as pyridine, pyrazine, pyrrolo and their derivatives existed in the aqueous product. Elemental analysis provided the elemental distribution of swine manure to products after HTL (Figure 6). Over 60% of the carbon and hydrogen, 50% of the nitrogen and 15% of the oxygen was transferred into toluene soluble oil product. About 13% of the carbon and over 50% of the oxygen was transferred into gas phase product-carbon dioxide. There is still about 17% of the carbon, over 30% of the hydrogen, about 45% of the nitrogen and over 30% of the oxygen remaining in the aqueous phase.

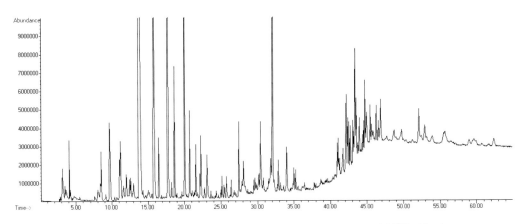

Figure 5. GC-MS of aqueous phase product from HTL of swine manrue at 240°C, 60 min.

Table 2. GC-MS of volatile compounds analysis in the aqueous phase product from HTL of swine manure at 240°C, 60min

#	Retention time	Name	Area (%)
1	3.12	Acetone	0.74
2	3.48	2-Butanone	0.33
3	4.09	Trimethylamine	0.13
4	8.00	Pyridine	0.46
5	8.39	Pyrazine	0.42
6	8.52	Pyridine	0.58
7	9.68	Pyrazine,methyl-	2.28
8	11.06	Pyrazine, 2,5-dimethyl-	0.78
9	11.20	Pyrazine,ethyl-	1.35
10	11.60	Pyrazine, 2,3-dimethyl-	0.51
11	12.02	2-Cyclopenten-1-one, 2-methyl-	0.58
12	12.46	Pyrazine, 2-ethyl-6-methyl-	0.41
13	12.62	Pyrazine, 2-ethyl-5-methyl-	0.48
14	13.01	Pyrazine, trimethyl-	0.50
15	13.66	Acetic Acid	14.98
16	15.76	Propanoic Acid	6.17
17	16.50	Propanoic acid, 2-methyl-	0.93
18	17.75	Butanoic Acid	7.77
19	18.28	Acetamide, N-ethyl-	0.31
20	18.66	Butanoic acid, 3-methyl-	1.79
21	20.02	Pentanoic Acid	3.51
22	20.74	Acetamide	1.26
23	21.56	Propanamide	0.72
24	22.13	Hexanoic acid	0.30
25	22.26	Phenol, 2-methoxy-	0.93
26	23.10	Butanamide	0.80
27	24.99	Phenol	0.11
28	25.14	Pentanamide	0.34
29	25.43	Phenol, 4-ethyl-2-methoxy-	0.22
30	25.74	2-Pyrrolidinone	0.38
31	26.39	Phenol, 4-methyl-	0.28
32	27.44	2-Piperidinone	1.06
33	28.07	S)-2-Hydroxypropanoic acid	0.85
34	30.42	Glycerin	1.12
35	30.49	Pentanoic acid, 4-oxo-	0.69
36	31.83	3-Pyridinol, 6-methyl-	1.16
37	32.10	3-Pyridinol	5.41
38	32.73	2,5-Pyrrolidinedione	0.12
39	32.87	5-Hydroxymethyldihydrofuran-2-one	0.51
40	34.03	Benzeneacetic acid	1.04
41	35.02	Benzenepropanoic acid	0.43
42	35.24	1-(2,4-Dihydroxy-3-methylphenyl)ethanone	0.34
43	40.95	Butanoic acid, 2-oxo-	0.49
44	41.06	3,6-Diisopropylpiperazin-2,5-dione	0.44

Table 2. (Continued)

#	Retention time	Name	Area (%)
45	42.17	3-Isopropyl-6-methyl-piperazine-2,5-dione	1.58
46	42.39	Uric acid	1.09
47	42.53	3,6-Diisopropylpiperazin-2,5-dione	0.54
48	43.07	Pyrrolo[1,2-a]pyrazine-1,4-dione, hexahydro-3-(2-methylpropyl)-	0.62
49	43.35	3-Isobutylhexahydropyrrolo[1,2-a]Pyrazine-1,4-dione	2.34
50	43.55	dl-Alanyl-l-leucine	0.85
51	43.96	2,5-Piperazinedione, 3,6-bis(2-methylpropyl)-	0.80
52	44.54	3-Isobutylhexahydropyrrolo[1,2-a]Pyrazine-1,4-dione	0.32
53	44.73	3-Isobutylhexahydropyrrolo[1,2-a]Pyrazine-1,4-dione	0.84
54	44.95	Uracil	0.83
55	45.46	Cycloglycylvaline	0.49
56	45.63	2,5-Piperazinedione, 3-methyl-	0.22
57	45.82	4-Methyleneproline	0.34
58	46.27	Pyrrolo[1,2-a]pyrazine-1,4-dione, hexahydro-	0.52
59	46.56	3-Hydroxymethyl-piperazine-2,5-dione	0.31
60	46.86	Cyclo-(glycyl-l-leucyl)	0.96
61	49.75	Thymine	0.44
62	52.13	Uracil	1.02
63	52.92	1-Pyrrolid-2-one, N-carbamoyl-	0.68
64	55.65	3-Benzyl-6-isopropyl-2,5-piperazinedione	1.04
65	62.39	Pyrrolo[1,2-a]pyrazine-1,4-dione, hexahydro-3-(phenylmethyl)-	0.39
Total			80.24

As of phosphorous, more than 85% of the phosphorous in the feedstock was transferred into the solid residue fraction. As mentioned previously, the fraction of nitrogen and phosphorous which does not end in the bio-oil could be used in the production of algae in the loop of E^2-Energy. The oxygen content of the bio-oil is usually about 10-20% and significantly higher than that of the conventional petroleum. The high oxygen content causes some undesirable qualities such as poor thermal stability, lower energy content and the tendency to polymerize. So the bio-oil generated via HTL needs to be burned directly as fuel oils, otherwise downstream upgrading processes are needed for further applications. Hydrodeoxygenation processes could be a solution for the oxygen removal from the bio-oil. And Elliott (2007) has recently published a critical review on the hydrodeoxygenation technologies to upgrade biomass-derived oils. Nitrogen in the bio-oil is another challenge for upgrading. The bio-oil generated from protein-containing biomass usually has much higher nitrogen content than the petroleum oil has. Specific catalysts and technology may be needed for the removal of this high nitrogen content.

The author of this chapter thanks the research group of Bioenvironmental Engineering led by Prof. Yuanhui Zhang at Department of Agricultural and Biological Engineering, University of Illinois at Urbana-Champaign for the discussion on E^2-Energy and for providing some of the valuable data.

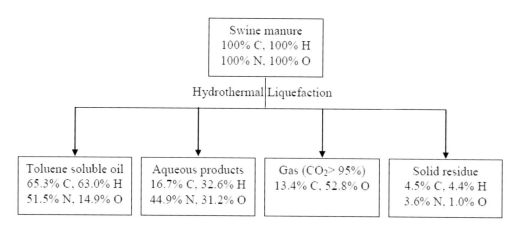

Note: 1) Percentage of Element A in product stream B= (Mass of Element A in product stream B/ Mass of Element A in dry swine manure feedstock)×100%. 2) As more than 95% percent of the gas is CO_2, it is assumed that all the gas is CO_2 during the calculation.

Figure 6. Total elemental mass balance of HTP of swine manure at 300°C, 30min.

REFERENCES

Appell, H.R., 1967. Fuels from Waste. Anderson, L., and Tilman, D. A., (Eds.). New York: Academic Press.

Appell, H.R., Fu, Y.C., Friedman, S., Yavorsky, P.M., Wender, I., 1980. Converting organic wastes to oil: a replenishable energy source. Report of Investigations 7560. Washington, DC: U.S. Bureau of Mines.

Appell, H.R., Wender, I., Miller, R.D., 1970. Conversion of urban refuse to oil. Bureau of Mines Solid Waste Program Technical Progress Report. US Department of the Interior.

ASABE, 2005. Manure production and characterization, American Society of Agricultural and Biological Engineers Standard D384.2 MAR2005. .

Berl, E., 1934. Origin of asphalts, oil, natural gas and bituminous coal. *Science*, 80, 227-228.

Berl, E., 1944. Production of oil from plant material. *Science*, 99, 309-312.

Biller, P., Ross, A.B., 2011. Potential yields and properties of oil from the hydrothermal liquefaction of microalgae with different biochemical content. *Bioresour. Technol.*, 102, 215-225.

Boocock, D.G.B., Kosiak, L., 1988. A scanning electron-microscope study of structural-changes during the liquefaction of poplar sticks by rapid aqueous thermolysis. *Can. J. Chem. Eng.*, 66, 121-126.

Catallo, W.J., Shupe, T.F., Comeaux, J.L., Junk, T., 2010. Transformation of glucose to volatile and semi-volatile products in hydrothermal (HT) systems. *Biomass. Bioenergy*, 34, 1-13.

Dong, R., Zhang, Y., Christianson, L.L., Funk, T.L., Wang, X., Wang, Z., Minarick, M., Yu, G., 2009. Product distribution and implication of hydrothermal conversion of swine manure at low temperatures. *Trans. ASABE*, 52, 1239-1248.

Dote, Y., Sawayama, S., Inoue, S., Minowa, T., Yokoyama, S.-y., 1994. Recovery of liquid fuel from hydrocarbon-rich microalgae by thermochemical liquefaction. *Fuel*, 73, 1855-1857.

Duan, P., Savage, P.E., 2011. Hydrothermal liquefaction of a microalga with heterogeneous catalysts. *Ind. Eng. Chem. Res.*, 50, 52-61.

Elliott, D., 2007. Historical developments in hydroprocessing bio-oils. *Energy and Fuels*, 21, 1792-1815.

Fu, Y.C., Illig, E.G., Metlin, S.J., 1974. Conversion of manure to oil by catalytic hydrotreating. *Environ. Sci. Technol.*, 8, 737-740.

Funazukuri, T., Wakao, N., Smith, J.M., 1990. Liquefaction of lignin sulfonate with subcritical and supercritical water. *Fuel*, 69, 349-353.

Goudriaan, F., Beld, B.v.d., Boerefijn, F.R., Bos, G.M., Naber, J.E., Wal, S.v.d., J.A.Zeevalkink, 2001. Thermal efficiency of the HTU process for biomass liquefaction, in: (ed) BA (Editor), proceedings of Progress in thermochemical biomass conversion, Oxford UK, *IEA Bioenergy, Blackwell Science*.

Goudriaan, F., Peferoen, D.G.R., 1990. Liquid fuels from biomass via a hydrothermal process. *Chem. Eng. Sci.*, 45, 2729-2734.

He, B.J., Zhang, Y., Funk, T.L., Riskowski, G.L., Yin, Y., 2000a. Thermochemical conversion of swine manure: An alternative process for waste treatment and renewable energy production. *Trans. ASAE*, 43, 1827-1833.

He, B.J., Zhang, Y., Yin, Y., Funk, T.L., Riskowski, G.L., 2000b. Operating temperature and retention time effects on the thermochemical conversion process of swine manure. *Trans. ASAE*, 43, 1821-1825.

He, B.J., Zhang, Y., Yin, Y., Funk, T.L., Riskowski, G.L., 2001a. Effects of alternative process gases on the thermochemical conversion process of swine manure. *Trans. ASAE*, 44, 1873-1880.

He, B.J., Zhang, Y., Yin, Y., Funk, T.L., Riskowski, G.L., 2001b. Effects of feedstock pH, initial CO addition, and total solids content on the thermochemical conversion process of swine manure. *Trans. ASAE*, 44, 697-701.

He, B.J., Zhang, Y., Yin, Y., Funk, T.L., Riskowski, G.L., 2001c. Preliminary characterization of raw oil products from the thermochemical conversion of swine manure. *Trans. ASAE*, 44, 1865-1871.

Itoh, S., Suzuki, A., Nakamura, T., Yokoyama, S.y., 1994. Production of heavy oil from sewage sludge by direct thermochemical liquefaction. *Desalination*, 98, 127-133.

Jena, U., Das, K.C., 2009. Production of biocrude oil from microalgae via thermochemical liquefaction process ASABE - Bioenergy Engineering Conference 2009, pp. 209-218.

Karagoz, S., Bhaskar, T., Muto, A., Sakata, Y., Uddin, M.A., 2004. Low-temperature hydrothermal treatment of biomass: Effect of reaction parameters on products and boiling point distributions. *Energy Fuels*, 18, 234-241.

Kruse, A., Gawlik, A., 2003. Biomass conversion in water at 330-410 °C and 30-50 MPa. Identification of key compounds for indicating different chemical reaction pathways. *Ind. Eng. Chem. Res*, 42, 267-279.

Kruse, A., Krupka, A., Schwarzkopf, V., Gamard, C., Henningsen, T., 2005. Influence of proteins on the hydrothermal gasification and liquefaction of biomass. 1. Comparison of different feedstocks. *Ind. Eng. Chem. Res.*, 44, 3013-3020.

Kruse, A., Maniam, P., Spieler, F., 2007. Influence of proteins on the hydrothermal gasification and liquefaction of biomass. 2. Model compounds. *Ind. Eng. Chem. Res.*, 46, 87-96.

Kumar, S., Gupta, R.B., 2008. Hydrolysis of microcrystalline cellulose in subcritical and supercritical water in a continuous flow reactor. *Ind. Eng. Chem. Res*, 47, 9321-9329.

Matsumura, Y., Minowa, T., 2004. Fundamental design of a continuous biomass gasification process using a supercritical water fluidized bed. *Int. J. Hydrogen Energy*, 29, 701-707.

Meeroff, D.E., 2001. Effects of ionizing radiation in wastewater treatment and residuals processing. PhD diss. Coral Gables, FL.: University of Miami.

Miao, X., Wu, Q., 2004. High yield bio-oil production from fast pyrolysis by metabolic controlling of Chlorella protothecoides. *J. Biotechnol.*, 110, 85-93.

Minowa, T., Inoue, S., 1999. Hydrogen production from biomass by catalytic gasification in hot compressed water. *Renewable Energy*, 16, 1114-1117.

Minowa, T., Kondo, T., Sudirjo, S.T., 1998a. Thermochemical liquefaction of Indonesian biomass residues. *Biomass Bioenergy*, 14, 517-524.

Minowa, T., Zhen, F., Ogi, T., 1998b. Cellulose decomposition in hot-compressed water with alkali or nickel catalyst. *J. Supercrit. Fluids*, 13, 253-259.

Modell, M., 1980. Reforming of organic-substances in supercritical water *J. Electrochem. Soc.*, 127, C139-C139.

Murakami, M., Yokoyama, S.y., Ogi, T., Koguchi, K., 1990. Direct liquefaction of activated sludge from aerobic treatment of effluents from the cornstarch industry. *Biomass*, 23, 215-228.

Nelson, D.A., Molton, P.M., Russell, J.A., Hallen, R.T., 1984. Application of direct thermal liquefaction for the conversion of cellulosic biomass. *Ind. Eng. Chem. Prod. Res. Dev.*, 23, 471-475.

NREL, 1998. A Look Back at the U.S. Department of Energy's Aquatic Species Program—Biodiesel from Algae. NREL/TP-580-24190. National Renewable Energy Laboratory. 1617 Cole Boulevard Golden, Colorado.

Ocfemia, K.S., Zhang, Y., Funk, T., 2006. Hydrothermal processing of swine manure into oil using a continuous reactor system: Development and testing. Trans. *ASABE*, 49, 533-541.

Patil, V., Tran, K.Q., GiselrÃ¸d, H.R., 2008. Towards sustainable production of biofuels from microalgae. *Int. J. Mol. Sci.*, 9, 1188-1195.

Perlack, R.D., Wright, L.L., Turhollow, A.F., Graham, R.L., Stokes, B.J., Erbach, D.C., 2005. Biomass as feedstock for a bioenergy and bioproducts industry: The technical feasibility of a billion-ton annual supply. Washington, DC: U.S. Department of Agriculture and U.S. Department of Energy.

Peterson, A.A., Vogel, F., Lachance, R.P., Froling, M., Antal, M.J., Tester, J.W., 2008. Thermochemical biofuel production in hydrothermal media: A review of sub- and supercritical water technologies. *Energy Environ. Sci.*, 1, 32-65.

Ross, A.B., Biller, P., Kubacki, M.L., Li, H., Lea-Langton, A., Jones, J.M., 2010. Hydrothermal processing of microalgae using alkali and organic acids. *Fuel*, 89, 2234-2243.

Suzuki, A., Nakamura, T., Yokoyama, S., Ogi, T., Koguchi, K., 1988. Conversion of sewage sludge to heavy oil by direct thermochemical liquefaction. *J. Chem. Eng. Jpn.*, 21, 288-293.

USDA, 2006. Agricultural Research Service, FY-2005 Annual Report Manure and Byproduct Utilization (accessed November 2, 2010).

USEIA, 2011. Annual Energy Outlook 2011 With Projections to 2035. DOE/EIA-0383(2011). Available on the WEB at: www.eia.gov/forecasts/ aeo/.

USEPA, 2008. Municipal Solid Waste in the United States: 2007 Facts and Figures. EPA530-R-08-010. EPA Office of Solid Waste. Washington DC.

Vardon, D.R., Sharma, B.K., Scott, J., Yu, G., Wang, Z., Schideman, L., Zhang, Y., Strathmann, T.J., 2011. Chemical properties of biocrude oil from the hydrothermal liquefaction of Spirulina algae, swine manure, and digested anaerobic sludge. *Bioresour. Technol.*, 102, 8295-8303.

Waldner, M.H., Vogel, F., 2005. Renewable production of methane from woody biomass by catalytic hydrothermal gasification. *Ind. Eng. Chem. Res.*, 44, 4543-4551.

Wang, Z., 2011. Reaction mechanisms of hydrothermal liquefaction of model compounds and biowaste feedstocks. PhD diss. Urbana, Ill. : University of Illinois at Urbana-Champaign.

Xiu, S., Shahbazi, A., Shirley, V., Cheng, D., 2010. Hydrothermal pyrolysis of swine manure to bio-oil: Effects of operating parameters on products yield and characterization of bio-oil. *J. Anal. Appl. Pyrolysis*, 88, 73-79.

Yokoyama, S.-y., Ogi, T., Koguchi, K., Nakamura, E., 1984. Direct liquefaction of wood by catalyst and water. Liq. *Fuels Technol.*, 2, 155-163.

Yu, G., Zhang, Y., Schideman, L., Funk, T., Wang, Z., 2011a. Distributions of carbon and nitrogen in the products from hydrothermal liquefaction of low-lipid microalgae. *Energy Environ. Sci.*, DOI: 10.1039/C1EE01541A

Yu, G., Zhang, Y., Schideman, L., Funk, T.L., Wang, Z., 2011b. Hydrothermal liquefaction of low lipid content microalgae into bio-crude oil. *Trans. ASABE*, 54, 239-246.

INDEX

G

H

N

O

S